Stress and Your Body

Robert Sapolsky, Ph.D.

THE
GREAT
COURSES

PUBLISHED BY:

THE GREAT COURSES
Corporate Headquarters
4840 Westfields Boulevard, Suite 500
Chantilly, Virginia 20151-2299
Phone: 1-800-832-2412
Fax: 703-378-3819
www.thegreatcourses.com

Robert Sapolsky, Ph.D.

Professor of Neurology and Neurosurgery
Stanford University

Professor Robert Sapolsky holds the John A. and Cynthia Fry Gunn Professorship of Biological Sciences at Stanford University, where he is also Professor of Neurology and Neurosurgery. Professor Sapolsky's laboratory focuses on the mechanisms by which stress and stress hormones can damage the brain and on the development of gene therapy strategies to save neurons from neurological insults. In addition, he has spent most of his summers since the late 1970s studying a population of wild baboons in East Africa, examining what social rank, personality, and patterns of sociality have to do with vulnerability to stress-related diseases.

Professor Sapolsky has been the recipient of many awards for his work, including a 2009 Walter J. Gores Award for Excellence in Teaching, Stanford University's highest teaching honor.

Professor Sapolsky writes regularly for nonscientists in such publications as *Scientific American, Discover, Natural History,* and *The New Yorker.* He is also the author of 5 books, including 4 nontechnical publications for the general public: *Why Zebras Don't Get Ulcers: A Guide to Stress, Stress-Related Diseases, and Coping* (3rd edition, Henry Holt, 2004); *The Trouble with Testosterone and Other Essays on the Biology of the Human Predicament* (Scribner, 1997); *A Primate's Memoir* (Scribner, 2001); and *Monkeyluv and Other Essays on Our Lives as Animals* (Scribner, 2005). ∎

Table of Contents

Table of Contents

Table of Contents

Stress and Your Body

Scope:

Few people taking this course are likely to be lepers, have liver flukes, or suffer from malaria. Few will have lost their mothers to childbirth or be malnourished. Westernized humans are unlike other animals because we are spared the classic infectious diseases, undernutrition, and poor hygiene. Instead, we live well enough and long enough that our serious diseases are ones of slow accumulation of damage, such as heart disease, diabetes, and cancer.

These are unique ways of getting sick. Imagine a person 20,000 years ago accidentally eating a bushbuck riddled with anthrax. The prognosis is clear—he has about a 3-day life expectancy. Imagine a contemporary person accidentally deciding that a healthy diet consists of lots of red meat, saturated fats, and a few drinks each day. The prognosis is not at all clear—she could be dead at 50 or running marathons at 85. Some of that variability arises from nuts-and-bolts biology, such as, how does her liver deal with cholesterol? But some has to do with issues never before seen as relevant to medicine, issues that generate bizarre questions such as, what is her psychological makeup? What is her social status? How do people of that status get treated in her society? Even things like is she the sort of person who eats a lot more when she is feeling worried or unloved? This is a strange realm for making sense of who is healthy and who gets sick. And it is critical to note that most of these diseases of slow degeneration and Westernized lifestyle can be caused or worsened by stress. Most of us will have the luxury of dying of a stress-related disease.

Nonetheless, we can try to delay that from happening. To hark back to a term from 9th grade biology, our bodies seek homeostasis, the state where there is an ideal blood pressure, temperature, level of glucose in the bloodstream, and so on. A stressor can be defined as anything in the outside world that disrupts homeostatic balance. Consider a zebra that has been attacked by a lion, with its innards dragging in the dust, still needing to flee. I think it is fair to state that this counts as being out of homeostatic balance. Or consider

1

that lion, half-starved, who must find the energy to run down a prey and survive. In both of those animals, there is activation of the stress-response (involving, among other things, the secretion of epinephrine). And that response is highly adaptive under those circumstances. The stress-response diverts energy from storage sites throughout the body to exercising muscle.

Blood pressure, heart rate, and breathing rate increase, accelerating delivery of nutrients to where they're needed—get that oxygen and glucose to the thigh muscles in 2 seconds instead of 3, and the animal is more likely to survive. Long-term, costly building projects throughout the body— such as growth, tissue repair, reproduction, and digestion—are inhibited. If an animal is running for its

Zebras and other animals activate their stress-response only when necessary.

life, it's not a bad idea to ovulate some other time; it can do it later, if there is a later. Its pain perception is blunted, its body gets better at clotting a wound, its immune system activates, and its brain is alert and processing information more acutely. This is all highly adaptive.

Then there are humans. We activate the stress-response if being chased by a predator. But, critically, we can activate that same response if we merely think we're about to be knocked out of balance—we have an anticipatory stress-response. If it is justified, that is a great thing. But if there is no actual physical stressor impending, and we do that regularly, we have entered the realm of anxiety, neurosis, hostility, and paranoia. Zebras do not worry about global warming, but we do. We activate the identical stress-response as do zebras and lions, but we can do so because of chronic psychological stress. And if that occurs often enough, our disease risk increases, because that is not what the stress-response evolved for. This is the central point of this course.

Chronically diverting energy from storage sites increases the risk of metabolic diseases such as diabetes. Chronically increasing blood pressure or deferring growth, tissue repair, or reproduction can exact a health price. In contrast to the situation with acute stress, chronic stress suppresses, rather than stimulates, the immune system, increasing risk for infectious diseases. And chronically activating the stress-response can cause memory problems, increase the risk of depression and anxiety disorders, and even accelerate brain aging. In other words, we humans are smart enough to make ourselves sick with thoughts, emotions, and memories—and we Westernized humans live long enough for the consequences to eventually haunt us big-time.

The first part of the course marches through various parts of the body (e.g., heart, stomach wall, and immune system) or physiological functions (e.g., sleep, learning, and memory), examining first what happens during the sort of stress experienced by a zebra or lion—how that is great adaptive news for them—and then, for each of those systems, how chronic stress winds up being bad news for us. The information is presented at the level of an educated individual who, nonetheless, hasn't gone near science since high school. The course then examines what it is that makes psychological stress stressful, and its relevance to depression, anxiety, and addiction. We examine the role of personality differences in explaining why some individuals cope with stress better than others, and we explore what socioeconomic status has to do with stress and health. By this point in the course, you should be depressed as heck. The final 2 lectures are an overview of stress management: Remarkably, there are reasons for optimism. ■

Why Don't Zebras Get Ulcers? Why Do We?
Lecture 1

Sit down a hippo and try to explain traffic jams, and it's going to have no idea what you're talking about. We do, though, and that's the critical point of the whole field of stress and disease. We turn on the exact same stress-response as do those mammals running for their lives or running for a meal, and we turn it on for psychological reasons.

When most of the beasts on this planet become sick, it is due to acute crises. You are a zebra, and a lion has leapt out and ripped your stomach open. Your innards are dragging in the dust, and you still need to get out of there. Or you're the lion who's half starved to death, and if you don't manage to chase down that zebra, you're not going to survive the night. You have been knocked out of homeostatic balance. Short-term physical crisis leads to the **stress-response**: You secrete adrenalin and other hormones to reestablish **homeostasis**. If you're a zebra or a lion, that's all you need to know about the subject.

The stress-response is a good thing for animals in the wild, such as zebras attacked by a lion.

What do we humans, especially Westernized humans, do instead? We worry about physiological states. We worry about our body slowly being done in by things like heart disease and stroke. In lots of ways, the central question in Westernized disease these days is why do some of us live to 50 and some of us to 85? Some of that has to with biology, but a lot of it has to do with issues like social status and psychological makeup. When you look at the diseases that get us sick these days, those diseases of slow accumulation over time, they are predominantly diseases that are sensitive to stress. Most of us will have the profound Westernized luxury of dropping dead someday of a stress-related disease.

How does stress impact our lives? How does stress impact our health? Not just any kind of stress: the psychological and psychosocial stress that we Westernized humans specialize in. If you're a human, yes, stress can be when you're knocked out of homeostatic balance. But a **stressor** can also be when you think you're about to be knocked out of homeostatic balance. If you think you're about to be knocked out of homeostatic balance, and you're really not, and you think that way all the time, there are medical ways to describe you: You're being neurotic, anxious, paranoid, or hostile.

> **We humans activate the stress-response for reasons of psychological factors, and that's simply not what the system evolved for.**

We humans activate the stress-response for reasons of psychological factors, and that's simply not what the system evolved for. If you do that chronically, you're going to get sick. The problem is that after a while, your stress-response is more damaging than the stressor itself, especially if the stressor was some psychological nonsense you made up. Everything you're doing with your body here is inefficient, but you got to do it because today is an emergency. If for psychological reasons, every day is an emergency, you never fix, you never grow, you never plan for the future. When you chronically turn on the stress-response, your body is forced to ignore the repair and growth functions it would normally be performing, and then you've got this big challenge of how do you recover afterward? This is what chronic stress is about: That same stress-response that was wonderfully adaptive and logical for that zebra or lion, do it chronically, and you pay a price. ■

Important Terms

homeostasis: A state of equilibrium, with physiological endpoints functioning in an optimal range.

stressor: An external perturbation that disrupts homeostasis; also, the psychological anticipation of such a perturbation occurring.

stress-response: The array of hormonal and neural adaptations in the body meant to reestablish homeostasis.

Suggested Reading

McEwen, "Protective and Damaging Effects of Stress Mediators."

Sapolsky, *Why Zebras Don't Get Ulcers*, chap. 1.

Questions to Consider

1. Why is the stress-response exactly what you want to have happening in your body if you're running away from a predator?

2. So why don't zebras get ulcers?

Why Don't Zebras Get Ulcers? Why Do We?
Lecture 1—Transcript

Here's the scenario. It's 2 o'clock in the morning. You're lying in bed wide awake. Tomorrow is a hugely important day. There's some meeting, some presentation, something where it is all on the line that you need to be coherent, you need to be organized, you need to be alert, and you need to be rested. You are lying there thinking, unless I fall asleep in the next 30 seconds, my entire career is over with tomorrow, and thus, you lie there more and more awake. Somewhere about 45 minutes into that worrying, a different worry creeps in. Somehow amid all of that worrying about your neuroses and sort of those fears of work tomorrow, suddenly it strikes you, oh my God. That pain in the side I've been having, that headache I've been having, I'm sick, I'm sick. I have a fatal disease. I have a fatal disease; it's all over with. It's not fair. I'm too young, all of that. You suddenly have a fatal disease.

When it's two in the morning and I'm getting all crazy like that, it's always a brain tumor because with a brain tumor, you can always panic yourself even more because you can attribute any symptom to that. Maybe you're lying there thinking it's a heart attack or a stroke or some such thing. I'm willing to make a bet though, you are not lying there thinking, oh my God, this time it's small pox, this time it's dysentery for sure, or I can just feel them I've got liver parasites the size of my fists crawling around in me. You're not going to be worrying about something like that. In that regard, you are not a normal mammal. You take a normal mammal and you look at the diseases that do them in, and it's ones where there's an acute challenge to their health. It is something major and serious.

What are we doing there? We're worrying about circumstances that slowly do us in. This is how we humans, especially we Westernized humans, differ critically from animals out there. For most of the beasts on this planet, you look at what gets them sick, and it is an acute crisis. You are some zebra and a lion has leapt out and ripped your stomach open. Your innards are dragging in the dust, and you still need to get out of there. What do we do instead? We worry about sort of physiological states. We worry about our body slowly going to hell on us over the course of 75 years, and this is a very different realm of disease.

For the most part, we are spared the infectious diseases, the diseases of poor hygiene, poor nutrition, and instead we have these diseases where you slowly fall apart over time. This is Westernized disease. This is a very different realm of who gets sick and who is healthy. In 1900, what were the leading causes of death in the United States? All sorts of things we don't worry too much about anymore. Pneumonia, tuberculosis, if you were a woman between ages 20 and 40, the single medically riskiest thing you could do is try to give birth, the number 1 killer of women in that range. What was number 1 on the list as a whole? Influenza, the flu, in 1918, worst winter of World War I, people being blown out of trenches all over Europe, and if you were sent to the war that winter, your chances of surviving were better than if you came down with the flu. Eight million more deaths in World War I, best estimates 40 million dead civilians from the flu. The flu? The flu, we don't worry about the flu anymore.

Instead we worry about these diseases where we slowly accumulate damage, these diseases like heart disease, like stroke, things of that sort. This, again, is a very different realm of who is healthy and who is sick. Twenty thousand years ago, you're some 20-year-old hunter gatherer, and you have screwed up. You have made a major medical mistake. You've eaten some reedbuck riddled with anthrax. The medical outcome is absolutely clear. You've got like a 2-day life expectancy. These days, you're a 20-year-old, and you've screwed up big time because you've decided a healthy diet consists of a lot of red meat, saturated fats, or cholesterol. It's not at all clear what the medical outcome is going to be. You may be dead in your grave when you're 50, or you may be running marathons with your grandkids when you're 85.

In lots of ways, the central question in Westernized disease these days is why do some of us live to 50 and some of us to 85? Some of that has to with nuts and bolts, biology, what your liver does with cholesterol. Things such as that. A lot of it, though, has to do with issues that nobody in medicine has had to think much about anymore. Utterly bizarre questions like, what's your social status? How do people with your social status get treated in your society? What's your psychological makeup? Even something as bizarre as, so do you eat a lot more carbohydrates when you're feeling unloved? Figure that one out, and you've just solved half the cases of diabetes in this country.

That is a very different realm of who is healthy and who is sick. When you look at the diseases that get us sick these days, those diseases of slow accumulation over time, these are predominantly diseases that are sensitive to stress. Most of us will have the profound Westernized luxury of dropping dead someday of a stress-related disease.

My name's Robert Sapolsky. I'm a Professor of Neuroscience at Stanford, and I'm the messenger with all the bad news. The strategy in this course is going to be to get a sense of, how does stress impact our lives? How does stress impact our health? Not just any kind of stress, the psychological, and the psychosocial stress that we Westernized humans specialize in.

Much of the course is going to be devoted to that, and I need to warn you right now in the fine print, if you stay awake to the end of that section, you are going to be depressed as hell because there's nothing but bad news between now and then. What we will transition to towards the end of the course is some realms for good news, coping, and why do some of us cope better than others?

Stress, of course we need to start off with some definitions. I start off with a term I guarantee you had it back in ninth grade biology. With any luck, you haven't thought about it since then. Remember the word "homeostasis"? Homeostasis, an ideal body temperature, an ideal level of glucose in your bloodstream, an ideal everything. A stressor is anything that knocks you out of homeostatic balance. Again, you're that zebra and your innards are dragging in the dust, and this counts as being knocked out of homeostatic balance; or you're the lion who's half starved to death, and if you don't manage to chase down that zebra, you're not going to survive the night. Short-term physical crisis, and the stress-response, you secrete adrenalin and "eleventy" other hormones we'll be learning about. The stress-response is what you do to reestablish homeostasis. If you're a zebra or a lion, that's all you need to know about the subject.

If you're a human, though, you've got to expand the definition in a critical way, which is, yes, stress can be when you're knocked out of homeostatic balance. In addition, a stressor can be when you think you're just about to be knocked out of homeostatic balance. If you're right, hooray for you. You've got this anticipatory stress-response, and that could be very adaptive. On the other hand, if you think you're just about to be knocked out of homeostatic balance, and you're really not, and you think that way all the time, there are medical ways to describe you. You're being neurotic as hell. You are being anxious. You are being paranoid. You are being hostile.

You are being profoundly human. Sit down a hippo and try to explain traffic jams, and it's going to have no idea what you're talking about. We do, though, and that's the critical point of the whole field of stress and disease. We turn on the exact same stress-response as do those mammals running for their lives or running for a meal, and we turn it on for psychological reasons. For 99% of the beasts on this planet out there, stress consists of 3 minutes of screaming terror in the savanna, after which it's either over with or you're over with.

What do we do? We turn on the same exact stress-response for a 30-year mortgage, and that's not what the system evolved for. The central concept of this whole course is: We humans are smart enough to turn on the stress-response, what you'll learn about, to activate the same stress-response as does an animal having a physical crisis, and we turn it on for thoughts, for memories, for things of that sort.

Here's an exercise. I want all of you to do this. Tonight when you're in bed, you're nice and relaxed, you're calm, your heart is beating slowly, think the following thought: "You know, that heart isn't going to beat forever." I mean really think about it. Think about the blood flow stopping in your bloodstream. Think about your toes becoming cold. Think about those blue lips, and I'm willing to bet, suddenly your heart is beating faster. You won't have just run up some flight of stairs with a cow on your back. You won't be doing anything that counts as a physical stressor, yet you will be lying there with your stress-response activated, and that's the key point.

We smart humans activate that stress-response for reasons of psychological factors, thoughts, emotions, memories, and that's simply not what the system evolved for. If you do that chronically, you're going to get sick. This is the corner piece of the stress-response. This is an idea that has dominated the field since the 1930s and has much to do with one of the godfathers of stress physiology, an Austrian physician named Hans Selye. Selye kind of was the locomotive for the stress field. Selye was able to get the whole thing going because he was very smart, and he was very intuitive. He was very creative and very insightful, and apparently, he was totally lame at handling laboratory rats. This is how the field began.

In the 1930s, Selye is this young assistant professor at McGill University in Montreal, and he's looking for some research project. Some biochemist down the hall has just isolated some unknown hormone out of ovaries or something. Nobody knows what the stuff does, so Selye decides that's it. I'm going to figure out the effects of this ovarian stuff on the body. What do you do? You go down the hall. You get a bucket load of the stuff from your buddy, and you come back and you start injecting lab rats with it.

Apparently, Selye simply was not very good with lab rats. He's in there every day with the rats, injecting the rats, dropping the rats, chasing the rats, and the rats are chasing him, and half the morning with a broom underneath the refrigerator trying to get them out of there. Months go by, and Selye examines these rats. He discovers something amazing. All of the rats have stomach ulcers. Selye is euphoric. He has just discovered the effects of this ovarian stuff on the body. It gives you a peptic ulcer.

Selye, being a good scientist, does something critical. He has also been running a control group, a control group of rats he has been injecting with not the ovarian stuff, but with just saline. He's been in there with the control rats injecting the rats, dropping the rats, chasing the rats, and the rats are chasing him. He checks them out, and they all have stomach ulcers. Your average scientist might give up at this point and apply to business school. Selye, however, is thinking about this, and he says, "This is totally screwed. I'm seeing the same thing in the controls and the experimentals. This can't have anything to do with this ovarian stuff. What do they have in common? Let's see. Well, I'm pretty inept at handling lab rats. Maybe what

I'm seeing is some sort of generalized response of the body to generalized unpleasantries."

Selye's critical insight there was to begin to systematically expose rats to generalized unpleasantries. He put some of them up in the roof of the building in the winter, down in the boiler rooms, rooms with loud noises, rooms with cats, and he'd always see the same thing, which is, they'd get a stomach ulcer. We know exactly what Selye had discovered. This is the tip of the iceberg of stress-related disease, and Selye was the person who popularized the term, this obscure term from metallurgy talking about torsional strains on metal, he's the person who popularized this notion of these animals are under stress.

Important historical qualifier: Selye spent an awful lot of his life to great acclaim and sort of pulling in crowds claiming he invented the term "stress as related to medicine." This was actually done by a giant of stress physiology in the 1920s, a man named Walter Cannon, who was one of those titans where he just begs to be turned into an oil painting. Cannon was the one who first introduced the term to medicine. Selye was the one who popularized it, and what he would say is, here are these rats undergoing these generalized unpleasantries, these rats undergoing stress, and there's this stress-response in the body that helps them adapt to it.

If that stress-response is turned on for too long, you're going to get sick. Without question, everybody in the field thought that Selye was out of his mind for this very simple reason: If you are trained in learning how the body works, there's this rule: The body comes up with a very specific solution to a very specific challenge. If you're hot, you don't shiver. You do something very different from that. Yet, here's Selye with his imaginary stress-response which you're supposedly turning on whether you are that zebra, that lion, too hot, too cold, you have this stereotype, this consistent stress-response.

Nonetheless, this actually makes a lot of sense because whether you are that lion or that zebra, if you are going to survive this short-term crisis, there are very similar things you're going to need to do with your body. First off, above all else, whether you are that zebra or that lion, you need energy. Not energy tucked away in your fat cells for some building project next spring, energy right now in the circulation to hand over to whichever muscles are going to save your life. The first thing your body does with the onset of stress is you send these hormones to your fat cells, your liver, storage sites throughout the body, and you empty them out of the storage forms of energy. You go to the bank, you empty out the savings account, and you turn it into cash, glucose in the bloodstream. That makes perfect sense whether you are that zebra or that lion. The next thing you do makes perfect sense as well. You've just done all this amazing biochemistry and dumped all this energy in this easily usable form into your circulation. You want to deliver the stuff as quickly as possible. What do you do? You increase your heart rate, your blood pressure, your breathing rate, all as part of the strategy, get that glucose, get that oxygen to your thigh muscles in 2 seconds instead of 3; you're that much more likely to survive.

Another thing that bodies do during stress, and again, this makes perfect sense whether you are that zebra or that lion, is you turn off all the long-term building projects. You do it later under more auspicious circumstances. You shut down digestion. By definition, that starving lion is not just staggering up from some all-you-can-eat buffet, and that zebra is not mobilizing energy thanks to digestion. Mobilizing energy, you do it from your fat cells in a couple of seconds. Digestion takes hours. It's this slow, expensive process. Humans use like 20% of their energy just on digestion, and this is no time for it. You shut down the digestive tract, and we all know the first step of this. Suppose you're speaking in public and you get stressed. What happens? Your mouth gets dry, and that's the first step of shutting down your whole gastrointestinal system.

What else do you shut down? You shut down growth. You shut down reproduction. Perfectly logical: These are big, expensive, optimistic things to be doing with your body, and this is no time for it. You're running for your life. There's a lion 2 steps behind you. Ovulate some other time. Hit puberty next week. Grow antlers some other day. Don't even think about sperm. A hallmark of the stress-response is you shut down secretion of growth hormone, growth tissue repair, all of that gets turned off. Every sex hormone on Earth begins to disappear from the bloodstream. Do it later if there is a later.

The next thing you do makes perfect sense if you are that zebra in great pain. Your innards are dragging in the dust. This might be a good time to perk up your immune system a little bit, protect you against infections. With the onset of stress, immunity is enhanced. Something else useful, you're bleeding like mad, that zebra, it might be a good time to get clotting enhanced in your body to try to stanch that blood flow. Something else makes a great deal of sense there also. You're that zebra. Your guts are ripped open. This is rather painful, and one of the other things that happens during the stress-response is you blunt pain perception: stress-induced analgesia. All of those are good things.

In addition, there's a bunch of stress hormones that get into your brain, and short-term, they do fabulous stuff for brain functioning. They increase the delivery of oxygen and glucose to your brain, and that's in part from that increased blood pressure and diverting energy and blood flow to where it's needed, your brain, the exercising muscle. Short term, you're learning and memory and recall is enhanced. You have that momentness, that alert instant there where you just are in this tunnel of concentration dealing with that stressor. You will remember it; that's the flashbulb memory. I am willing to bet every single one of us, no matter how old we wind up being, we will remember exactly where we were when we heard the news that Angelina Jolie was being appointed to the Supreme Court. This is an important thing. The Teaching Company recommended I not talk about something topical because it may become obsolete. This is something that will persist through the ages. This will become part of our cultural legacy.

Your brain needs to work better at those times. So look at all the things you're doing here. You're mobilizing energy. You're delivering it where it's needed. You're shutting off unessentials. You're thinking more clearly. You're enhancing immune defenses. You are trying to blunt pain, all the sorts of things you would want to do if you are your normal mammal who has just had some sort of physical injury. All you need to do to appreciate that is look at a couple of rare human diseases where people can't turn on the stress-response, can't do all the things we just went over. One of them is called Addison's disease; another is Shy-Drager syndrome. These are not diseases where now you're more at risk for diabetes. These are diseases where the guy goes running for the commuter bus and drops dead from hypoglycemic shock. If you plan to get stressed like a normal mammal, if you plan to sprint across the savanna or sprint across a parking lot, you had better turn on the stress-response that was just outlined, or else you've got like a 30-second life expectancy.

We've got a first critical punch line here, which is: If you plan to get stressed like a normal mammal, you had better turn on the stress-response. For most of us, though, the critical issue is: What if you turn the stress-response on too often, too long, for purely psychological reasons? You're going to get sick.

Selye, 70 years ago, was the first person to wrestle with this notion: Why is it that chronic stress makes you sick? He came up with an explanation which dominated the field for the next 40 years, which is too bad because he was totally wrong. Here's what he thought. Along comes a stressor, knocks you out of homeostatic balance, you turn on the stress-response, and you reestablish homeostasis. Everything's great except the stressor goes on for too long, and you enter what Selye called the exhaustion phase. You run out of the stress-response. Your adrenals run out of adrenalin. Your pituitary runs out of its pituitary hormones. You are left there in a state where you can't battle whatever the stressor is.

Turns out, this never happens. Nobody has ever been so stressed that they run out of adrenaline. The problem isn't that you are just exhausting yourself fighting against the stress. The problem is the central point of this whole field. The problem is that after a while, your stress-response is more damaging than the stressor itself, especially if the stressor was some psychological nonsense you made up. Everything you're doing with your body here that we just outlined, everything is inefficient, and bad news and pennywise and dollar foolish, but you got to do it because today is an emergency. If for psychological reasons, every day is an emergency, you never fix, you never grow, you never plan for the future.

Here's a way to think about it. You've got 2 kids in the park, and they're on a seesaw. They're perfectly happy going back and forth, and they're having a great time. They're giggling, and they forget that they lost gloves and mom is taking pictures and all of that. Along comes a change. This is a basal-unstressed state. Along comes an acute stressor. You tell the kids, try to balance both of you up in the air for as long as possible. The kids are somewhat successful. They can manage it, and it's just fine. This is your body dealing with a short-term stressor.

Instead, along comes chronic stress, and the way to think about it now is you don't have 2 little kids on the seesaw anymore, you've got 2 huge elephants who you've just told, balance this seesaw up in the air. This is not going to work very readily. For one thing, you're going to pay a price. The elephants could be doing something useful at the time. They could be off painting your house or mowing the lawn. They could be off helping the process of building, repairing, and instead, they're devoting all their energy to pulling off this balancing act.

There're more problems now as well, which is the elephants are going to make a mess of the environment around them. They're going to be tossing Twinkie wrappers everywhere because they need to snack nonstop. They'll have stomped down the flowers getting over to the seesaw. They will be causing a lot of wear and tear on your system as a whole. There's an additional sort of subtle price that they wind up having under the circumstances, which is at some point you tell the elephants, that's great. No more balancing. That was terrific, good going. They've got to get off the seesaw. As we well know, if you get the timing wrong, somebody will crash down. What we have here is this choreography problem of the elephants getting off at the same time so that they don't break the seesaw and one of them doesn't smash to the ground. You have a problem that will run through the world of stress-related disease, which is it can often be very tough to recover from your stress-response.

By the way, I was at some conference years ago where people came up with this analogy for the elephants. We spent hours working on this, and before you knew it, about half of Earth's stress physiologists, who were locked in this room, were talking about metaphors of elephants on pogo sticks, or sumo wrestlers on seesaws. Nonetheless you get the point. When you chronically turn on the stress-response, you're ignoring repair, planning for the future. When you chronically turn on the stress-response, you've got wear and tear on that seesaw and everything around you, and then you've got this big challenge of how do you recover afterward? This is what chronic stress is about, and we've got this critical issue. That same stress-response that was wonderfully adaptive and logical for that zebra or lion, do it chronically, and you pay a price. One example of the many we will be learning about in far more detail.

You have increased your blood pressure because you're sprinting for your life and the lion is coming after you and you don't suffer from hypertension under that circumstance. You are doing something very adaptive. On the other hand, if you boost up your blood pressure all the time because of the traffic jams, things of that sort, you're not saving your life. You are suffering from stress-induced hypertension. Over and over, we are going to be dealing with this basic dichotomy here that's going to run through the entire course. If you plan to get stressed like a normal mammal, punch line number 1, you had better turn on the stress-response. If you get stressed like a psychosocially sophisticated human, you are constantly going to be paying the price of chronic activation of the stress-response, chronic activation of a system that simply did not evolve for being chronically activated.

This is going to be the strategy of the course. What we're going to do over the next couple of lectures is get a sense of what are the nuts and bolts of the stress-response? Which hormones are you secreting? Which physiological systems in your body are you turning off? This will give us the tools for the rest of the course. What we'll transition to then afterward is looking at specific systems. What happens with your body during stress—with growth and tissue repair, with digestion, with reproductive function—always dealing with this dichotomy? What's the short-term response like when you're a zebra or a lion, and what's the price we're paying when you turned it on like a sophisticated human?

A couple of qualifiers have to kick in here. First one is that this is not the case of stress causing heart disease, of stress causing diabetes. What we will see over and over is stress is not a causative factor; stress is an exacerbative factor. It makes preexisting disease worse. It lowers the threshold for you coming down with some disease that's already menacing you. What stress does is put you on the edge of a cliff, and almost anything comes along at that point and pushes you, you're that much more likely to go over the edge. So, not the sort of thing that mainstream medicine hated about the stress concept early on, the notion of stress causing disease. That's not true. Viruses cause disease, bacteria cause disease, mutations, diet, all of that. Stress worsens it.

Another qualifier that's going to run through here, which is that homeostasis concept has been replaced in recent years with something much fancier, the allostasis concept. What that's basically saying is when you're trying to solve a homeostatic challenge, a stressor, you don't solve it just locally. The homeostatic concept is you're running out of water, you're dehydrated. What do you do? Your kidneys retain water. The allostatic concept brings in a far more realistic picture of what happens instead. Yes, your kidneys retain more water, but you also change how your sweat glands are working. You begin to crave water. What allostasis is about is this notion of the whole body being involved in adaptive responses. What we'll see is, the fact that the whole body is involved increases the odds that one of those adaptations somewhere along the way is going to be getting you in trouble.

Here are a couple of more qualifiers for you. If you have a background in this area, you will be horrified by the simplifications I'll be making. Nonetheless, that's necessary some of the time because it's impossible to go over the details within this time frame: some of the time because no one in their right mind wants to learn it, unless they're staking their career on it; some of the time, because nobody really knows how it works, especially me. Therefore, we will be doing a lot of simplification along the way.

Again, this large strategy, what your body is doing with an acute stressor, how great that is, what your body is doing along the lines of falling apart with chronic stress—and throughout we will have this challenge which is hanging on with all this bad news up through three-quarters of this course, hanging on because the main point here is, there's good news at the end.

The Nuts and Bolts of the Stress-Response
Lecture 2

When you have a thought, have an emotion, have a memory, things change in your body. Your pancreas releases some hormone you've never even heard of. Your spleen is texting your thymus. Something is happening with blood flow in your big right toe, and what we have is this ... capacity, again as these sophisticated psychosocial humans, to turn on physiology with mere thought.

L et's take a look at the nuts and bolts of the human stress-response. Broadly, there are two systems in the body responsible for it. The first is the nervous system, through which your brain influences events throughout your body; the second is the release of hormonal messengers. How do these two systems work? How are they regulated? And most importantly, what happens with these systems during stress?

The part of the nervous system that handles the stuff you don't have much control over, things that are typically automatic, is called the **autonomic nervous system**. This autonomic nervous system comes in two halves: The first half is the sympathetic nervous system, which controls things like the stress-response. In contrast, the parasympathetic nervous system mediates calm, vegetative functioning. When you eat a big starchy meal or take a nap, you turn on the parasympathetic nervous system. If you get disemboweled by a lion, you turn off the parasympathetic nervous system and turn on the sympathetic. For the most part, they work in opposition, and the stress-response is all about turning on the sympathetic nervous system to an extremely severe extent.

So what regulates the sympathetic nervous system and the broader autonomic nervous system? This is illustrated by a wonderful concept that has run through the field of behavioral biology for some years, known as the triune brain. Obviously, this is not what the brain is really about, but it's a way to conceptualize what's happening, particularly with respect to the autonomic nervous system. The first level of the triune brain is the part of your nervous system that has your hypothalamus and all sorts of brain stem areas. This part of the brain does regulatory stuff: Your body gets cold, there are sensors that send information up to this part of the brain, and your muscles start shivering. The second layer is the **limbic system**, which is about emotion: lust, rage, petulance, and so on. Sitting on top is the third layer, the **cortex**. The cortex, the most recently evolved part of the nervous system, is about abstract stuff: abstract reasoning, processing, and long-term memories. Think about children in refugee camps, think about your mortality, and you might turn on the stress-response; the nervous system reacts as if this is a physiologically real event.

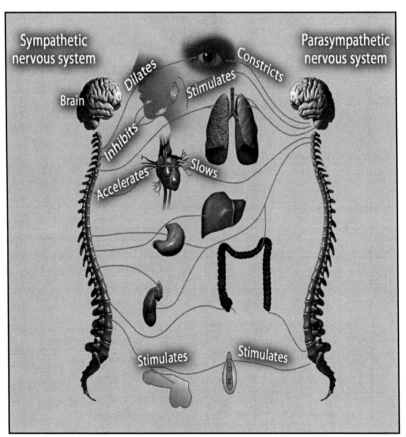

Figure 2.1. The autonomic nervous system.

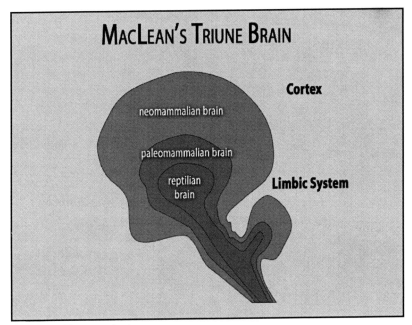

MacLean's Triune Brain

Cortex

neomammalian brain

paleomammalian brain

reptilian brain

Limbic System

Figure 2.2. The triune brain.

The second type of regulation is by way of hormones. A **hormone** is a chemical messenger from a brain cell or from cells throughout the body; hormones are blood borne and as a result can affect events throughout your body. The brain releases hormones that tell the pituitary gland what hormones to release, which tell the peripheral glands. Which hormones are secreted during the stress-response? After epinephrine, there is a class of steroid hormones that come out of the adrenal glands called glucocorticoids. Stress also increases secretory rates of prolactin, glucagon, and beta-endorphin. Then there are the hormones whose secretion is inhibited during stress, like growth hormone, insulin, and the reproductive hormones.

The interactions of these hormones will be covered in detail in the next few lectures. Note, however, that not everybody has the exact same stress-response. The fact that individuals differ in how their bodies respond to stress is great, because once we figure out the folks who are doing it just right, then we've got a model to go after. ■

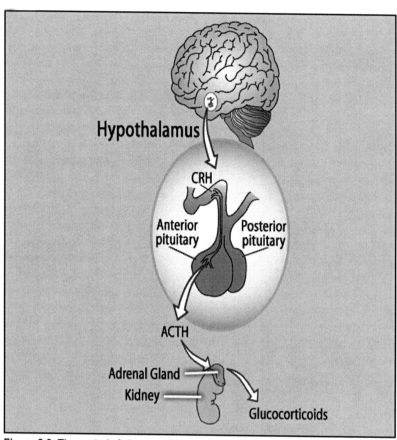

Figure 2.3. The control of gluccocorticoid secretion.

autonomic nervous system: A part of the nervous system that mediates aspects of the body's function that are often automatic, or involuntary. Consists of the sympathetic nervous system (generally involved in arousal and stress-responses) and the opposing parasympathetic nervous system (generally involved in calm, vegetative bodily function).

cortex: The outer surface of the brain, it is the most recently evolved and involved in the most abstract brain functions. Most pertinent to this course is the frontal cortex.

hormone: A chemical messenger released by glands into the bloodstream, where it travels and has effects elsewhere in the body.

limbic system: A region of the brain that plays a central role in emotion.

neurotransmitter: A chemical messenger with which one neuron communicates with another. Examples include serotonin, dopamine, and norepinephrine.

Suggested Reading

Sapolsky, *Why Zebras Don't Get Ulcers*, chap. 2.

Questions to Consider

1. How does your brain control hormonal events throughout your body?

2. What are some of the critical hormones secreted during stress, and what do they do?

The Nuts and Bolts of the Stress-Response
Lecture 2—Transcript

Why, hello. Perhaps you have been listening to Wagner with great pleasure for the last 30 seconds. However, fortunately, I have not been. I have had these earphones on where I've been listening to the theme song from *Gilligan's Island*, and that's great because I hate Wagner. I cannot stand Wagner. Listening to Wagner elevates my blood pressure and constricts my stomach, and I can't stand the guy's music. Maybe you've been having a different response; maybe, inexplicably, Wagner makes you feel at one with the world, and maybe it slows down your heart rate and your breathing rate; maybe you've increased your blood flow to your genitals if you're really weird.

Nonetheless, despite you perhaps liking Wagner and having all those responses, and me loathing the guy's music, we have one thing in common, which is, stuff is changing in our bodies. Different processes have changed. All sorts of things are working differently for a very simple reason: We thought something. We've had some emotion. We're suddenly dealing with this extraordinary fact first emphasized in the last lecture, which is we humans are unique, are sophisticated enough that we can think of things. We can remember something from our childhood. We can feel an emotion evoked by a piece of music. We can do any of that and we could change how our body works.

A wonderful example of this: There has been a lot made by gerontologists about this very striking fact about all sorts of orchestral conductors who live to be 120 and they're conducting way up to the end. What's the explanation for that? One of the things that's emphasized is all the aerobic exercise you get conducting and that increasing your heart rate to an optimal range. Here's a wonderful story. Apparently a study was once done on Arturo Toscanini, who was a great example of one of those lasting-forever conductors, and where he was not getting all this aerobic exercise conducting. Instead, he was sitting and listening to one of his recordings, and his heart rate increased to the same extent as if he was conducting himself.

What we've got here is a very dramatic example of when you have a thought, have an emotion, have a memory, things change in your body. Your pancreas releases some hormone you've never even heard of. Your spleen is texting your thymus. Something is happening with blood flow in your big right toe, and what we have is this critical point that runs through everything coming following this, which is we have this capacity, again as these sophisticated psychosocial humans, to turn on physiology with mere thought.

The question becomes: How do we do that? Broadly, there are 2 systems in the body responsible for it. The first is the nervous system, the way in which your brain can influence events throughout your body by way of the nervous system; the second is by way of hormones, the release of hormonal messengers. What this lecture is about is getting a broad sense about how these 2 systems work, how they're regulated, and most importantly, what happens with these systems during stress.

To begin, the nervous system, that neural regulation by your brain of events throughout your body, requires you to have a spinal cord. Most of your spine mediates boring stuff. It makes you sign checks, and shake hands, and fox trot, and all sorts of thing that you have voluntary control over where you are sending messages from your brain to your voluntary muscles, a system called, not shockingly, the voluntary nervous system. That's not the one that's critical for this lecture. Instead, we have a part of the nervous system that does the good stuff, the stuff you normally don't have much control over, blushing, goose flesh, orgasms, and pupillary contractions, the things that are typically automatic, and thus termed the automatic nervous system, or more formally, the autonomic nervous system. This is the means by which your nervous system changes events throughout your body by way of your spinal cord.

This autonomic nervous system comes in 2 halves, and that's going to be critical throughout the course as well, 2 halves. The first half is the sympathetic nervous system. The sympathetic nervous system, all hell breaking loose, emergency, arousal, fight-or-flight, secreting adrenaline, the whole stress-response, all of that sympathetic arousal. In contrast, you have the second system, the parasympathetic nervous system, which mediates calm, vegetative functioning. When you eat a big starchy meal, you turn on the parasympathetic nervous system. When you take a nap, you turn on the parasympathetic nervous system. If you get disemboweled by a lion, you turn off the parasympathetic nervous system and turn on the sympathetic. For the most part, they work in opposition, and what we will see is stress and the stress-response is all about turning on the sympathetic nervous system to an extremely severe extent, screamingly sympathetic tone in your body, while turning off the parasympathetic.

How do these work? How do these regulate parts of your body? An example, your heart, we already know what the main core of the cardiovascular stress-response is about, which is, you're that zebra running for your life. You need to increase your blood pressure and your heart rate to deliver more energy to your exercising muscles. What happens with this autonomic nervous system at the level of your heart? You turn on the sympathetic nervous system, and it speeds things up while you're decreasing parasympathetic tone.

In the heart, what the sympathetic nervous system is about is increasing activity. Meanwhile, in the last lecture we learned another example of what happens in your body, the gastrointestinal tract. You will remember that business. You get stressed; you get nervous; your mouth gets dry; those first steps of shutting down the whole gastrointestinal system. What we've got there is a case where the sympathetic nervous system, the emergency arousal, is decreasing activation of this particular organ. In order to pull off this emergency stress-response business, as we saw before in the previous lecture, some organ systems you activate, some you inhibit, and it's the sympathetic nervous system that's predominantly responsible for this.

The question, of course, becomes: What regulates the sympathetic nervous system? What are the regulators of this broader autonomic nervous system? There are parts of the brain where you decide, voluntarily, you're going to do this with your finger and there are certain neurons, brain cells that have been identified that do that. What regulates all this stuff where you think about a memory from your childhood, and your heart rate changes? What regulates this automatic nervous system? To begin to appreciate it, we need to pull in a wonderful concept that has run through the field of behavioral biology for some years. One originated by a man named MacLean, Paul MacLean, one of the giants in the field in the 1950s, what has come to be known as the triune brain; the triune brain, the 3-layer version of the brain. Obviously, this is not what the brain is really about, but it's a way to conceptualize what's happening, particularly with respect to the autonomic nervous system.

You've got your first level of the triune brain, which is the part of your nervous system that has all these ancient pathways, your hypothalamus, all sorts of brain stem areas. Do not panic if those terms are new to you. The main point, there is, this is one of the most ancient parts of the brain. This is a part of the brain where, similar to a lizard's, has virtually the same part of the brain there, the same regulatory subareas, the same projections. What's this part of the brain about? It's doing regulatory stuff. Your body gets cold, and there are sensors which send information up to this ancient reptilian part of the brain, and suddenly your muscles start shivering. You get some signal sent up there saying, "Oh, God I'm bleeding," and before you know it, there are signals coming down changing your cardiovascular tone, exactly the same in us as in a reptile. We've got this first part of this triune-brain way of thinking about the nervous system.

The second layer is limbic system, on top of the triune, reptilian section, limbic system. Limbic system is about emotion. Limbic system is about lust, rage, petulance, and all that stuff. Limbic system is about mammals. Yes, reptiles have a limbic system, fish, all those guys, but they don't have much of one. Lizards are not renowned emotional lives. It's not until mammals that you hit a really well-developed limbic system. What's that doing? That's the "moose that sees some other male moose dominating and trying to come into his territory with his antlers." I don't know if moose actually have antlers, but some male doing some territorial threat, and, you, the other male, being threatened; your heart rate increases. It is taking information about the world, which is emotional in nature, and turning it into a signal down to that reptilian part of the brain. Suddenly your heart is beating faster, not because you're running and you're getting signals there, not because you're bleeding, but because you've seen something. You have thought something. You have had a strong emotion evoked.

Sitting there on top though, is the third-most layer in this triune organization, the cortex. The cortex, this gleaming new part of the nervous system, the most recently evolved. Yes, once again, reptiles, fish and birds, they have a cortex. It is something that is not really elaborated until you get to mammals, and is not really, really elaborated until you get to primates. The cortex is about all that abstract stuff, abstract reasoning, processing, long-term memories, all of that, and that becomes very pertinent here. Hemorrhage, and thanks to the reptilian brain, you turn on the stress-response. See that menacing moose, and thanks to the limbic system, you turn on the stress-response. Think about children in refugee camps, think about ozone layers thinning out, think about your eventual mortality, think about a fictional character who evokes emotions in you, and suddenly, you might turn on the stress-response. Suddenly your cortex does a classically cortical thing, some abstract thought, and suddenly your heart is beating faster. Suddenly, your breathing rate may have decreased. Suddenly your salivary glands are doing something different. Suddenly, you've regulated your autonomic nervous system. What that implies is for one thing, what the cortex has is lots of ways of speaking to the limbic system and speaking to that reptilian part of the brain. You think a thought, and in some ways, that reptilian part of the brain reacts as if you're hemorrhaging. Somehow it reacts as if this is a physiologically real event.

You had better bet, throughout this course as we deal with us and our stressors, not our stressors being chased by predators, our stressors of psychosocial nature, what we're going to be dealing with is this ability of the cortex to do its abstract sort of thing, and suddenly your body reacts as if it were a real menace. This is another way of stating the central concept of the course. By the time we get to these psychosocially sophisticated humans and primates, we have that ability to change the body's functioning with thought, with emotion, with memory. If it's the right kind of adverse thought, emotion, memory, and you do it chronically, you will be suffering from the consequences of activating your stress-response too often.

In a lecture to come, in 2 in fact, we will be dealing with one of the more interesting domains of what your cortex can do to the rest of your brain. Your cortex thinking about extremely sad things, and suddenly, your body reacts differently. What's the building block we've just seen neuroanatomically? As we will see, this is a lot about what a depression is about. Obviously highly simplified, nonetheless, some sort of a sense of how to begin thinking about how the brain regulates psychosocial manifestations throughout the body. That's our first half.

Remember, we've got our 2 halves here. The first one is the nervous system, regulating the autonomic, the automatic, the involuntary, and the unconscious parts of your body by way of neuroprojections down your spine, this autonomic nervous system; and as we've heard, there's a second type of regulation which is by way of hormones. Hormones evoke a whole lot of fancy definitional stuff. Here's a hormone. Here's what it consists of. You've got, for example, a brain cell, a neuron which dribbles out some chemical messenger, and it goes a thousandth of an inch until it hits the next neuron, and it changes something or other in that neuron's function. What you've got is a neurotransmitter. Instead now, you have that neuron that secretes this same exact chemical messenger, except this time instead of going a tiny distance to the next neuron, it gets in the bloodstream where it can circulate throughout the body and affect something going on in your ankles. What we've just defined is a hormone. A hormone is a chemical messenger which can come from a brain cell or cells throughout the body, as we'll see, and it is blood borne, and as a result, it can affect events throughout your body.

Of course amid all of the hormones that are coming down the pike that we will learn about and all of their consequences, some of which are bad news in the face of chronic stress, the question then becomes: What regulates hormone release? The same sort of question as what regulates that autonomic nervous system, what regulates hormone release; and figuring out the answer to this has been a great chapter of history of physiology.

What regulates hormone release? Hormones come from glands. That's kind of a definition of a gland. A gland secretes hormones, chemical messengers that get blood borne. A gland secretes hormones, glands like ovaries, testes, adrenals, and thyroid, that sort of thing. What tells them when to secrete their particular hormones? What everyone thought they knew endlessly, absolute, iconic, textbook knowledge was, these glands know what they're doing. These glands are autonomous. These glands themselves decide: When am I going to secrete progesterone? When am I going to secrete thyroid hormone? The glands are self-regulating. The glands somehow know when to do their thing.

This was a dominant model around 1900, and in fact, it gave rise to one of the truly weird chapters of endocrine history, and it had to do with aging. Scientists at the time were trying to figure out what aging is about and they were just figuring out at the time that there is some interesting hormonal stuff that comes out of the testes, testosterone. There's interesting stuff there. I don't think they had quite the term at that point. The theory then became: What causes aging? Aging is due to declining levels of testosterone, taking away your vigor. As we'll see, there are 2 problems to that. One is that this, in fact, is not entirely the case of what goes on and testosterone does not play this role. Second problem is that it ignores aging in like 51% of the population, those folks without testes. In any case, this is what all those aging male scientists focused on at the time. So if you believe, number 1 that declining testosterone levels with aging have a lot to do with the aging process, and number 2 that the testes know what they're doing, they decide when to secrete the testosterone thus aging testes are not as good at secreting it, you come up with what was state-of-the art medicine at the time, which is, give some guy a new set of testes. What was done during this magical era of endocrinology is people would have bits of goat testes or monkey testes transplanted, put under their skin. In the view at the time, the testes would be off and running, these new ones with young vigorous amounts of testosterone release, and that would just reverse the aging process. This was all the rage. Captains of the industry, heads of state, would go off to fancy sanitariums to get themselves their monkey gland extract. This was known as the monkey gland phenomenon because people at the time were not allowed to say outrageous, blasphemous terms like "testes," but this was the monkey gland craze.

It turns out that none of this is what was going on because your testes don't know what they're doing, nor do your ovaries, nor do your kidneys or your thyroid or your adrenals. These glands, these peripheral glands, turned out not to be autonomous. In other words, they were not deciding when to secrete their hormones. Someplace else in the body was doing this. Thus we transition to the next level of regulation. Of course you may ask, nonetheless, why all of these guys, after they were getting their monkey gland transplants were reporting these wondrous effects of rejuvenating. I think what we have is this grand placebo effect. You go to this place. You pay a ton of money, and they transplant all sorts of distressing monkey parts into your butt, and you've got a strong incentive at that point to suddenly feel like a young stud again, one big placebo effect.

The peripheral glands don't know what they're doing. What does, though? We transition up at this point to the pituitary gland. By the 1940s, 1950s, what became clear is it was the pituitary secreting its whole array of hormones which would then go in the bloodstream and tell the various glands what to do, tell them when to secrete their hormones. This gave rise to one of the great sound bites of physiology, and this was what the pituitary was. In fact, I endlessly encountered this, like lots of folks in my generation. I grew up reading the *Reader's Digest* in the bathroom, and amid all their articles, they had this one continuing series, "I Am Joe's Liver," "I Am Joe's Stomach," "I Am Joe's Heart," "I Am [Jo's] Ovaries," this whole sort of series of articles they had, and somewhere in there, eventually you would get the "I Am Joe's Pituitary." Out would come the inevitable sound bite there, which is the pituitary is the master gland.

Turns out, the pituitary isn't the master gland, and by the 1950s, top people in the field were realizing that the pituitary doesn't know what it's doing on its own. It is not autonomous; it's getting directions from someplace else. This shifted to what, at the time, was an outrageous notion, which is the brain is the master gland. The brain is releasing hormones that tell the pituitary what hormones to release, which tell the peripheral glands. This was outrageous at the time because endocrinology had this somewhat sort of lowbrow feel to this, and neurobiologists and brain scientists did not like the notion one bit that this gleaming, analytical, computer-like brain actually was like drooling hormones out of some gland. This seemed very unappetizing, and it took a huge amount of time for people to actually prove that the brain, specifically the hypothalamus, a part of the brain that sits just above the pituitary, the hypothalamus releases hypothalamic hormones which tell the pituitary what to do.

The search for hypothalamic hormones was this grand, grand race between 2 individuals, 2 scientists—one named Andrew Schally, the other named Roger Guillemin—who started off working together. Presumably one night over the test tubes, one of them made a snide comment about the other one's hairdo or something. They broke up this collaboration, and they began one of the great competitions in science, the competition to isolate the first hypothalamic hormones. It took them years and years and years, and because, as far as everybody else was concerned, these imaginary hormones—if they existed— were in such tiny amounts because all they had to do was just go down here and tell the pituitary what it does all it needed to do was travel a half inch or so that there wasn't going to be much of the stuff. How do you isolate it? How do you prove the stuff is there? These guys had to pioneer these approaches of getting thousands of pig hypothalami that they got from stock houses, and cow hypothalami where they would then extract various factors from there and throw them onto pituitaries that were sitting in petri dishes and see if the pituitary suddenly did something different that made sense. Ah-ha, somewhere in this thimbleful of stuff we poured in, there's this hypothalamic factor that's relevant. Huge amount of work, all of this, competing for who got contracts with which stockyard, grad students in each of the 2 labs sort of not talking to the ones from the other ones, huge competition amid this great skepticism as to whether these hypothalamic hormones even existed. It took them years and decades, and eventually they showed that the hypothalamus is the master gland. You'd better bet, the limbic system and the cortex is telling the hypothalamus when to secrete its particular hormones that tell the pituitary what to do, which then tells the peripheral glands.

These 2 guys got their Nobel prizes for doing so and, bizarrely, you might ask what would seem to be a simple question is well which of them won the race, which got there first? It depends on quite how you define winning, and I won't go into the details of that because whomever I wind up casting a vote for, folks on the other side of the argument will come and stab me for doing so. This, though, was a major landmark event showing how the brain is the thing that ultimately regulates hormones, the endocrine system. Thus you have what are now termed axes, endocrine axes. You can have the ovarian axis where the brain secretes a particular hormone which tells the pituitary to secrete its particular hormone which goes to the ovaries, and suddenly out comes estrogen. Or you could have the thyroid axis. The brain secretes a different hormone which gets the pituitary to secrete a different one and gets the thyroid gland to secrete thyroid hormone, these endocrine axes.

We've got all of this working that way. Mind you, there are a few exceptions. Not all hormones are under the control of the brain, but for our purposes, the hypothalamus to pituitary to peripheral gland sequence is what we will work with, and what we will work with also is that notion of the limbic system and cortex telling the hypothalamus when to secrete its hormones, along with limbic and cortical influences on that anatomic nervous system. How do these things wind up working? What you've got are an array of hormones which constitute the stress-response and an array of autonomic components. What we'll go over now are the major players in the stress-response. I cannot possibly emphasize too much at this point, so do not panic. Do not panic when hearing these terms. If they are important, you will hear the names of these hormones a gazillion times in the lectures to come. This is merely just to introduce the first players. Do not even dream of writing them down.

Which hormones are secreted during the stress-response? We've already heard that the sympathetic nervous system is turned on, and the main hormone that it regulates is adrenaline, in the United States typically known as epinephrine, in England and commonwealth countries as adrenaline. It comes out of the adrenal glands. The sympathetic nervous system sends a message to the adrenals, out comes adrenaline, epinephrine. The next major player is a class of steroid hormones that come out of the adrenal glands as well called glucocorticoids. I happen to be in love with glucocorticoids because I've spent the last 30 years studying them; human version, hydrocortisone, we are going to hear tons more about these. Other players that get secreted increased secretory rates during stress: prolactin, glucagon, beta-endorphin. We will get back to these. Meanwhile in the next county, there are the hormones whose secretion is inhibited during stress, the parasympathetic nervous system, hormones like growth hormone, insulin, the reproductive hormones. We will see how all of these pieces fit together.

A couple of final qualifiers here, everything that I described here as the classic stress-response is built around bringing about the classic, clichéd sound bite about what the stress-response is about, something mentioned earlier. It is turning on the fight-or-flight response. Whatever the number of Fs are in there, this was the classic picture first pulled together by Walter Cannon, one of the godfathers of stress physiology, back in the '20s.

The stress-response is about emergency arousal, fighting, fleeing, but it turns out that's not what was always happening, and a few years ago, a scientist named Shelley Taylor began to point out that this may be an artifact by scientists spending way too much time studying this weird subset of subjects: males. The stress-response in males is predominantly about fight-or-flight. In females—it can be in lots of species—doing affiliated behaviors, running and making sure your kids are OK. That sort of thing mediated by completely different hormones; and just showing she means business, Taylor came up with a sound bite of her own, often what the stress-response is about is tend-and-befriend. We've just made the picture a little bit more complicated. Some of it is about fight-or-flight, some of it tend-and-befriend. Nonetheless, we've now gotten the major players: increased secretion of epinephrine, glucocorticoids, glucagon, prolactin, those guys, decreased activation of the parasympathetic nervous system, growth hormone. Again, we are going to hear more about all of these.

Here as a couple of final qualifiers as well. What I'm implying here is with any sort of stressor—physical or psychosocial—you turn on the exact same stress-response. I've been emphasizing this since the first lecture. In other words, you secrete epinephrine and glucocorticoids. You don't secrete the exact same amount for every type of stressor. A very trendy thing in the field now is looking at stress signatures, particular stressors have different epinephrine to glucocorticoid ratios, minutia. For our purposes, each stressor turns on roughly the same stress-response.

A final detail, and one that seems like sheer obscurity, which is: "Oh, yeah, not everybody has the exact same stress-response." There are individual differences. As we will see, individual differences are what the rest of this course is about. It is about coping, it's about learning to do things differently. The fact that all individuals differ in how their bodies respond to stress is great, because once we figure out the folks who are doing it just right, then we've got a model to go after.

That now sets us up for our first transition in the course, now that we've got the major players of the stress-response in hand, to begin to look at how it plays out in a particular physiological system: the cardiovascular system. What is the acute stress-response that's good news? What is the chronic stress-response about which is terrible news?

Stress and Your Heart
Lecture 3

> This brings up a point ... that's very well summarized by Elie Wiesel—concentration camp survivor, Nobel Laureate—a phrase that he has often used, which is, the opposite of love is not hate. The opposite of love is indifference. ... Physiologically, quite similarly, ... extreme love, extreme hate, what your sympathetic nervous system can be doing is quite similar.

If you wanted to pick the definitive, iconic outpost of your body that gets done in by chronic stress, the cardiovascular system is the one. There's a lion there, and you have to go running for your life; you had better hope you turn on the cardiovascular stress-response.

It's actually very simple to do: You secrete **glucocorticoids** and **epinephrine**. You turn on the sympathetic nervous system and turn off the parasympathetic. Your heart rate goes up; your blood pressure goes up. The entire process is very adaptive because now you're delivering more blood, more glucose, and more oxygen throughout your body. Because this is a crisis, you're saving your life by sending blood where it's needed, the thigh muscles and the lungs, for example. Meanwhile, you divert blood away from the parts of your body that don't need it, such as your gut and your reproductive organs.

So what happens when you do all of this too long because of chronic stress, especially chronic psychological stress? Increase your blood pressure for 30 seconds and run away from the lion—you're saving your life. Increase your blood pressure chronically, and you are suffering from hypertension.

How does that happen? You have periods of the heart working really hard, pumping with more force, pumping more frequently. Blood pressure is increasing. It's going through the blood vessels with more force, distending the blood vessels out more from the sheer force of it. The blood vessels, in response, slowly begin to build up more muscle wrapping around them. This makes the blood vessels more rigid, which requires more force to get the blood through there. You increase the blood pressure evermore, and we've got a vicious cycle here. That's how you begin to get problems with hypertension.

What's the price that you pay? Ultimately, the heart is just a big old mechanical pump, and it has a lot of the same principles if you make it work very hard. It begins to wear out after a while. Enough of that slamming of blood against the walls of the blood vessels and you begin to get little bits of damage there, little bits of tearing and scarring that wind up getting inflamed. You begin to get a bit of a plaque. Now along comes fat and glucose and cholesterol, and that stuff is more likely to stick onto this inflamed little plaque.

> **Once the coronary vessels are damaged, when you increase blood flow during a period of stress, they no longer vasodilate; they constrict.**

That's a problem, but you can set yourself up for a second problem, and this is one that has been shown in a lot of experimental settings. You have hypertension, which could lead to damage to your blood vessels. Very interesting research shows that if you couple hypertension with a high-fat diet, you get far more vascular damage than either alone. What this brings us to is the third outpost of what can go wrong. It turns out coronary blood vessels, the blood vessels bringing blood to your heart, are not vessels you want to damage from chronic hypertension. Normally there is something really helpful that coronary blood vessels do when they're perfectly healthy. In a crisis, you need more blood delivered to your heart, so a healthy coronary blood vessel will vasodilate: increase, become looser so more blood can go blasting through. But once the coronary vessels are damaged, when you increase blood flow during a period of stress, they no longer vasodilate; they constrict.

You're totally up the creek now. You've got damaged coronary blood vessels, and exactly when your heart needs more energy during a major stressor, these blood vessels stab you in the heart by constricting even more. Your heart, thus, does not get enough blood flow. It doesn't get enough oxygen, enough glucose, or enough energy, and you have myocardial ischemia. Your heart muscles are not getting enough of the stuff they need. ∎

Important Terms

epinephrine: A hormone released during times of stress by the adrenal glands under the control of the sympathetic nervous system; it is also known as adrenaline. Epinephrine plays a key role in virtually all aspects of the stress-response.

glucocorticoid: Any of a class of hormones released from the adrenal gland during stress that play a key role in virtually all facets of the stress-response. The primate/human version is cortisol, also known as hydrocortisone. Synthetic versions often prescribed by physicians include dexamethasone and prednisone.

Suggested Reading

Sapolsky, *Why Zebras Don't Get Ulcers*, chap. 3.

Questions to Consider

1. How is the cardiovascular stress-response perfect for your body while you're escaping a predator?

2. How does chronic stress cause atherosclerosis?

Stress and Your Heart
Lecture 3—Transcript

We are now ready to start with our first organ system, looking at the cardiovascular system. We now have 2 lectures' worth of preparation under our belts, the first lecture giving us the organizing theme for this entire series, being this dichotomy. If you are turning on the stress-response because you are getting stressed like a normal mammal, you are doing something acute, energetic, explosive that's not going to last for too long. The stress-response is wonderful, saves your life, highly adaptive. On the other hand, a central theme of this entire course is if you turn on the stress-response too long, too often, for purely psychological reasons, that is when you set yourself up for getting sick.

That was the main theme coming out of Lecture 1. Lecture 2 provided us with the tools, the toolbox, of how you go about activating the stress-response, which hormones you begin to secrete more of—epinephrine, glucocorticoids, some other ones—which hormones you secrete less of—growth hormone, those reproductive sex hormones—and collectively, this is what powers your body to do that wonderfully adaptive stuff in the face of an acute stressor, and all of that unhealthy disease-causing stuff in the face of chronic stress.

With that said, now we can begin to apply those exact principles to the cardiovascular system. In a lot of ways, if you wanted to pick the definitive, the iconic outpost of your body that gets done in by chronic stress, this is the one. Right off the bat, we know exactly how to apply the short-term logic. You are walking home from work, you're not quite paying attention, you come around the corner, and oh no, there's a lion there and you have to go running for your life, and you better hope you turn on the cardiovascular stress-response at that point.

It's actually very simple to do. If you don't worry about much in the way of details, you need to secrete glucocorticoids and epinephrine. You need to turn on the sympathetic nervous system, back one lecture, that SNS. Also, as we know from the previous lecture, if you are going to turn on the sympathetic, you are going to turn off the parasympathetic. You've now got lots of epinephrine, lots of glucocorticoids, in your bloodstream. Epinephrine directly increases cardiovascular activity. Glucocorticoids are interesting. They make it possible for epinephrine to work even more effectively—really fancy biochemistry there. What they also do is they get up into your brain in very primitive "brain stemy" areas and send messages to the neurons there, the neurons that send messages down to your heart. Suddenly then, everything kicks into gear. Everything is more activated. Your heart rate goes up. Your blood pressure goes up, blood pressure secondarily from the heart rate going. You are pumping the blood out. More frequently, it comes bashing back with more force pumped out again. The entire process is very adaptive because now you're delivering more blood, more glucose, more oxygen, all over your body. You don't want to deliver it all over your body, though. This is a crisis and you're not saving your life by increasing blood flow to your ears; you're saving your life by sending it where it's needed, the thigh muscles for example, which are going to save your life, your lungs which have to be breathing fast enough to supply the oxygen, the parts of the brain being stimulated by those glucocorticoids, the part of the brain that powers your heart, your lungs, all of that. Those are the ones that need more blood. Meanwhile, there are parts of your body that don't need the excess blood where you decrease the blood flow. You divert it away from there. You divert it from your gut, from your reproductive organs, all of that, and this makes wonderful sense.

This was actually something that was first noted around 1833. This was a study by a bunch of physician scientists. There was a man who had gotten some gunshot wound, apparently in his gut, and it had left a gaping hole there. While the doctors were about to fix him up there, they noticed something interesting which was it was nice and red and rosy underneath with the blood flowing there. They would get the guy angry about something, and it would suddenly get pale. It would blanch, it would be a much lighter color, the blood flow to the intestines would decrease. This is just sheer speculation, but maybe the guy was getting angry because the damn doctors were sitting there as though they were doing a science project on him instead of sewing him up. This was some of the first evidence that stress will divert blood flow from an unessential area like the gut, that same logic from the first lecture: digest food, grow, reproduce, do all that stuff later if there is a later. It's not essential right now. Deliver the blood where it's needed.

That's great, you've increased your heart rate. You've increased your blood pressure, your breathing rate. You're delivering the energy where it's needed, that's terrific. One additional thing you need to do though. You're that zebra, you've just gotten ripped to shreds by a lion, and you're bleeding like mad. What do you want to do at that point? This may be a good point to try to get some more blood into your system, try to decrease the amount of blood flowing out, and try to replace it. How do you decrease the blood flowing out? One of the things you do at that point is you make a certain type of red blood cell, a platelet, a certain type of blood cell, and thanks to epinephrine, during a crisis the platelets get stickier, they get gummier, more viscous; and what do they do? They facilitate forming a clot to stop the outflow of blood.

That's a great adaptation to decrease the amount of blood going out. You've got though another problem here, which is you've lost a lot of the blood already. You want some replacement blood. How are you going to do that? One solution is to make yourself some more blood cells, more red blood cells and white blood cells, and that's great. That's a great solution, but it's going to take you days or weeks to build those up again, so how else can you replace missing blood? Get some more water into your circulation. Increase your blood volume with more fluid. That'll make it easier to increase the blood pressure, get some more fluid in there. Where are you going to get the fluid from? You're obviously in this physical crisis, and you're not going to suddenly get a lot more thirsty and drink a terrine of something, but where can you get water from? You can get it from your kidneys. What are your kidneys usually doing? They're sitting there, filtering water in and out of your circulation, salt balance, all sorts of stuff, and what you need to do is send a message down to the kidneys saying re-absorb some of that water. Don't turn it into urine. What you secrete is a hormone from your pituitary called ADH, antidiuretic hormone. A diuretic is something that makes you urinate. Tea for example is a diuretic. An antidiuretic hormone is something that makes you antidiurese; it makes you stop urinating and causes your kidneys to retain more of the water.

That's great, that's terrific; your blood pressure has gone up. Your heart rate has gone up. You're delivering it where it's needed. You're clotting blood if you're bleeding badly, and you've got this great mechanism here by which you reabsorb water out of the kidneys back into your circulation to maintain blood volume. This makes wonderful sense except this brings up one of these questions, a question which is so rarely aired in our public schools, part of the tragedy that is public education these days, so little discussed in educational venues. This is this mystery of an enigma wrapped within a mystery, which is why is it if you're so, so, so stressed, sometimes you're going to pee in your pants? This doesn't make any sense because we've just seen the logic during the stress-response is, reabsorb water from the kidney, all of that. Why is it, though, that you have this paradoxical finding, nonetheless, that with the onset of severe stress, you lose control? This is sufficiently the case that in many of the states where there are executions still, people are typically executed in diapers because you tend to wet your pants.

In order to appreciate the answer to this, we have to wrestle with the deep, abiding question of why do we have bladders? A bladder is kind of weird. The kidney is great. The kidney is wonderful. As we said, you put water in, you take water out. You futz around with sodium. It's great; you could do it all day long. It's a great hobby. By the time stuff gets down to your kidneys, leaves your kidneys, and then heads to your bladder, your bladder is just this bladder thing. It doesn't do anything regulatory. It just stores stuff. By the time the urine goes south of your kidneys there, you can kiss it goodbye. You can't get it back from the bladder. It's just sitting there.

What's a bladder for in a lot of species? All sorts of species scent mark. What they do is individuals use their bladder, build up urine, and they go and they urinate around the periphery of their territory. That gives all sorts of "stay-out-of-here-I-mean-it" signals to anybody else smelling the urine. Scent marking is a very frequent use for urine in various species. That makes sense to have a bladder. However, we're not a scent-marking species. That's typically not what we do, although there are some interesting exceptions. I was actually reading recently, when General George Patton was leading the troops into Germany during World War II, finally getting into Germany, apparently there was the point when they got to the Rhine River that Patton walked out to the middle of the bridge, and in front of his adoring, triumphant, cheering troops, he very ritualistically peed into the Rhine and announced, "I've been waiting a long time to do that." Actually this seems to be a frequent theme in the military. I'm not quite sure why, but apparently also during the Korean War, very often you had American troops lined up on one side of the Yalu River, Chinese on the other, and apparently at this interface, this point of stalemate, the American troops would regularly line up and urinate into the Yalu River, take that, as they scent mark there.

Despite these deeply moving historical circumstances of people urinating like hamsters, nonetheless, we still have this mystery. What's a bladder for? It's not clear. The most important thing about it is it doesn't seem to be doing much, and here you have your classic acute physical crisis. You are running for your life. The lion is coming after you, and suddenly you've got your choice. You could run for your life with or without 5 pounds of fluid sloshing around there on the bottom. You void your bladder. You get rid of the excess urine. We now see exactly how the system works here, what's going on, acute stressor, increased blood pressure, increased heart rate, retain the fluids there, clot, send it where it's needed or else, makes wonderful sense for the short-term stress-response.

Now we barrel into our, by now, obligatory second half of this dichotomy. What happens when you do all of this too long because of chronic stress, especially chronic psychological stress? What you do is increase your blood pressure for 30 seconds, run away from the lion. You're saving your life. Increase your blood pressure chronically, and you are suffering from chronic hypertension, chronically elevated blood pressure. A little bit of the nuts and bolts first. How does that happen? You have periods of the heart working really hard, pumping with more force, pumping more frequently. Blood pressure is increasing. It's going through the blood vessels with more force, distending the blood vessels out more from the sheer force of it. The blood vessels, in response, slowly begin to build up more muscle wrapping around them in response to this distension. They build up more muscle, which makes the blood vessels more rigid, which requires more force to get the blood through there. You increase the blood pressure evermore, and we've got a vicious cycle here. That's how you begin to get problems with hypertension.

What's the price that you pay? First off, at the level of your heart. What happens with heart function when you are chronically hypertensive? You get cardiologists, and they're pretty impressed with the heart and would try to convince you of the same. Ultimately, the heart is just some big old mechanical pump like you could buy at Sears, and it has a lot of the same principles if you make it work very hard. It begins to wear out after a while. One version of the wearing out is if blood pressure is greatly increased, your heart muscle walls will pay for it. The heart pumps out the blood from one of its chambers, and the blood circulates around and comes back into a different chamber of the heart. By definition of being pumped out with a lot more force, it's going to slam back in there with more force and pound away on the wall there, and it happens to be the left ventricle, that's the area that takes the brunt of returning blood under high force. The muscle there begins to enlarge. You've got a hypertrophy of the left ventricle. What is that wobbly sort of extra muscle on that side? It begins to set the heart up for irregularities.

That's a problem. That's a first step there where you can get into trouble thanks to chronic hypertension. What about at the level of your blood vessels themselves? What could be happening there that gets you into trouble? Where you get your biggest problems has to do with the principle that runs through a lot of physiological systems in your circulatory system, your pulmonary system, a process called bifurcation. Coming out of your heart, descending for example, is one big huge blood vessel called the descending aorta—don't worry about the name of it—one big, huge blood vessel which after a certain distance splits into 2, bifurcates into 2. After a while there are 2 smaller vessels. Each one of those is going to split into 2, bifurcate, bifurcate, bifurcate endlessly until you've bifurcated your way down into little capillaries. What the circulatory system is about is a whole bunch of these bifurcations.

What's one of the things that happen when you increase blood pressure? The bifurcation, the point right where it divides, that's the point of the wall of the blood vessel that is splitting this river of blood and splitting it in 2. Another way of stating it is that's the part of your blood vessel that's getting pounded with the most force there. You increase blood pressure, and you begin to have a problem that's straight out of ninth grade physics, and it describes all sorts of fluids moving through any sort of tube. This is why your bathroom plumbing wears out after a while. By definition, if you've got a tube and you've got fluid moving through it, and it moves through with more force, you've increased your blood pressure. Move it through with more force, and you eventually begin to get fluid turbulence, and little eddies, and little tsunamis of blood there, and as you begin to get the turbulence, what it does is it slams into the walls of the blood vessels with more force. Again, particularly taking the brunt of it are those points of bifurcation.

Enough of that slamming against the walls of the blood vessels and you begin to get little bits of damage there, little bits of tearing, little bits of scarring, little bits of spots there that wind up getting inflamed. That turns out to be a critical process there, one that's appreciated more and more in cardiology. You begin to get little bits of inflammation around these spots of vessel damage. Inflammation, there are all sorts of inflammatory cells that wind up getting in there, start sticking to there, and suddenly, it's beginning to glom things up there a bit. You're beginning to get a bit of a plaque. Why does that get you in trouble? It's for lots of reasons. Now along comes fat and glucose and cholesterol, and that stuff is more likely to stick onto this inflamed little plaque. Where are the fat and glucose and cholesterol coming from? That's exactly the stuff you're mobilizing out of storage sites to feed your exercising muscle, so you get this double whammy here between the metabolic stress-response and the cardiovascular one.

This whole business about inflammation has really come to the forefront in the field. Twenty years ago, if you could only measure one thing in the bloodstream and you wanted to get a sense about how somebody's cardiovascular system was doing, what would you measure? You would measure somebody's cholesterol levels. That was the number everybody got obsessed over. That was the number you would use a pickup line at parties, bragging about how low your cholesterol was. That was just the defining point of the field. Of recent years, people have realized more and more, your amount of cholesterol is important, but something else is more important. In other words, you could have just cholesterol coming out the wazoo. You could be eating 3 dozen eggs a day, and if you had absolutely unblemished healthy blood vessel walls, the cholesterol really doesn't have much to stick to. It's not until you begin to get inflammation, inflammatory damage there, that the cholesterol has a spot that it is going to home in on, the inflammation appears to be the starting step. It's for that reason that there has been this transition in the field from, we can only measure one thing, measuring cholesterol, over to measuring one thing, something called CRP, C-reactive protein, which is a marker of the amount of inflammation.

That's a problem, but you can set yourself up for a second problem here, and this is one that has been shown in a lot of experimental settings. You have hypertension, and that could set you up for damage to your blood vessels. Very interesting research, very clear- cut research, done with a non-human primate, showing that if you couple hypertension with a high-fat diet, you get far more vascular damage than either alone. This turns out to make perfect sense. One reason is obvious, you get more fat, and we've just heard if you've got inflamed damaged blood vessels, more fat there is going to be more likely to glom on and cause an arthrosclerotic plaque and plug up your blood vessels. As we're going to hear in a subsequent lecture, people are just realizing there's a really interesting, unexpected additional reason, which is, you have a high-fat diet and you're going to get more fat stored in your body. Something that just knocked fatologists on their rear as this became clear is fat cells are able to secrete certain inflammatory messengers, totally interesting and unexpected. What's our implication here? A high-fat diet is always also going to increase the amount of these inflammatory signals coming out of your fat cells.

When you have a high-fat diet, whatever damage there is to the blood vessels, they're more likely to get inflammatory plaques forming, and the elevated fat, glucose, cholesterol is more likely to stick onto, and you're going to get more atherosclerotic disease. What that sets you up for are a number of different types of potential disasters. You block the blood vessel here entirely, or it's partially blocked and you get enough blood force, enough sheering force, that eventually you knock this little plaque loose, you get what's called a thrombus, and that could get you into trouble now if it goes wandering up into one of your heart vessels, coronary heart vessels, and clogs things there. You might have a heart attack. If it gets into a vessel in the brain, you have a stroke, and not good.

What this brings us now to is this third outpost of what can go wrong. We've now seen how chronic hypertension, how chronic stress-induced hypertension can be bad news for your heart muscles, can be bad news for your blood vessels. Now to focus in on a particular type of blood vessel, one I just alluded to, the blood vessels bringing blood to your heart, your coronary blood vessels. When you think about it at first, this actually doesn't make any sense at all. Wait a second, your heart, which is just swimming around in oceans of blood, your heart has to have specialized blood vessels feeding it blood when it's the heart? What it does is it's in contact with blood. This initially makes no sense, but think about how you might work in the building that regulates water flow through some reservoir, town reservoir and you work 15 feet away from the reservoir, and you're thirsty. If you're thirsty, you don't go out to the reservoir with a bucket and drop it down in there and pull some water out of there to sip the rest of the day. What do you do? You do what you do anywhere else in that city; you go to a water fountain that's in there in the building. It is exactly equivalent to what happens in the heart. Heart muscle can't feed itself from these oceans of blood blasting in and out, so you have coronary blood vessels.

It turns out coronary blood vessels are not vessels you want to damage from chronic hypertension. Normally there is something really helpful that coronary blood vessels do when they're perfectly healthy. Along comes the lion, you're running for your life, it's a crisis, you need more blood delivered to your heart because your heart is working so hard. In a healthy coronary blood vessel, something terrific happens there, they vasodilate, they increase, they become looser so even more blood can go blasting through there and bring energy, and your heart can keep up with demands. That's great. Begin to damage those coronary blood vessels, that inflammatory plaque stuff, and something so insidious, so unfair happens at that point in terms of how things can go so, so wrong. What begins to happen is once those coronary vessels are damaged, when you increase blood flow during a period of stressor, these vessels no longer vasodilate. They constrict. They constrict, and exactly when your heart needs a ton of blood, there's less of it coming through. This is not a good thing. How does this work? It turns out there are some chemicals that are released from the coronary blood vessels when the heart is working hard that vasodilate, a bunch of these. Interestingly, one of those chemicals is related to nitric oxide, so they normally work there, but begin to get damaged coronary blood vessels with plaques and stuff, and these nice, helpful vasodilatory signals are unable to get out there.

You're totally up the creek now. You've got damaged coronary blood vessels, and exactly when your heart needs more energy during a major stressor, that's exactly when these blood vessels stab you in the heart by constricting even more. Your heart, thus, does not get enough blood flow. It doesn't get enough oxygen. It doesn't get enough glucose, doesn't get enough energy, and you have cardiac ischemia, myocardial ischemia. Your heart muscles are not getting enough of the stuff they need. Studying that was traditionally kind of hard to do because the only way you could see if somebody had this problem with cardiac ischemia would be to put them in this very artificial setting, take them into the doctor's office and make them run to the point of exhaustion on a treadmill when you've got all the electrodes, stuck up with them. You could get information, but this admittedly is a very artificial setting. Not a lot of people who are potentially having emerging heart disease are having problems with it because they are running up dozens of flights of stairs nonstop and then seeing what their blood pressure was like. Instead, the problems pop up throughout the day.

The question became: What's happening to function of coronary vessels throughout the day? When you begin to have vessels that are damaged, who knows? You can't measure it. Some years back somebody came up with the wonderful technology where you can measure it. You could do what soon was called ambulatory cardiology where you've got these little devices there to monitor, and it could monitor what's going on with your heart throughout the day, and back came a surprise, which is people who begin to have damaged coronary blood vessels, they're having those little ischemic insults to their heart muscles just all the time throughout the day. This is not the realm of massive, sudden physical stressor and that history of stress-induced damage to your blood vessels. You begin to pay for it then. It was shocking to everyone how often you get little problems with that, and how often then the heart muscle is not getting enough energy and it hurts. Angina is the term for it.

We've seen here ways in which you can get into trouble by too much sympathetic arousal with chronic stress damaging your heart muscles, damaging vessels throughout your body, damaging the coronary blood vessels, all of that conceptually due to too much of a "let's kick into action" signal coming, too much sympathetic nervous system. There's a flip side to it as well, which is you can also get into trouble if you have too little of the inhibitory signal coming in there, too little of parasympathetic tone. You remember sympathetic emergency arousal, parasympathetic, calm, vegetative. Activate the parasympathetic nervous system, and your heart is going to slow down by way of something called the vagus nerve.

You can get into trouble either by too much sympathetic screaming at your heart, or too little vagal calming, or if you're really in for trouble, both of them are going wrong, and this is another way you can have problems there. Interesting way you could pick up on that, showing just how delicate this whole system is. Inhale, take a breath in, and you slightly stimulate your sympathetic nervous system, and your heart rate increases a little bit. Exhale, and you stimulate parasympathetic and things slow down a little bit. If the system is working wonderfully, every time you inhale, you get a little sympathetic hiccup, exhale parasympathetic and you look at the pattern of beats, they're a little bit longer, a little shorter, a little bit longer, they're quite variable. Begin to have a damaged parasympathetic nervous system, if stress has been driving it to the point where it really doesn't do what it's supposed to do, you inhale, and your heart rate speeds up a little bit. You exhale, and because the parasympathetic nervous system has been driven into a coma, you don't get as much of a slowing down. What does that look like? You look at somebody's heart rate pattern, and there's not as much of that variability. That's a very hot subject these days for picking up problems with parasympathetic nervous system.

All of these are scenarios where chronic stress will chronically pound away at your blood vessels, your heart, all of that. All of that can potentially culminate into one of the great crises which is sudden cardiac death, and we all know the dramatic version of it. Guy gets terrible news, and he's wailing, and suddenly he clutches his chest and keels over dead in sudden cardiac arrest, and for the most part this is a movie plot. This is very rare. Nonetheless, it pops up in all sorts of settings. One example is during the 1991 Gulf War there were attacks from Iraqi SCUD missiles onto Israel; and the number of people killed by missiles was considerably smaller than the number of people who had heart attacks during the period of the missile strikes. Sudden cardiac arrest, massive increase in cardiac demand, you're running away from a lion. You're running a marathon. You are just euphoric and hyperactive and agitated because you've just taken some guy's pawn in this chess game. Whatever it is, you can push things to a point where down you go, it is too extreme.

This brings up a final, really interesting point, which is: What about when you get people who have heart attacks, even sudden cardiac death, not because a lion is chasing them, but because they're in the middle of something wildly pleasurable, the archetypical example being, of course, the person who has a fatal heart attack right in the middle of sex. What is that about? We're talking about stress here. What's this going on? What this brings in here is the possibility of something such as fatal pleasure. It makes perfect sense. If you are leaping up with joy or leaping up with terror or leaping up with rage, you're leaping up. It's taking muscular work. Your heart has to work harder, and when you look closely at what the heart is up to when it's in an activated state, you cannot tell whether this is someone who is just about to commit murder or someone who is just about to have an orgasm.

This brings up a point that will come back again and again, and it's one that's very well summarized by Elie Wiesel—concentration camp survivor, Nobel Laureate—a phrase that he has often used, which is, the opposite of love is not hate. The opposite of love is indifference. In his context, what it's about is the opposite of love is not hate. The way you express the opposite of love is to perhaps be indifferent to somebody's suffering, to be indifferent to a people's suffering, to be indifferent enough not to have a rule of "never again will this happen to anyone." The opposite of love is not hate. Physiologically what we've just seen is, quite similarly, the opposite of love is not hate. Extreme love, extreme hate, what your sympathetic nervous system can be doing is quite similar. What all parts of your body are doing can be quite similar. This is a theme that will come back again and again.

What do we have at this point? We have our first organ system under our belts here, and we have our first clear evidence that this dichotomy really works. Short-term cardiovascular stress-response, wonderful adaptive news; chronic, it gets you into trouble in all sorts of ways. And this is the format, this is the general structure for all the lectures to come for a while as we move from one organ system to the next.

Stress, Metabolism, and Liquidating Your Assets
Lecture 4

Adult-onset diabetes, insulin-resistant diabetes, used to be this incredibly obscure outpost of disease. This was a problem that our great, great, great, great grandparents never thought about. ... It is a disease becoming more prevalent with Westernized lifestyle, putting on weight, becoming sedentary. ... This once obscure disease is slated to become the planet's biggest killer within a couple of decades or so, according to the estimates of the World Health Organization.

Metabolism is the process of how food goes from your gut to beginning to be useful to your body. There are basically 3 constituents in food: protein, carbohydrates, and fat. Your stomach and intestines do their thing, breaking down protein into amino acids, breaking down complex carbohydrates into simple sugars, and breaking down fat into fatty acids and glycerol. You are well fed: You've got, if anything, surplus amounts. What do you do? You store the stuff away in a complex storage form. You do exactly the opposite of the digestion that you have just gone through.

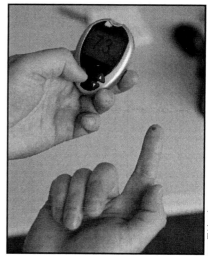

A glucometer measures the concentration of glucose in the blood.

How do you do that? The pivotal hormone that's involved is **insulin**. You secrete insulin in response to elevated nutrient levels in your bloodstream, or even in anticipation of a meal. Along comes an acute stressor. You need energy not stored away but powering whichever muscles are going to save your life. You break down the storage forms of energy and flush them into the circulation. And you do something else: You secrete glucocorticoids,

glucagon, and epinephrine. You mobilize stored energy forms, and you shut down insulin secretion so that you're not storing anything. This is not a good thing. Your metabolism normally allows you to store energy for the future. But when you enter a cycle of chronic stress, you mobilize energy, store it away, then mobilize it again. Our biochemistry of storage and mobilization is not 100% efficient; it costs a little bit to break them down and mobilize them again and again.

Metabolic syndrome encompasses an array of symptoms that increase your risk of metabolic disease and/or cardiovascular disease.

Another potential problem is **diabetes**. If you've got juvenile (Type 1) diabetes and are chronically stressed, this starts a vicious cycle. Each time you get stressed, you're releasing a flood of sugar into your bloodstream and then storing it away. You are doing the very opposite of what blood sugar control is about in diabetes: You're getting huge oscillations all over the place. Chronic stress makes glycemic control (control of sugar) more precarious for a person with diabetes. Type 2, or adult-onset, diabetes is coming to haunt modern Western societies. The problem here isn't too little insulin; it's an excess of nutrients. Typically, you are getting older in a Westernized way: You put on weight, you become more sedentary, and you've got all these excess nutrients in your bloodstream. What's the logical thing you would be doing at this point? Store away the excess. But your problem is you've stored so much away already that your fat cells are full. One additional step occurs: Your brain indirectly sends a signal to fat cell storage sites throughout your body and says, "Don't listen to any insulin. Become resistant to it; lose your sensitivity to it."

This insulin resistance can lead to hyperglycemia, which can lead to cardiovascular damage and increase your risk of metabolic disease. Suddenly, they are completely intertwined, which is the rationale behind the large catchment term for what can go wrong in this realm, **metabolic syndrome**. Metabolic syndrome encompasses an array of symptoms that increase your risk of metabolic disease and/or cardiovascular disease. It illustrates the concept that you can't put parts of your body into completely separate categories; you solve local challenges to homeostatic balance with adaptations far flung throughout your body. ∎

Important Terms

diabetes: Type 1 (juvenile) diabetes is an autoimmune disorder in which the pancreas is unable to secrete insulin. Type 2 (adult-onset; a.k.a. insulin-resistant) diabetes is a disorder, typically brought on by obesity, in which cells throughout the body have become resistant to the effects of insulin.

glucagon: A hormone released from the pancreas during stress that helps mobilize energy from storage sites in the body.

insulin: A hormone released from the pancreas that promotes the storage of glucose throughout the body. It is normally secreted when blood glucose levels rise; secretion is inhibited in the early phases of the stress-response.

metabolic syndrome: An emerging concept in medicine focusing on the fact that there is often overlap between the causes and symptoms of cardiovascular disease and of metabolic diseases such as diabetes; the syndrome refers to a constellation of symptoms that can include hypertension, obesity, hyperglycemia, and insulin resistance.

Suggested Reading

Rubin, *Diabetes for Dummies*.

Sapolsky, *Why Zebras Don't Get Ulcers*, chap. 4.

Questions to Consider

1. What do you normally do with excess energy in your circulation?

2. How does stress push you into adult-onset diabetes if you are just on the edge of having the disease?

Stress, Metabolism, and Liquidating Your Assets
Lecture 4—Transcript

We are back, ready for our next organ system to fall apart in the face of chronic stress. What we will focus on in this lecture is metabolism. Metabolism, the movement of energy into storage sites, out of storage sites, from your digestive tract into the circulation, and you already know what the punch line for this entire lecture is, which is when you have excess food, you store it away. When you are running for your life, you get the stuff out of storage, and it's all just minor details from here.

Metabolism, where do you start off? Metabolism, the process of how food goes from your gut after you've eaten it, to beginning to be useful to your body. Broadly there are 3 constituents that you can get into food. It's protein, it's carbs, and it's fat. Protein is made up of amino acids, and as per usual, do not panic if this is a level of detail that's more than you want, get the broad themes. Protein is made up of amino acids. You eat protein. Your stomach and intestines do their thing, and what you dump into the bloodstream are amino acids, the broken-down building blocks of protein.

Same thing, carbohydrates are complex collections of sugars, like glucose, from your gut to your bloodstream. It's the process of breaking down complex carbohydrates down to simple sugars. Finally, same theme, fat— fat going from your gut broken down into its constituent parts, fatty acids, glycerol. You've got your basic fuel, your energetic fuel in your bloodstream in the form of amino acids, in the form of free fatty acids, in the form of simple sugars, and we've got our first situation which is you've got excess of that stuff in your bloodstream. You are well fed. You've got, if anything, surplus amounts. What do you do? You store it away.

You store it away, and what you do is you store it back in the complex form that it started off in, and what we have here is our economic metaphor. You've got excess money, most of us don't put all our extra coins, making up our gazillions of dollars, we don't stuff them in our mattresses anymore. We take advantage of the large, complex world of economics, which I understand nothing about. You store it away as stocks and bonds, soybean futures, and who knows what else. You store the stuff away in a complex storage form. What do you do? You do exactly the opposite of the digestion that you already have gone through. You take the circulating amino acids. You stick them together as proteins, and you store them in various parts of your body. You take those simple sugars that are circulating around. You stick a bunch of them together, and you store them in the form of glycogen. Take those individual constituents of fat—free fatty acids, glycerol—you put them back together, and you store those away, very simple.

We've got this economic metaphor going for us, and when you have excess resources available what you do is you store them away. Along come the mechanisms to explain that. How do you do that? How does your body sense that you have an excess of nutrients in your bloodstream? How does it store it away? The pivotal hormone that's involved in all of this is insulin. Insulin which you secrete in response to elevated nutrient levels in your bloodstream, remarkably enough, insulin, which you even secrete in anticipation of a meal. If you eat dinner at 6 o'clock every night, quarter of 6, you are secreting insulin in preparation for storing away all those nutrients for the long term. What part of your nervous system does that? Parasympathetic nervous system sending projections down to your pancreas which is where insulin comes from, all built around where you're about to get an influx of nutrients and send out that signal to store it away.

Insulin is this hormone of plenty. Insulin is this hormone of gluttonous excess, probably the gross national insulin levels in our country peak the evening after Thanksgiving dinner, and we have a hormone of planning for the future. Per usual, along comes an acute stressor, an acute stressor where you're running for your life from the lion, our usual scenario. What do you need to do? You need energy not stored away, but powering whichever muscles are going to save your life. What do you do? You reverse everything that we've done just now. You break down the storage forms of energy, and you flush them into the circulation. You turn it back into cash. Hormones responsible, as promised, we are coming back to some of the ones that were mentioned briefly in Lecture 2, glucocorticoids, epinephrine by way of the sympathetic nervous system, glucagon, an otherwise obscure hormone. What are all of these about? Glucocorticoids, glucagon, they go and they take that stored glycogen and turn it into glucose in your circulation. They mobilize the storage form of carbohydrates into circulating sugars. They are doing the same thing with your proteins in storage sites. Have those proteins broken down to their constituent amino acids, dump them in the bloodstream, break down the storage forms of fat, all with this logical message, you are running for your life, and you need the energy in the circulation, not stored away for some building project long in the future. You do something else in addition. You stop the secretion of insulin, very logical, which is the last thing you want to be doing is sending some signal to your body saying store away energy at the same time that you're trying to mobilize it. This is not a good thing. You secrete glucocorticoids, glucagon, epinephrine. You mobilize stored energy forms, and you shut down insulin secretion so that you're not storing anything.

We've got the basics here. What happens next? What's going to happen next is perfectly obvious, our transition here from running for your life to what do you do in the face of chronic stress. What you've got here is lots of potential for problems. First one, we go back to our financial metaphor, and once again, on thin ice for me, but apparently there is this problem. You've got such a gross excess of money that you stick it away in the bank in some long-term savings account. What you do is you agree to some deal there which is I will put this away and not touch it for x amount of time, and in exchange, I'll get this vast amount of interest when it comes out the other end. One of the neat things that you also get is the possibility of a penalty for early withdrawal. In other words, you store away the energy there, you store away your resources, and you suddenly get into this neurotic psychologically stressed state where you want to reverse the whole process, and you pay a penalty.

We've got this metaphor. You store stuff away in the bank, and suddenly you get anxious and you go, you pay the penalty, and you withdraw it, and an hour later you decide you're not anxious after all. You deposit it again, and the next day you withdraw and you pay another penalty. The exact same thing with metabolism, you store energy for the future because you've got excess. You get into a stressed state, mobilize it, store it away, mobilize it again, this cycle of chronic stress, this cycle of chronically activating, mobilizing energy storage, and then sticking it back again afterward. What's the equivalent of a penalty? None of our biochemistry of storage and mobilization is 100% efficient. You pay a little bit of a penalty in terms of all of the biochemistry, it costs a little bit to generate those storage forms. It costs a little bit to break them down again, back and forth you go.

That's the first problem you get into. The second potential problem is one with a rather specialized disease, one unfortunately which is becoming more prevalent, but it's one where glucose, sugar in the bloodstream, is at the very heart of what goes wrong, juvenile diabetes. Two different types of diabetes, one version, most broadly is you're not secreting enough insulin. The other problem is where, if anything, you've got too much insulin. We will see shortly that's a gross simplification, blah, blah, all the usual; but starting first with juvenile diabetes. In that, there's something wrong with your pancreas. There's something wrong with the cells in your pancreas that secrete insulin, some evidence that there's a genetic component, a vulnerability, your immune system attacks your pancreas, whatever it is, those cells are damaged, and you're not secreting enough insulin right now.

Back to what we saw before, which was the storage issue. You've got excess nutrients in your bloodstream, and you want to store them away. You do that with insulin as we heard, except thanks to your juvenile diabetes, you are not able to store it for lack of insulin. You get too much sugar in your bloodstream, and the places in your body that need the sugar don't get them. You take yourself synthetic insulin, and if you take too much of it, it clears away too much glucose. What you do virtually nonstop as a juvenile diabetic is you try to keep your blood glucose levels within a normal range. There has been a wonderful amount of technological advances in terms of getting feedback, juvenile diabetics finding out what their blood glucose level is with a high frequency manipulating their intake. As a result, this is what juvenile diabetes management is all about, keeping blood glucose levels in a nice steady range.

You've got juvenile diabetes and you are chronically stressed, chronically you get stressed, you get over it, you get stressed again, what are you doing each time? You're releasing a flood of sugar into your bloodstream and then you're storing it away. What are you doing? The very opposite of what blood sugar control is about in diabetes, you're getting these huge oscillations all over the place. In other words, what chronic stress does is make glycemic control, control of sugar, more precarious in a diabetic. This is where you see a very frequent problem with juvenile diabetics; juvenile diabetics, which are by definition, very often juvenile diabetics are juveniles. Occasionally they act juvenile, which is to say they don't do all the nice prudent things you're supposed to do with your diabetes, and instead they don't eat the right food, they don't eat it at the right frequency, they don't get enough sleep, and what you've got is wreaking havoc again with your blood glucose levels. All that stress does there is push you even more in that direction.

What about the next realm of trouble with chronic stress? What about another type of diabetes? We've gotten this main pattern here so far which is you want to mobilize stored energy processes into your bloodstream in the face of stress, and mind you there's a very subtle version of mobilizing energy out of storage sites in the face of stress. What's the most stressful thing that happens to us each day in the course of perfectly calm functioning? Getting up in the morning, having to start functioning, moving those muscles that have been quiescent for hours, what you see is the hormones of the metabolic stress-response just within their normal non-stressed range happen to peak around the time you wake up because that's starting the day with this increased energy demand. You're some nocturnal species. You don't wake up until the evening, and then you go about your business. Those hormones peak their levels, in the evening, right around the time you wake up, up go glucocorticoid levels, epinephrine, glucagon, dealing with the incredible stress of waking up every morning.

Real stress, though, real big time stress and real big time stress chronically, we're now looking at another way you get into trouble. First version, as we saw, this inefficient use of energy. Store it, mobilize, store it, mobilize, and you pay this penalty of early withdrawal of inefficient storage and mobilization; you pay the price there. Second version that we just saw, which is the chronic metabolic stress-response, wreaks havoc with juvenile diabetic glycemic control. Now we're into the other type of diabetes. This is the type of diabetes that is coming to haunt Western societies big time. This is what is known as adult-onset diabetes, also known as insulin-resistant diabetes.

There are all sorts of other terms for it. What this is is exactly the problem of juvenile diabetes, exactly the opposite problem ultimately, though. Exactly the same problem blood sugar levels, exactly the opposite problem. The problem here isn't too little insulin, you've got no problem with insulin. The problem here is an excess of nutrients. What are you doing? Typically, you are getting older in a Westernized way which is to say, you put on weight, you become more sedentary, and you've got all these excess nutrients in your bloodstream from all the cholesterol and carbohydrates and proteins you've been consuming. What's the logical thing you would be doing at this point? Excess, let's store it away. Let's secrete a ton of insulin, and let's store it away, but your problem is you've stored so much away already, that your fat cells are full. Your fat cells are full, and you've got a big problem at this point, which is it can't get any fuller.

Back to the metabolic stress-response, what do you do? As we heard, you secrete glucagon and glucocorticoids and epinephrine to mobilize energy. You block insulin release. There's one interesting additional piece in there, and it's essentially built around the notion that your brain doesn't trust your pancreas. Your brain believes your pancreas can screw up readily. Here comes a stressor where you need to mobilize energy. What would be the stupidest thing to do at that time? Secrete insulin, at the same time we've already seen the pancreas stops insulin secretion. The brain doesn't trust it though. The brain is convinced those idiots down in the pancreas are still going to be drooling out a little bit of insulin. One additional step occurs, which is, your brain indirectly sends a signal to fat cell storage sites throughout your body, and what it says is, don't listen to any insulin. Don't respond to an insulin signal in case they're still secreting insulin down in that pancreas, become resistant to it, lose your sensitivity to it.

What happens during the stress-response is your body, very logically under the acute circumstances, pushes you toward insulin resistance. How does this work? An enormous amount of research has gone into it, basic kind of biochemistry stuff. Do not panic again, but insulin binds to an insulin receptor just like every hormone binds to its own personal receptor. What you've got with insulin-induced resistance in these cases here, which is something gets uncoupled so that insulin binds to its receptor, but its receptor which then was supposed to send a signal saying store the nutrients, doesn't listen to it. The receptor becomes ineffective. This is a mechanism that people are spending their whole careers working out the nuts and bolts of. The main point is, run for your life and you are getting a signal throughout the body not only to not secrete insulin, but don't respond to insulin. Do it chronically, and your body is giving off signals all over the place saying don't listen to insulin. You become insulin resistant.

Here's the scenario again. You are eating to great excess and your fat cells are full. Essentially what they're saying there is forget it; we're full. We've got no more space. We're fully occupied. There are no more beds; hit the road. Go to someplace else; the inn is full. We're not responding to insulin anymore. That's the mechanism by which too much stored energy, being overweight, begins to make fat cells less responsive to insulin. Then along comes chronic stress superimposed on top of that, and what's the stress-response system saying? It's saying, what a great idea. That is a brilliant idea to not respond to the insulin. You've got this double whammy. You're having insulin resistance because your fat cells are completely full, and they're just not responding anymore because they're completely full. In addition, just in case they're still a little bit responsive to insulin, if you are chronically turning on the stress-response, you are saying yeah, become even more insulin resistant. What you're now skating into the neighborhood of is insulin-resistant diabetes.

What's the problem there? Is the problem that you don't have enough energy throughout your body? Absolutely not, that's the problem in juvenile diabetes. You're not sending an insulin signal saying store energy, take up energy, that's not the problem. You've got plenty of insulin. The problem is amid too much energy stored away, you've got all this excess stuff now in your bloodstream because there's stuff there that's not getting stored because the storage cells are not responding to insulin. You've now got fat and glucose and cholesterol just circling around in your bloodstream with nothing to do, just looking for problems like glomming onto those damaged blood vessels as we saw in the last lecture. You get hyperglycemia. You get elevated blood sugars along with the fats and such, and they just get into trouble if they've got no place to go; and they've got no place to go because your fat cells are full, and because you're chronically stressed and your body is saying, don't even listen to any insulin out there.

The characteristics of adult-onset diabetes is not that you are lacking energy in cells throughout the body, they've got more than they can use. Elevated insulin, elevated glucose levels in the bloodstream, often elevated fat levels, triglycerides in your blood, and stuff like that just circulating 24-7 is not a good thing. It gets into trouble often in terms of the cardiovascular damage we heard in the last lecture.

That is a problem. That is a huge problem because adult-onset diabetes, insulin-resistant diabetes, used to be this incredibly obscure outpost of disease. This was a problem that our great, great, great, great grandparents never thought about. As said, it is a disease becoming more prevalent with Westernized lifestyle, putting on weight, becoming sedentary. This once obscure disease is now right on the edge of being our number 1 killer, its consequences. This once obscure disease is slated to become the planet's biggest killer within a couple of decades or so, according to the estimates of the World Health Organization. This once obscure disease of adult-onset insulin resistance is now occurring at a higher frequency among kids than even juvenile diabetes is.

This is part of where we are getting in major metabolic trouble, and all that chronic stress does is tell your body what a great idea, do even more of it. Here's this whole problem here with the potential for chronic stress to worsen your symptoms of adult-onset diabetes. We've had our theme here once again, you have excess energy and everything is perfectly fine. You store it away. You have an emergency, you acutely take the storage stuff, dump it in your bloodstream, and it powers your muscles; that's wonderful. You do it chronically, and you mess up blood sugar levels. You make it harder for a juvenile diabetic to control their blood glucose levels. Stress plays havoc with diabetic control, and you increase your risk, as we've seen, of adult-onset diabetes.

You've already heard one thing here, one interesting thing, which harks back to the previous lecture. That business, you've got all this glucose in your bloodstream because you have adult-onset diabetes and you're not storing the stuff; and the circulating glucose, the fat going along with it, is likely to glom onto those bits of blood vessel damage with the inflammatory cells. Suddenly, we have leapt from the world of metabolic disease, diabetes and such, and suddenly we're back half an hour into cardiovascular disease. This has been a very interesting shift in the field over the last decade or so.

It used to be, you have screwy blood glucose levels, and you go to a physician who deals with metabolism. Meanwhile, if somebody else has a problem with high blood pressure, they go to someone who specializes in the cardiovascular nervous system. If everything goes right, there are 2 types of doctors, specialists, and they never talk to each other. They go to completely different conventions. They have different languages. Their children can't marry. These are 2 totally different realms of disease. What should be apparent by now is they intertwine; and what you've got is the kind of circumstances that play havoc with your metabolic profile with chronic stress, increases your risk of cardiovascular disease. The problems you get with cardiovascular, excessive mobilization with chronic stress increases your risk of metabolic disease. Suddenly, they are completely intertwined, and this intertwining is the rationale behind this large overall sort of catchment term for what can go wrong in this realm, metabolic syndrome.

Metabolic syndrome, in its original version know as syndrome X, I believe, until people got more of a sense of it and it got a real name, metabolic syndrome is the syndrome, the array of symptoms that increase your risk of metabolic disease and/or cardiovascular disease. The 2 of them suddenly intertwine, and this is a realm in which you get a whole hodgepodge of things wrong. You've got increased blood pressure. You've got vascular resistance due to damage in your blood vessels. You've got elevated glucose levels. You've got your fat cells not responding to insulin. It's a whole connection of these things going wrong. Yes, you can have a bunch of metabolic things going wrong, and at the same time, you can have a whole separate world of cardiovascular problems. What we've seen instead is they interact. Here are 2 ways in which it could occur, just as examples. One example we've heard already: Have the metabolic end of problems in metabolic syndrome, have those problems of insulin resistance, and you're not storing away your glucose, and thus you are getting into trouble circulating glucose, the circulating fats you're not storing. What we've heard already is they are now more likely to get stuck onto those points of vascular damage of inflammation. That's not a good thing.

There we see one intersection. Another way in which they can intersect, and this represents a fascinating shift in this field, which is an utterly bizarre thing: What do your fat cells do? What does your fat do? They store fat; they get fatty. They get plump and jolly; they store away nutrients. That's what your fat cells do. It's turning that out fat cells can do something else, they can generate signals of inflammation in your body. It's an utterly bizarre thing, in fat cells you generate some immune inflammatory activators that are supposed to be coming out of white blood cells in your immune system. Fat turns out to be an endocrine gland of releasing hormones signaling molecules related to inflammation. You can begin to guess here what our second scenario here is of a interaction between metabolic problems and cardiovascular problems. You've got a little bit of damage to your blood vessels, thanks to that high blood pressure, and what's the next step that can go wrong? You begin to get inflammatory cells glomming on there to the injury site. If you've got a lot of fat stored away, what's going to happen? You're having a higher sort of basal level of inflammation in your body. You're increasing the odds of inflammation glomming on to that area of damaged blood vessels. We've got a metabolic problem, increasing your risk of a cardiovascular problem.

That's what metabolic syndrome is all about. It's this whole business that you can't put parts of your body into completely separate categories. This is a theme that should be coming through over and over. This is a theme that came through in the first lecture. Remember homeostasis, ideal body temperature, ideal everything, and the fact that towards the end of the first lecture, I noted that there's a new fancy term going around for modern state-of-the-art notions about homeostasis, this new term allostasis which is getting a whole lot of attention these days. I mentioned the example there which is suppose you're getting dehydrated. Boring old, local homeostatic type solution, your kidneys retain more water. What we saw was the more far-flung fancy realistic version, the allostatic version of it is, instead, yes, your kidneys retain more water, but you begin to sweat less, you have a sense of thirst coming out of your brain. You solve local challenges to balance, homeostatic balance, with all sorts of adaptations far flung throughout your body. That's the allostatic notion.

Where does that come in here? The very simple fact that you don't get challenges to only one small part of your body. They all interact. You get a small challenge going on in your levels of fat storage, and suddenly you're setting yourself up for cardiovascular disease. What the allostatic concept is all about is you can't break the body down into separate parts, which makes perfect sense, but it's hard to remember that. One of the realms in which it's hard to remember that is you've got some problem or other, and you go to your physician who orders up a blood panel, and out the other end, you get this array of blood test results. A lot of us have seen those things, you get this long list of the various things that were measured. Then you have a normative range, what the average level is and what are the levels that are considered normal, below the average above the average, and you get a whole bunch of little Xs on your printout there saying what your own levels are compared to the normal range. Get them outside the range, below, above and something counts as a problem, because you have abnormal levels of whatever it is—blood glucose, hemoglobin, hematocrit, whatever it is—and thus your doctor picks it up by scanning down that chart with all the results there and seeing if there's any of these little Xs outside the normal range. You've got one that's on this side of the norm but within that range, and the doctor says, well, you know, it's a little less of the stuff than we would like, it's a little bit more of the stuff than we would like, but it's still in the normal range. What the allostatic notion, what the metabolic syndrome notion, what the whole notion that you have intersections so that it makes no sense to break the body into cardiovascular, metabolic and all these little buckets, what all of those collectively say is: Even although all of those measures in your bloodstream may be normal, it may be abnormal to have so many of them almost abnormal, a whole collectivity of things going wrong. It's the theme that nothing in your body is a separate little domain.

As we've gone over our basic theme now here, short-term stress-response, good news, long-term chronic, we've seen a first theme in the last few lectures, one that's going to run through all of them; they're not separate areas. A problem in one domain, you're going to pay a price in the other, metabolic dysfunction, cardiovascular, as we'll see, calling these lectures about this particular subject, this particular organ system is just as a convenient way of dealing with them. They don't separate.

Stress, Overeating, and Your Digestive Tract
Lecture 5

Let's now think about chronic stress. You've got someone who says, "Oh my God, I'm so stressed. I get stuck in traffic every day, I have a horrible boss, my relationship is unsteady, all of these sorts of things, and I am like totally stressed nonstop, 24-7." This is not like totally stressed nonstop 24-7. You want to know what totally stressed 24-7 is about, you look at somebody with a whole body burn, and you look at somebody in septic shock. That's stress 24-7. ... What we call everyday chronic stress is instead lots and lots of intermittent stressors.

Let's look at the gastrointestinal tract. Once the food gets into your mouth and then your esophagus, your stomach, and your intestines, what role does stress play? Of course the first issue is how desirous you are of putting food in your mouth. What does stress do to appetite? About two-thirds of people eat more than usual when they're stressed. Why? A piece of what's occurring is psychological. It turns out those two-thirds of people have something in common, which is on a regular basis, when they are eating a meal, they are consciously regulating the amount of food they take in. Along comes stress, and what happens is you say, this is an incredibly stressful period, enough of that self-regulation; I am going to gorge. What you do during stress is you tend to suspend some of the regulatory processes, some of that self-discipline.

Work-related stressors are among the causes of gastrointestinal disorders.

There's an additional reason why most people wind up eating more food when they're under stress. Your brain, with the onset of stress, secretes a particular hypothalamic hormone that causes the pituitary to secrete a hormone that stimulates the adrenals to release glucocorticoids.

Alongside the insulin effect we learned about in Lecture 4, something else happens. The glucocorticoids stimulate appetite so that you replace all the energy you depleted running for your life. At the end of stress, it takes quite a few minutes for glucocorticoid levels to go back to normal. In other words, after any given stressor, there's a period of increased appetite.

There is a great dichotomy between 2 different types of fat: abdominal fat and gluteal fat.

Let's now think about chronic stress. If you spend all day having bursts of intermittent stressors, you are spending a lot of the day recovering from them. Your appetite increases, and generally you crave carbohydrates: bread, sugars, treats, and candy. For even more bad news, we now consider where those excess calories go. They go into your fat cells, but all fat cells are not the same. There is a great dichotomy between 2 different types of fat: **abdominal fat** and **gluteal fat**. Abdominal fat is more dangerous, for a whole bunch of reasons. It releases inflammatory signals, which can be a greater risk in your torso than in other parts of your body; it sits close to your liver, which could lead to fatty liver; and its sheer mechanical pressure pulls your spine forward. Abdominal fat puts more stress on your body.

What happens to your gastrointestinal tract under chronic stress? All sorts of things can go wrong: You turn off the digestive tract, and if you do this chronically, disease risk is going to crop up. Gastrointestinal disorders are a bit confusing, but they basically come in 2 flavors: organic bowel disorders and functional bowel disorders. Organic bowel disorders are those that have an explanation, such as an abnormality in the structure of your small intestines or lactase not performing correctly. Functional bowel disorders are what they diagnose you with when they haven't a clue what's up. But we do know that functional bowel disorders are exquisitely sensitive to stress. This is the realm of things like irritable bowel syndrome and spastic colon. This is the realm in which emotions, by way of the autonomic nervous system and stress hormones, can greatly regulate your bowels.

This reemphasizes the central concept of the overlap between the organic and psychogenic bases of disease. If all you do is concentrate on 1 piece of the story, you're not going to know what's going on. It's the intersection that is critical and informative. ■

Important Terms

abdominal fat: Fat deposits around the gut. Chronic stress preferentially promotes the deposition of abdominal fat, which is of the type that is worse for cardiovascular health.

gluteal fat: Fat deposits around the buttocks.

Helicobacter pylori: A bacteria that causes a large percentage of cases of peptic ulcer. Chronic stress can impair the ability of the body to repair such ulcers.

ulcer: An area of tissue erosion (e.g., on skin or on the stomach lining).

Suggested Reading

Adam and Epel, "Stress, Eating and the Reward System."

Sapolsky, *Why Zebras Don't Get Ulcers*, chap. 5.

Questions to Consider

1. What does stress have to do with craving carbohydrates?

2. Despite the discovery of a flashy bacteria that causes ulcers, why does stress help explain why only some people infected with the bacteria develop an ulcer?

Stress, Overeating, and Your Digestive Tract
Lecture 5—Transcript

This is Robert Sapolsky reporting live from the 87th Annual Rose Bowl Parade, and it is a beautiful day in Pasadena. It is clear and sunny, the crowds are large and enthusiastic. In a time like this, one must think about irritable bowel syndrome. What did we do in the last lecture? What did we do? We thought about what happens to nutrients once they're digested, hit your bloodstream, the whole world of storing energy mobilizing it, all of that that we went through before.

In this lecture, what we focus on is the gastrointestinal tract. Once the food gets into your mouth and then your esophagus, your stomach, and your intestines, what does stress have to do with that realm? Starting with your mouth, of course the very first issue is how desirous are you of putting food in your mouth? What does stress do to appetite? We all know what stress does to appetite, which it does something or other to appetite. If you talk to people, and you say, well, when you're stressed, do you eat more than usual? About two-thirds of people will say yes. When you're stressed, do you eat less than usual? About one-third of people say yes as well. What do we suddenly have? We have the shocking finding, officially, that stress changes appetite. This doesn't do us any good at all. What is actually going on? What's happening that influences why two-thirds of people or so become stress hyperphagic, they eat more. The others tend to eat less. What's happening with that?

A piece of what's occurring is psychological. There's a psychological component to this. It turns out those two-thirds of people have something in common, which is on a regular basis, when they are eating a meal, they are consciously regulating the amount of food they take in. They're watching their diet. They're making sure they eat something healthy. They are passing on some dessert that is tempting, and along comes stress, and what happens is you say, this is an incredibly stressful period, enough of that self-regulation. I am going to gorge. It's like if all you do is watch on television some pensive, introspective, British period piece play, when secretly you would love to be watching professional wrestling, and along comes some horrible stressful period, and you say, screw this with the English drama, I'm going to watch professional wrestling and then watch some roller derby. What you do during stress is you tend to suspend some of the regulatory processes you have going on, some of that self-discipline stuff. I'm stressed; I'm going to eat more.

Two-thirds of people, on the average, have that sort of psychological makeup. There's an additional reason why most people wind up eating more food when they're under stress. This has to do with an incredibly complicated piece of endocrinology which will make perfect sense when you think about it. Back to our basic endocrinology, those axes having to do with the brain as the master gland. We've already heard about glucocorticoids, those key stress hormones that come out of the adrenal. You already know all about them and what they do. As promised, your adrenals don't know what they're doing. Your brain, with the onset of stress, secretes a particular hypothalamic hormone which causes the pituitary to secrete a hormone which stimulates the adrenals to release glucocorticoids.

There's something with the dynamics of this which is very, very critical. You secrete that hypothalamic hormone within a second or 2 of the onset of stress. If you deeply care about such minutia, this hormone is called corticotropin-releasing hormone—do not write that down—the hypothalamic stress hormone. With the onset of stress, your hypothalamus releases that stress hormone within seconds. Obviously it's going to take a longer time to start secreting glucocorticoids because the hypothalamic stress hormone has to do something at your pituitary, which then drools out its stuff, so the very earliest phase of the stress-response is dominated exclusively by that hypothalamic stress hormone. Once glucocorticoid levels kick up with the stressor going on for a while, the profile is elevated levels of both the hypothalamic stress hormone and glucocorticoids.

End of stress, your hypothalamus takes like 2-and-a-half seconds to shut off its secretion of that hypothalamic hormone and it takes quite a few minutes for glucocorticoid levels to go back to normal. In other words, hypothalamic hormone up by itself, first couple of seconds of stress, both hypothalamic hormone and glucocorticoids up, you're in the middle of a stressor. Only glucocorticoids up, and it's over with. What we introduce now, for the first time since the elephants, is the importance of the recovery stage.

What's the stress-response stage about? We already know what it's about in terms of energy: You're mobilizing energy and sending it to your exercising muscle. That's all over with, and what you now need to do is store that energy back where it came from. How do you do this? We heard from the last lecture that whole song and dance about insulin, but something else happens. Your appetite increases so that you replace all that energy you depleted running for your life. What does that? We already heard that glucocorticoids when they're elevated during a stress-response, when those hypothalamic hormone levels are up also, they're involved in mobilizing energy. Once you get to that phase where all you've got are the elevated glucocorticoid levels, that recovery phase, what glucocorticoids do is they stimulate appetite. They stimulate this recovery process. Again, this is the first time we are seeing the critical role of one of these stress hormones, not in mediating the stress-response, but mediating recovery from it. We've got something critical that I've already told you; the end of stress, and it takes just a couple of seconds for those hypothalamic stress hormones to go back to normal. End of stress, it takes quite a few minutes for glucocorticoid levels to go back to normal. In other words, after any given stressor, there's a period afterward of increased appetite.

Let's now think about chronic stress. You've got someone who says, "Oh my God, I'm so stressed. I get stuck in traffic every day, I have a horrible boss, my relationship is unsteady, all of these sorts of things, and I am like totally stressed nonstop, 24-7." This is not like totally stressed nonstop 24-7. You want to know what totally stressed 24-7 is about, you look at somebody with a whole body burn, and you look at somebody in septic shock. That's stress 24-7. What we mean in an everyday sense when we say, oh my God, I'm just stressed all the time, what we actually mean is we turn on the stress-response over and over repeatedly throughout the day. The car that almost doesn't start, and then the horrible traffic. Then the sneaking into work 10 minutes late without the boss seeing, and what we call everyday chronic stress is instead lots and lots of intermittent stressors.

What happens then? What we just saw was for any given one of those intermittent stressors, typically the amount of time that you're turning on the stress-response can be pretty brief, and the amount of time the stress-response goes on is pretty brief. We're talking about these brief, intermittent stressors, and the amount of time it takes to recover where your appetite is stimulated is longer. In other words, if you spend all day long having these bursts of intermittent stressors, you are spending a lot of all day long recovering from them with your appetite increased, and suddenly you have chronic stress increasing appetite.

That is definitively not a good thing. We begin to see here why most of us eat more during periods of stress, and why those nutrients tend to get stored away. Now the next piece of trouble we get into has to do with not just the fact that we eat more during stress, but we eat more of certain things, and this one we all know about. You do not get wildly stressed and decide now is the time to switch over to a spinach diet. You get stressed and like most of us, what you do is you crave carbs. You crave carbohydrates, bread, sugars, treats, and candy, all of that. You get a carbohydrate craving. What is this about? This is certainly not a clever thing. The least you can do is if you're overeating because of chronic stress is eat healthy stuff, and instead, we all tend to get into this carbohydrate craving. Remarkably, this does you some good. Remarkably, you increase those blood sugar levels. Remember back by now, we know dietary carbs get broken down into simple sugars, and they fuel your muscles and all of that stuff we know about. One of the other things they do is they lower glucocorticoid levels.

In other words, when you are stressed, eating carbs is antistress. This is not just gibberish about, oh, I'm going to feel much better if I scarf down 8 Hershey bars during this period. Increasing carbs in your diet during acute stressors help turn off glucocorticoid secretion, and that's perfect because your glucocorticoid levels go back to normal that much faster. That's great; that's adaptive during recovery, and this is amazing. With chronic stress, not only do you eat more, you get this craving for carbohydrates. In some wonderful work done by Mary Dallman at the University of California, San Francisco, who has worked out precisely how this works, which part of your hypothalamus is measuring the glucose in your bloodstream. Which parts are sensitive to fatty acids. Which take information about what's in your bloodstream and then affect your diet, and then affect your appetite, and then affect your glucocorticoid secretion. We've got this big regulatory loop here which winds up having this important implication, not only do you start eating more during chronic stress, during frequent intermittent stressors, not only do most of us do that, but the craving we get is for the worst possible kind of food at that time, so bad news.

Let's have even more bad news; what we now consider is where those excess calories go. We know where all those excess calories go. They go into your fat cells, but here we have an extremely important feature of fat physiology. It's the fact that all fat cells are not the same. The fact that it depends on where in your body the fat is being stored, and here we come to the great dichotomy between 2 different types of fat, fat that winds up in your belly, abdominal fat, and fat that winds up in your rear end, gluteal fat, abdominal fat versus gluteal or truncal fat. You have this very simple deal here which is one of them is a lot worse than the other. One of them gets you into a lot more trouble. What you have is a different body shape, a different body morphometry. A different body shape depending on whether you are putting on abdominal fat or gluteal, and the jargon used in the field is when you put on abdominal fat, you look like an apple. Whereas, if you put on gluteal fat, you look like a pear, and being overweight, having excess fat at extremes one could take on an apple profile or a pear profile; and the official deal is the apple version of it is the one that's not good for you. The apple version is the one that gets you into trouble, the abdominal fat.

Why should this be? It's for a whole bunch of reasons. First off, the very first one, abdominal fat is, as you heard, like any sort of fat, releasing all sorts of inflammatory signals and some of the most vulnerable blood vessels in your body to those inflammatory messages happen to be more in your torso. That's not good. The next thing, abdominal fat is sitting real close to your liver, and that could produce the dread state of a fatty liver, not a good thing; that's bad. Another thing that winds up being bad is sheer mechanical pressure. Abdominal fat is pulling your spine forward, gluteal is like increasing, lowering your center of gravity. Abdominal fat puts more stress on your body.

We begin to see one of those awful facts that explains all sorts of disturbing things about the universe. You remember back to insulin, how does insulin work? Insulin goes floating around in the bloodstream and binds to an insulin receptor. As I noted, that's the same thing with all of these hormones out there, and glucocorticoids do their thing by binding to glucocorticoid receptors. We have a key thing which is some parts of the body have more glucocorticoid receptors than other parts, and it turns out fat cells have lots of glucocorticoid receptors. Abdominal fat cells are the ones with the most.

In other words, along comes a stressful period, and in the aftermath, you are set up for increased appetite. You are set up for that increased appetite taking the form of the worst possible food you can be eating. On top of it all now, with chronic stress you are set up to store that excess fat in exactly the part of the body where you don't want to be doing it, in the abdominal fat stores, not a good thing. It turns out that individual differences come in here, and this was something promised at the end of the second lecture. All of this physiology, all of this complexity, works different in one person than another, and this helps to begin to explain why some people are more prone toward putting on weight with chronic stress. It could be because they get more of a food craving. Perhaps they secrete more glucocorticoids. It could be because that carbohydrate business is even more effective at turning off secretion; all these different possible domains of how things work differently in one person than another. It could also be because you happen to have more glucocorticoid receptors in your abdominal fat; or another version could be, at the end of stress, as I said, it takes a few minutes for your glucocorticoid levels to go back down to normal. Maybe you just happen to be the sort of person where it takes a lot longer than average for the levels to go back to normal. For every one of those intermittent stressors, you are soaking your system in more glucocorticoids during the recovery period than most people do, more of the craving, more of this craving for the carbohydrates, more of the storing it away in all the bad places, possible realm of individual differences. Some really nice work by Elissa Epel, again, of the University of California, San Francisco, focusing in on those individual differences, looking at people who are really prone towards abdominal fat deposition, and one of the explanations is, some of these are folks who are very slow in having their glucocorticoid system recover back to normal after a stressor.

What's also running through here is a theme. We've got excessive eating. Long ago we had the 4 horsemen of the apocalypse, and sloth and greed, and all sorts. We have modern versions which are eating to excess and smoking and drinking too much and not exercising. In lots of ways, there's sort of a moral thread that runs through the issue of proper weight, which is being overweight represents some sort of loss of discipline. Yes, indeed that's true in some cases. We're also seeing, though, how much of this stuff has to do with just the nuts and bolts of what sort of biological deck of cards you've wound up with. We all differ as to how many glucocorticoid receptors and how jumpy our adrenal is and how much the part of the brain that is sensitive to the carbohydrates' wonderfully calming influences, how sensitive it is to it. We begin to see all these individual differences coming in.

We've gotten this array of ways in which things can go wrong. Your appetite increases. Your appetite increases for the worst possible stuff. You tend to deposit it as the worst kind of fat, and lots of individual differences come in there. This is the world of apples versus pears. Mind you, you go to the doctor, and almost certainly, the physician is not going to say, uh-oh, you're getting a little more "apple-ish" than last time. The formal way in which this is measured is the waist, girth, how far around your belly, how far around your hips, your waist-to-hip ratio. In other words, how much of the abdominal fat you have versus how much of the gluteal. That's the formal way in which it's measured. You don't get an "apple-ish" number, but it's tapping into that exact same concept.

What's going on in your gut? We've seen a ton here about appetite. How about your gastrointestinal tract? With chronic stress, all sorts of things can go wrong. The general logic here is obvious, what we know already which is acute stressor, run for your life you've got better things to do than digestion. Turn off the digestive tract; we know the scenario in our sleep now. Chronic stress, if you chronically shut down the gastrointestinal system, somehow disease risk is going to pop out the other end. Where does the disease risk come from? How do we normally turn off our bowels during stress? Very simple, you've heard this already. Onset of stress, turn off the parasympathetic nervous system, turn on the sympathetic, and that winds up sending a signal, decrease contractions in your stomach. Decrease contractions in your small intestines, decrease salivary secretion, that whole pathway we know about. Shut down your gastrointestinal system. You've got better things to do right now, et cetera. One exception, though, one interesting exception which provides a remarkable parallel to something we heard a couple of lectures back, you are profoundly, utterly, traumatically stressed, and one of the things that tends to happen with people is in moments of crisis like that, they lose control over their bladder. In the same way, sometimes you lose control over your bowels. What's that about? Same exact sort of story, same severity as with the bladder business. Again, in lots of states people when they are executed have diapers put on them, and that's that same logic again, which is people often lose control over both their bladder and their bowels. What's happening here is this very interesting dichotomy.

The onset of stress: sympathetic nervous system sending a signal, stop the stomach contractions, stop the intestinal contractions, and increase the contractions of your large intestines, your colon. Small intestines, less activation, large intestines, more constriction, This makes great sense. Small intestines are like your kidney. You're absorbing stuff out of it, nutrients, all sorts of regulatory steps. Large intestines, once stuff hits there, there's like no nutritional content to it; this is just stuff heading out for recycling. This is stuff that's going to get dumped. All you do with your umpteen feet of large intestines is reabsorb some water so you don't desiccate like a prune going to the bathroom, not very interesting, not essential. We've got that same choice again as you run for your life from the lion, you could do it with or without 5 pounds of dead weight down there in your large intestines. Same logic again, void your bowels as you were voiding your bladder. With the onset of major stressors, you increase contractions in your large intestines pushing stuff out faster.

That's great, that's exactly why you want to be soiling yourself as you're running away from the lion. What about in the face of chronic stress? What we get into here now is an extremely confusing domain of gastrointestinal disorders. They come in 2 flavors. You have either an organic bowel disorder or a functional bowel disorder. This is a very fancy way of saying you have bowel disorders where people know what the disease is versus ones where nobody has a clue. Organic bowel disorders, there is an explanation. There's an abnormality in the structure of the absorptive whatever's in your small intestines, or you've got your lactase not doing the right stuff. They know what's going on. Functional bowel disorders is what they diagnose you with when they haven't a clue what's up, and they got to give you some sort of name because they're going to charge you out the wazoo. On the other end of this, functional bowel disorders are ones that are exquisitely sensitive to stress. This is the realm of things like irritable bowel syndrome, or spastic colon. This is the realm in which emotions, by way of the autonomic nervous system, by way of stress hormones, can greatly regulate all that stuff with your bowels.

What's going on with things like spastic colon, with stress-induced bowel abnormalities? Remember what we had a few minutes ago, this amazing beautiful choreography with the onset of stress. Ideally you want to decrease contraction in the small intestine, and increase them in large. End of stress, you want to reverse the process. Here comes another stressor, you do it again, and have chronic enough of stress and the choreography, the timing gets out of whack. Suddenly you've got things contracting when they shouldn't, and you've got the runs. Suddenly things are not contracting when they should, you've got an opposite problem. It's a problem of simply coordinating this fairly subtle adaptation. Get chronically stressed and things simply don't work very well down there.

This is remarkably common. Just to inject a sort of autobiographical note that I know all of you want to hear about in courses like this: Every major juncture in my life has been filled with the runs a few days before. My Bar Mitzvah; going off to college; defending my thesis; in preparation for proposing to someone, my wife; and on my wedding day; all of that, in all of those cases all sorts of uncoordinated things were clearly going on with my small and large intestines. Wasn't that personal note pleasing?

You've got these disorders. You've got these disorders of stress messing up the coordination in these different parts of your gastrointestinal system. There are 2 ways that can happen. One is if you're sending too much of a stress signal—turn off, turn on, go the other way—all of that, the other is if your bowels happen to be overly sensitive to normal stress signals. What is becoming clear is some folks with irritable bowel syndrome, the problem is not chronic activation of the stress-response. The problem is hypersensitivity to normal stress signals.

How can you show this, and this is the sort of science that's done that's really wonderful. You take a bunch of people and some of them have spastic colon, irritable bowel syndrome, and some of them don't. You've got your 2 groups, and you give them an experimental stressor. They have to sit there for 10 minutes with their hand in a bucket of ice. They have to do some time-pressured math test, they have to give some sort of public speech when that disturbs them greatly. They have some sort of stressor, and you look at how much their large intestines increase contracting. The folks with the irritable bowel syndrome problems, for the same stressor, they increase the contractions more.

One version of the problem is hypersensitivity to a stress signal. The other version is another group of people with these functional bowel disorders have elevated levels of stress hormones; their sympathetic nervous system is overactive, things of that sort. We see all sorts of ways in which that can go wrong. Final domain, being classicists here, we have to return to the stress-related disease that started the entire field, ulcers. Ulcers, back to Hans Selye and his stressed rats in the 1930s, back to that very first sign, chronic stress you get an ulcer, everybody knows this. Chronic stress, stress and ulcers, stress and ulcers completely intertwined, the stress-related disease.

Then about 20 years ago there was this revolution in ulcerolgy. These 2 Austrian scientists discovered actually ulcers are caused by a bacteria, a bacteria called *Helicobacter pylorus*. What happens, people who have ulcers, like 90% of the cases in the West, what they have is a *Helicobacter* infection in their stomach. What do these bacteria do? It generates these things called oxygen radicals and it blows holes in the wall of your stomach.

It's a bacterial disorder. This was a major, major discovery. This got these guys the Nobel Prize. This was an enormously important finding because suddenly it says that ulcers arise from a bacterial disorder. They're organic in nature. They are not psychogenic. There is nothing to do with this stress stuff. This was the greatest news among gastroenterologists, the day everybody suddenly learned about *Helicobacter* like every gastroenterologist on Earth went out and celebrated that evening. Never again were they going to have to sit down with their patients and make eye contact, and ask them how's it going. Anything stressful in your life? It's got nothing to do with stress. It's a bacterial disorder; give them their antibiotics, next. Suddenly, stress has nothing to do with ulcers. Stress has everything to do with ulcers for a very simple reason, only about 10% of the people with *Helicobacter* infections get an ulcer. It's not enough to merely have the bacterial infection. You've got to have something else. You've got to have the bacterial load, and you've got to have some sort of lifestyle risk factor, and in their overlap comes the highly increased risk of ulcers. Where do the lifestyle risk factors come in? That's the stress. That's the stress component to ulceration. There's one domain of ulcer that's completely due to stress, they're called stress ulcers, and those emerge over the course of a couple of days, and they're life threatening. These are whole-body-burn induced ulcers. Back in the normal range of ulcers, these *Helicobacter*-driven ones, only 1 out of 10 people with the bacteria get the ulcers. It's the intersection between the bacterial load and the stress.

Where does that come in? Here we see one of our great lessons from this course. The stress-response, those glucocorticoids, those other stress hormones, they're not causing ulcers. They're not generating this disease. What are they doing instead? Back to the very first lecture, you're running for your life, and digest some other time. Don't bother with digestion; stop the stomach contractions. You're running for your life and divert your blood to where it's really needed, your muscles. You're running for your life, and don't repair anything going wrong in your stomach walls, because it's an emergency, do it later. Do it later. If you are chronically stressed, what happens is all the time you've got the starts of little ulcers here and there if you have *Helicobacter*. Normally, you're pretty good at repairing it. Instead, because you are chronically stressed, over and over your body is saying, do it later, do it later. Stress does not cause ulcers; stress impairs your defenses, your ability to repair ulcers in their earliest stage.

What we have here is a central concept in this course, which is the overlap between the organic basis of disease, and a psychogenic basis. What you see very importantly here is if all you do is concentrate on one piece of the story, you're not going to know what's going on. It's the intersection that is critical and informative.

Stress and Growth—Echoes from the Womb
Lecture 6

Take a newborn rat, and over the first couple of weeks of its life, pick it up every day and handle it. Pet it for a few minutes. ... What this counts as is stimulation, and remarkably this is now a rat who, as an adult, will have lower glucocorticoid levels, that will have better learning and memory, and as it turns out will have a more neurologically intact old age.

What does stress have to do with child development? The critical fact is that environment doesn't begin at birth. Environment begins in fetal life, and thus the consequences of stress can begin in fetal life also. What's environment like for a fetus? What it's about is what mom is experiencing, because you share her circulatory system, and the hormones in her bloodstream will wind up, to some extent, in your own circulatory system. The amount of nutrients is relevant, as are things like extremely loud noises.

You don't want to be a stressed fetus. There are 2 realms of consequences of fetal stress. The first is what you're like at birth; at the simplest level, more fetal stress equals a lower body weight at birth. The other, more subtle, point is that fetal experience influences what sort of adult body you're going to have as you respond to adult environments. Things get regulated in a permanent sort of way during fetal life. This phenomenon has been termed **fetal origins of adult disease**, a completely new area of research built around the notion that environment doesn't begin at birth. An awful lot of what's going on in fetal life causes programming of how adult responses are going to be.

It's the same outcome in a child as opposed to a fetus. Chronic activation of the stress-response does all sorts of bad stuff. If you stress an infant rat, you produce an adult rat with higher glucocorticoid levels and who has trouble turning off glucocorticoid secretion at the end of stress. Your rat will have a somewhat activated stress-response all the time and be more vulnerable to relevant diseases. Your rat will be not as good at learning and memory and will be more prone toward anxiety. Chronic stress leads to all sorts of long-term consequences.

The other component that comes into the equation is mothering style. Different styles of mothering can represent and generate a more stimulatory environment, or a less or more stressful one. Studies on rats and primates have shown that mothering style translates into different adult stress-responses in the offspring. So experience, prenatal and postnatal, can

Prenatal and childhood stress lead to a variety of negative health outcomes in adulthood.

shape the sort of hormonal profile and brain you have as an adult. Early experience—taking the form of severe stress, but also mild stress, degrees of stimulation, and mothering style—produces different profiles in adulthood, and even in following generations.

If you are stressed prenatally for 3 minutes, are you going to pay a price? No, there are enormous amounts of variability from one individual to another. Developmental stress does not guarantee that you will suffer those effects. The other piece of good news is that the negative effects are not necessarily permanent: There's a tremendous capacity to reverse them throughout life. ∎

Important Terms

benzodiazepines: Anxiety-reducing tranquilizers such as Valium and Librium. The brain contains receptors for them, indicating that the brain makes still-undiscovered natural versions of these drugs.

fetal origins of adult disease (FOAD): This is an emerging concept in medicine, focusing on the fact that events during fetal life can program lifelong aspects of bodily function. As the example covered most in this course, fetal malnutrition often causes increased insulin secretion throughout life.

The Dutch Hunger Winter Phenomenon

In 1944, Holland was occupied by the Nazis. For a number of reasons, including the uprising of resistance among the Dutch against the Nazis, the decision was made to punish Holland and divert all of the food that winter to Germany. Holland, with its reasonably good Westernized diet, suddenly plunged into famine. Something very interesting came out of this.

Suppose you are a second- or third-trimester fetus during the Dutch Hunger Winter. You are experiencing starvation, as there are fewer nutrients in mom's bloodstream. Your body concludes that there's not a whole lot of food out there in the world. Thus, your body gets programmed to be thrifty. Every bit of food that hits your bloodstream, quick, store it away, secrete insulin like crazy. Every bit of salt that you have, your kidneys are really good at retaining it because who knows when the next salt is coming.

The Dutch Hunger Winter ends, and you're back to a normal, healthy Dutch diet. Everything else being equal, 50 years later, you will be about 20 times more likely to have metabolic syndrome, because your body learned as a fetus to be really thrifty at storing away nutrients, and you have programmed your metabolic system to work that way forever. This is one of a number of examples of a new area of research called fetal origins of adult disease.

There's an even more interesting ripple to this, which is it turns out that Dutch Hunger Winter effects are multigenerational. If you were a Dutch Hunger Winter fetus, and 30 years later you are pregnant, your thrifty metabolism will impact your fetus. You have a perfectly typical diet during your pregnancy, but you are more efficient at taking nutrients out of the bloodstream, so your fetus is getting fewer nutrients than it should. In other words, Dutch Hunger Winter babies generate Dutch Hunger Winter babies, and their grandchildren show some of these same tendencies.

Suggested Reading

Godfrey and Barker, "Fetal Programming and Adult Health."

Sapolsky, *Why Zebras Don't Get Ulcers*, chap. 6.

Questions to Consider

1. How is it that environment doesn't begin at birth?

2. Why does being starved as a fetus make you more likely to have diabetes at age 60?

Stress and Growth—Echoes from the Womb
Lecture 6—Transcript

All of us are different sorts of people, we have different tastes, we have different habits, and we have different values. Nonetheless, all of us have one thing in common which is we grew up at some point. We went through fetal development; we went through child development.

What the next 2 lectures are about is: What does stress have to do with child development? You already know the punch line in your sleep. You're running for your life. You're a young individual running for your life, you're a kid and your body has better things to do under those circumstances than deposit calcium in your long bones. Grow later if there is a later. Short-term stress-response, highly adaptive; chronic stress-response, you impair growth. That's the concept that will run through the next 2 lectures. Chronic stress, environmental stressors, can disrupt the normal growth process. The point of this lecture is one critical fact, that is: Environment doesn't begin at birth. Environment begins in fetal life, and thus the consequences of stress can begin in fetal life also.

What's environment like for a fetus? What's stress like for a fetus? What it's about is what mom is experiencing, because you share something absolutely critical with your mother when you're a fetus. You share her circulatory system, and the hormones in her bloodstream will wind up, to some extent, in your own circulatory system. The amount of nutrients will become relevant in there. You have all sorts of ways in which maternal experience is translated into fetal experience. Even something as straightforward as extremely loud noises, fetuses can respond to it. It turns out amniotic fluid is this great vibratory resonating environment. What's going on in the outside world can affect the fetus.

What we have as the simple punch line here is: You don't want to be a stressed fetus. You don't want to have the same sort of stressors that follow the same logic built around grow tomorrow, grow tomorrow. What this begins to bring in are 2 realms of consequences of fetal stress. The first is, what you're like at birth, and in the simplest sort of level, more fetal stress equals a lower body weight at birth, what sort of individual you're like at birth. The other, a much more subtle point is, fetal experience, fetal stress influencing what sort of adult body you're going to have, responding to adult environments.

The second subtle point, the notion of fetal experience translating into how your body works as an adult brings in all sorts of new concepts. Concepts which can be summarized with terms that are absolutely metaphors for the fact that a fetus makes decisions about what sort of organism to grow into, that a fetus is programmed by experience, by environment. These are metaphorical terms. Things get set down. Things get regulated in a permanent sort of way during fetal life.

What do I mean by this? Let me give a first example, and this is an absolutely extraordinary one. We are all used to this typical sequence of scientific knowledge in this realm. You study something in laboratory animals. You see how it works, you understand its world, and then you see if it works in humans. This is a case where it started with humans. This is a phenomenon known as the Dutch Hunger Winter; 1944, World War II, Holland is occupied by the Nazis. For a number of reasons, with the uprising of resistance among the Dutch against the Nazis, the decision was made to punish Holland and divert all of the food that winter to Germany. Suddenly, Holland, with its reasonably good Westernized diet, plunged into famine. Over the course of that famine, something like 16,000 people starved to death, absolute disaster. Something very interesting came out of it. Suppose you were a fetus, a second or third trimester fetus during the Dutch Hunger Winter, what's going on? You are experiencing that starvation insofar as there are less nutrients in mom's bloodstream, your experience of this environment stressor.

It turns out that one of the things that a fetus decides, one of the things in which a fetus is programmed to respond to, one of the things going on there is, the fetus in effect is deciding, well, how much food is there out there in that world I'm heading into soon. Be a fetus at that time during starvation and what your body concludes is, there's not a whole lot out there. Thus, your body gets programmed to be thrifty. What do we mean by thrifty? Every bit of food that hits your bloodstream, quick, store it away. Translated from a few lectures ago, every bit of nutrients that hit your bloodstream, secrete insulin like crazy. Every bit of salt that you have, kidneys are really good at retaining it because who knows when the next salt is coming, be really thrifty at storing stuff.

Dutch Hunger Winter ends, and suddenly you're going back to a normal, healthy Dutch diet. Everything else being equal, 50 years later, you are now close to 20 times more likely to have metabolic syndrome because your body learned, as a fetus, to be really efficient, really thrifty, really good at storing away nutrients, and you have programmed your metabolic system to work that way forever after. Mind you, if you were a newborn during the Dutch Hunger Winter, if you were a first trimester fetus, it didn't work that way; you don't see this Dutch hunger phenomenon. It happens second and third trimester when a fetus is programming its response to nutrients, how a tripwire of insulin secretion it has. It's during that time that you are programming your adult metabolism.

There we see a really disturbing, remarkable phenomenon. This turns out to be one of a number of examples of this, a number of examples that have been summed by an epidemiologist named David Barker as fetal origins of adult disease, FOAD, this completely new area of research built around the notion that environment doesn't begin at birth. An awful lot of what's going on in fetal life causes programming of how adult responses are going to be— remarkable. Soon people were studying this in laboratory animals, seeing experimental versions of prenatal stress, and you see the exact same thing. You can generate a Dutch Hunger Winter phenomenon. You can show that prenatal stress, and as an adult, you have a less than optimal stress-response. You have elevated levels of glucocorticoids basally, when there is no stressor, in the absence of stress.

Prenatally stressed rats as adults secrete more glucocorticoids than they're supposed to, bad news. Prenatally stressed rats as adults take a longer time to recover after the end of the stressor, for their glucocorticoid levels to go back to normal. Prenatally stressed rats as adults are more vulnerable to metabolic syndrome, all sorts of things, even the domain of behavior, anxiety. There's this chemical your brain makes which is called an endogenous benzodiazepine—don't panic, the synthetic, the drug version of it is something like Valium or Librium, antianxiety drugs—and just like all the other examples we've heard, the benzodiazepines that your brain makes interact with benzodiazepine receptors to decrease anxiety. A prenatally stressed rat as an adult has fewer of those benzodiazepine receptors in its brain, more of a predisposition then toward anxiety.

Even in the realm of learning, prenatal stress and something about those elevated glucocorticoid levels disrupt aspects of brain development, aspects relevant to learning and memory. Prenatally stressed rats, everything else being equal from birth on, have more memory problems, aren't quite as good at learning, at consolidating new things, in part, because they have elevated glucocorticoid levels as an adult. Beginning does this disrupt cognition—stay tuned, that's going to be an entire lecture—but also because of that prenatal environment disrupting brain development. Look at this, we've got this whole world of prenatal stress which could influence your levels of stress hormones as an adult, how readily you recover from a stress-response, your brain chemistry that deals with anxiety, learning, vulnerability to metabolic disease. Again it's that critical punch line which is: Environment doesn't begin at birth.

There's an even more interesting ripple to this, and what it winds up doing is having Dutch Hunger Winter effects that are, in fact, multigenerational. Here's what I mean. You were a Dutch hunger fetus, Dutch Hunger Winter fetus, and 30 years later, you are now pregnant, you are having a child. Thanks to that fetal experience, you have a thrifty metabolism. You secrete insulin like crazy, so you're really good at stealing nutrients from your circulation, you retain salt, all that sort of stuff. You are having a perfectly typical diet during your pregnancy, but as I just said, you are stealing an atypically large amount of it from your fetus. You are more efficient at taking nutrients out of the bloodstream, so for that perfectly normal diet, your fetus is getting less nutrients than it should. Certainly not starving, but insofar as you're absorbing more of it than normal, your fetus is getting less of it than normal. In other words, Dutch Hunger Winter babies, when they become pregnant, generate Dutch Hunger Winter babies. It's multigenerational. This has now been shown in the Dutch Hunger Winter humans; their grandkids show some of these same tendencies. It has been shown in laboratory rats as well. This is multigenerational. Mind you, it's not as big of a phenomenon, it's one where it's a ripple of prenatal effect that, with each generation, gets smaller and smaller. But nonetheless, this is remarkable. Fetal life can leave an imprint, can leave an echo, can leave scar tissue of disease risk multigenerationally.

This is really critical in lots of ways because you look at this, and you say, wow, this could easily be mistaken for something else. In other words, you take a rat that has been made a Dutch Hunger Winter rat as a result of fetal malnutrition, and as an adult is much better at storing calories. As an adult, when she's pregnant, gives birth to babies who are a little bit prone toward this Dutch Hunger Winter phenomenon. You do a laboratory experiment which is, as soon as the babies are born, you take them away from the mom. They're raised by a different mother. It's called cross-fostering, a standard technique in these experimental studies, and you see a trait in these babies that were fostered elsewhere, a trait that they don't share with their adoptive mother, a trait that they share with their biological mother. As seen here, this propensity toward metabolic syndrome. You look at that, and you say well, all they had in common was their shared genes, took them away right at birth. If they have this same tendency toward this metabolic disease as their biological mom, it must be genetic. It's passed on over time. What we see here is again, that truism, which is environment, doesn't begin at birth. If you're not careful, some of these prenatal programming effects might be mistaken for, in fact, being genetic.

We take this, now, and we transition to the next logical phase, which is moving from all this prenatal stress stuff into postnatal, the sort of stress you experience during childhood. How does that work? What are the general consequences? You know already exactly what it's going to be. It's the same punch line in a child as opposed to a fetus. Chronic activation of the stress-response does all sorts of bad stuff, and it's in a very similar realm, very similar sorts of punch lines. If you stress an infant rat, stress not by nutrient deprivation—so in this case you're not producing a Dutch Hunger Winter effect—stress in all sorts of different possible ways, you produce an adult rat with higher glucocorticoid levels. You produce an adult rat who has trouble turning off glucocorticoid secretion at the end of stress, a rat with a somewhat activated stress-response all the time when there's nothing stressful going on, a rat more vulnerable to a bunch of those diseases. You get a rat that is not as good at learning and memory, whose brain in the cognitive realm hasn't developed all that well. You get a rat that is more prone towards anxiety. You get a rat that has fewer of those benzodiazepine receptors in there. You have parts of the brain like the hippocampus, which does not develop as normally. Stay tuned, we'll hear plenty about that. You've got all sorts of these long-term consequences, the same sort of picture there.

What this begins to bring in is something even more subtle. The first question that might arise when grasping all these prenatal and postnatal stress effects is: Well, how much do I have to worry about it in terms of is this a Dutch Hunger Winter phenomenon? Everybody who has a fairly normal diet as a fetus, everything is fine, and just only at the extreme that suddenly you get this increased metabolic risk. No, what you see instead is across the whole normal range of prenatal nutrition, across the whole range as manifested in birth weight as a percentage of body length, this is not just about the extremes.

Once you recognize that it's not just about these extreme states but instead the whole array of developmental stressors, moderate, medium, severe, all of that, the whole array of prenatal effects, suddenly you realize, there's something that's got to come into the equation which is mothering style. Different styles of mothering can represent and generate a more stimulatory environment, a less, a more stressful, all of that. Suddenly you've got this whole issue of does mothering style have an influence on the nature of metabolic programming, what sort of stress-response the offspring has as an adult. There has been some wonderful work done on this by lots of investigators. One of the leading ones is named Michael Meaney at McGill University, a fabulous scientist and also an old friend and collaborator, who gave a very modern spin to a timeworn phenomenon in this field. Take a newborn rat, and over the first couple of weeks of its life, pick it up every day and handle it. Pet it for a few minutes. Take it away from its mom for a few minutes and then put it back. Do that every day for 3 minutes or so, and what you have now done is neonatally handled that rat. What this counts as is stimulation, and remarkably this is now a rat who, as an adult, will have lower glucocorticoid levels, that will have better learning and memory, and as it turns out will have a more neurologically intact old age, the right amount of stimulation.

Meanwhile, do something else. Pick up a rat and pet it, and put it away from mom for 180 minutes, for 3 hours rather than 3 minutes. Then bring it back to mom, and you now produce an adult with a hyperactive stress-response and impaired cognition, and what you see is it's the exact same stimulus, maternal deprivation and tactile stimulation, 3 minutes, great thing, 3 hours, terrible thing. What we will come to in later lectures, where's the transition from stimulation to stress?

This very well-established phenomenon, this neonatal-handling business, when you stop and think about it, whatever is going on inside these baby rats did not evolve in order to give grad students doctorates out of petting rats 3 minutes a day. What's the equivalent in a rat's real world, and what Meaney first showed was this translates into mothering style. You take the baby rats away from mom for a certain length of time, and you bring the rat back and mom changes her behavior. What you see is when the baby is away for only 3 minutes, mom becomes more attentive. She grooms the baby more; she licks the baby more. Take the infant away for 3 hours, put him back with mom, and there's a certain degree of detachment that goes on. Mothering style, what this handling phenomenon is mostly about is, what sort of maternal behaviors are elicited when you return the pup.

Meaney then took it one step further. Forget this taking the pup out of the cage and petting it and taking it away from mom for differing lengths of time. Just do something now much more straightforward which is look at the style of mothering. What's the normative range of mothering among rats? Remarkably enough, some rats are more attentive moms than other rats. The normal range of variability applies to all sorts of other species, absolutely straightforward. Some rats lick their pups more than other rats do. Some rats groom their babies more, some groom them less, some are more or less physically rough with them, are more interactive, all those sorts of things you can imagine. What they see in their studies is the extent to which there is maternal licking and grooming will cause programming in adulthood. Get a mom who does an optimal amount of licking and grooming of her baby rat there, and she produces an adult with lower glucocorticoid levels, better learning and memory, all that sort of stuff.

That's absolutely remarkable, and it turns out that there's all sorts of ways in which rat mothering style translates into a different adult stress-response in the offspring. Turns out to work the same way in nonhuman primates, and that can take all sorts of forms, very simple sort of one, how anxious of a monkey mother do you have? What does anxiety in a mothering style look like in a nonhuman primate? A baby gets up and goes walking to start exploring the world. How far away from mom can it go before mom reaches over and grabs her kids and yanks them back, saying, the world is not a safe place when you get this far from me. Anxious monkey mothers, the kids go a tiny distance before mom communicates anxiety and ooh, it's scary, come on back. Less anxious mothers even further away, and that translates into different stress hormone levels. That translates into different adult profiles of stress-responses. That's absolutely amazing.

We've now seen a couple of remarkable things here. One, environment doesn't begin at birth and these really long-term persistent effects on physiology, on disease risk, as a function of fetal stress experience. We've now seen very similar sorts of themes in postnatal experience while growing up. What we see is this is not just about extremes; this covers the range of differences in stimulation and stress that's encompassed even in differences in mothering style among rats and monkeys.

What has become a huge question in the field, a huge challenge, and one which has to be in there the second you start thinking about stuff working this way is, how does it work this way? How do you translate how much a mother rat licks her pups into what sort of glucocorticoid levels those pups are going to have in their old age in some cases? How does that work? That is an extraordinarily tough problem to try to make any headway with because this is not obvious how does licking turn into a different hypothalamus or perhaps pituitary or adrenals. How did this stuff work? This is where Meaney and his collaborators have come up with some extraordinary findings, this whole new area of molecular biology. Close your ears if this is more detail than you want, but this whole new field called epigenetics.

You've got genes which direct the construction of certain proteins, and when a gene activates, it generates a certain protein that it codes for. That's great, genes as determining the workings of the entire universe. When does a gene know when to activate? It turns out in your DNA, not only are there lots of genes, but there are on and off switches, things in the outside world that will activate a particular gene to produce its protein product, all that sort of thing. It turns out epigenetics, what epigenetics is about is, early experience can cause a permanent stage of a switch being held on all the time or being held off all the time. What Meaney pioneered in showing is that mothering style causes certain epigenetic changes in the brain having to do with what sort of glucocorticoid level there will be in adulthood. It's still not clear how you get from licking to this epigenetics stuff. The nuts and bolts are getting worked out these days, how you do that. At least it's understood now how differences in prenatal/postnatal experience produce propensities toward certain genes being more active than others, or less active, remarkable finding in the last few years. Go to those Dutch Hunger Winter adults, the human ones, and look at certain key genes in them and there have been those epigenetic changes. What sorts of genes? Not genes coding for eye color, how wide their feet are, or anything, genes having to do with insulin actions; perfect, exactly what you would expect.

What we see here is the way in which experience, prenatal and postnatal, can shape the sort of hormonal profile you have as an adult, the sort of brain you have, early experience, taking the form of severe stress, but also mild stress, degrees of stimulation, and mothering style producing different profiles in adulthood. Producing, as we saw most remarkably, even profiles in the next generation and the next. It's right around this point where, if you are a parent, you grind to a screeching neurotic halt because here's a whole new realm in which you can screw up your kids.

I have to do something confessional here which is tell you a few of the ways in which my wife and I have been horrible, horrible parents. There was the time when my wife was pregnant with our first child, our son, during the third trimester, where we went to what turned out to be a really loud concert, and right in the middle of it, our son kicked. We said, "Oh my God. We're stressing him. This auditory environmental stressor, we have screwed up." Then there was the time that we meant to put on some video, one of those great educational ones, a video for 4-year-olds, about plate tectonics or something, and we messed up with the machine. For about 15 seconds instead, there was some horrible violent cartoon, and we messed up. Then there was the time in order to placate my second child, our daughter, we actually let her have some sugary cereal. Oh, we have messed up forever. We all know that neurosis, the notion that do something wrong with your child and there will be long-term consequences. Oh my God. That's crazy. You've got to get this stuff under control, and then along comes this whole field saying experience, remarkably subtle differences in experience, beginning as a fetus, produce the sort of adult you will be. Produce perhaps even the sort of children you'll have, these long-term effects, these fetal origins of adult disease. Suddenly you get that much crazier as a neurotic parent. Look at the ways in which early experience has long-term consequences.

In response to all this neurosis, there's some bad news and some good news. Some of the bad news you've already heard, which is: Is this a world only of extreme adverse experience versus everything else, you get a pretty normal outcome? No, we just saw that this covers the whole normal range of variability, amount of prenatal nutrition mapping onto adult metabolic profiles. This is not just about them and their horrific parenting and prenatal lives. This is something that appears to apply across the whole range of development.

Next source of bad news, which is, how big are these effects? If you're sort of a mainstream medicine type and you hear about stuff like this, the first response is, that's ridiculous. There's no way stuff can work like this. Then when it is shown, yes, there are prenatal programming effects, the next thing you do to kind of deny the importance is say, yes, yes, yes. I give up. It's real, but these are not big effects. These can be enormous effects. The Dutch Hunger Winter phenomenon, as I mentioned, be a prenatally stressed Dutch fetus during that Dutch Hunger Winter, and your increased risk of metabolic syndrome, obesity, hypertension, diabetes, your increased risk 50 years later is not a tiny effect; it's almost a 20-fold increase.

We got bad news. A normative range of developmental experience produces a normal range of better or worse adult profiles, and these are big effects. These are not little hiccups of biology. Now here's the good news. How inevitable is this to occur if you are stressed prenatally for 3-and-a-half minutes? Are you going to pay a price? No, there are enormous amounts of variability from one individual to another. Developmental stress does not guarantee that you are up the creek in that way. The other piece of good news is, are these things permanent? Prenatal stress, and suddenly are you guaranteed to have a miserable hyperglycemic 80th birthday? No, what's also clear is amid the persistence of these effects, there's a tremendous capacity to reverse them throughout life.

We've got some plusses and minuses. As you think about this, what's the undercurrent of all this parental anxiety of, did I do too much of this and too little of that, all this nutsiness. What's intrinsic in all of it after a while is what's the optimal parenting style? This is a domain of complete craziness. You get some interesting insights into it when you look at work of anthropologists who look at mothering styles as they vary cross-culturally. There are differences. There are dramatic differences across cultures. How much physical contact does a baby spend with its mother? How much physical contact does it have with nonmothers? How long on the average does a baby cry in this culture before it's picked up? At what age do babies stop sleeping with their mothers? There's tremendous variability in that.

You look at this, and suddenly you're sort of thinking well, if I can only learn enough about these cross-cultural patterns, I could come up with the perfect mothering style which will have like the Trobriand Islander diet, the Ituri Pygmy preschool curriculum, the Kwakiutl exercise regime, and it doesn't work that way.

An anthropologist at Cornell named Meredith Small wrote a wonderful book that gets at this issue. You look at all of the variability in parenting style across cultures, and what you realize is, there's no optimal style. There is no style that is most natural, most embedded in our hominid history. What we do in culture after culture is we raise children to become the sort of adults that we value. What you wind up seeing in our own society, in our own culture, is an example of this, perfectly captured by this old Harry Chapin song, "Cat's in the Cradle," which is this yuppie and baby-boomer song of middle-aged regret, which is my boy grew up just like me.

Stress, Growth, and Child Development
Lecture 7

The general consensus in the field is [stress dwarfism] is a remarkably rare disease. This is a once-in-a-career disease to see, extremely rare. Except, it's not so rare. It pops up all over the place. It pops up in areas of—perfectly logically—extreme stress, for example ... these poor kids who were raised in the Romanian orphanages shortly after the fall of Communism there.

If you are a young person and are chronically stressed, you're not going to grow as fast. What are some of the mechanisms underlying this? Some very straightforward ones like elevated levels of glucocorticoids, elevated activation of the sympathetic nervous system, and decreased secretion of growth hormone. The cardiovascular stress-response also plays a role: Your blood pressure goes up to deliver energy to the thigh muscles, but you decrease blood delivery to unessential areas like your gut. If you are a kid and are chronically decreasing blood flow to your gut, you're not absorbing nutrients as readily.

The effects of stress on child development are not subtle, and at an extreme, you get one of the truly bizarre, disturbing outposts of medicine: **stress dwarfism**, a disease of kids who are so stressed that they stop growing entirely. These are children who have no obvious disease. There is no malnutrition. There are no parasites. You look in the bloodstream, and there's no growth hormone. You give them synthetic growth hormone. Nothing happens; the whole system is shut down. What you have here are the consequences of truly sustained stress. You check around with that kid's background, and out comes some appalling psychological stressor. The good news is the consequence of removing that child from that stressful setting: Get them into a different setting, and everything gets better. There is a profound capacity of stress to disrupt growth but also a remarkable capacity of children to recover from it.

A remarkable therapy was worked out a few decades ago by a psychologist at the University of Miami named Tiffany Field. She noticed that one of the triumphs of modern medicine had a major downside: Kids in neonatal intensive care units are taken care of with all sorts of sophisticated equipment, but in the process, they don't have a lot of physical contact with people. Field came up with the idea of physically stimulating severe preemies, going in and massaging their backs 3 times a day. She discovered something remarkable, which was about a 50% increase in the growth rate in the preemies who were stimulated in this way. The babies were more alert, they were more active, they went home at an earlier stage—and looking at them months later, their growth rates were still enhanced.

We know you secrete less growth hormone during stress. But what does growth hormone do? In kids, it makes you grow. And it turns out that in adults, it helps remodel your bones. Growth hormone plays a huge role in depositing new calcium into bones. Along comes chronic stress, growth hormone levels drop, and you are now depositing less calcium into your bones. What's that going to set you up for? Brittle, prematurely aged bones and osteoporosis. The moral of the story is chronic stress at any age is not a good thing. ∎

King Frederick II, Early Endocrinologist?

King Frederick II of Sicily, a 13th-century despot, carried out a remarkable experiment. The members of his court were having an argument about what the natural language of humans is. One thought it was Greek, another Latin or classical Hebrew, and Frederick II was holding out for Italian. So what did he do? He commandeered some children in his kingdom and had them raised in complete isolation for a number of years—no one talking to them, just someone silently running in and leaving food for them; minimal contact with other humans. The notion in this experiment was that at some point they would open the door and the children would come out reciting in classical Greek or whatever the natural language of humans was. Eventually they opened the door, and the kids did not come out speaking classical Greek; the kids did not come out at all. They had died from the extreme of stress dwarfism.

stress dwarfism (a.k.a. **psychogenic dwarfism, psychosocial dwarfism**): A disorder in which growth in a child is significantly impaired by severe psychological stress.

Sapolsky, *Why Zebras Don't Get Ulcers*, chap. 6.

1. Is stress dwarfism as rare as most clinicians think?

2. What are the effects of stress early in life on the developing brain?

Stress, Growth, and Child Development
Lecture 7—Transcript

We're back, I've got on a new pair of socks, and I'm freshly shaven, so ready for more, part 2 of stress and growth. You'll remember the main point of the previous lecture, amid our logic chronic stress—bad news for growth—was the fact that environment does not begin at birth, that whole world of prenatal stress, that whole world of prenatal programming of adult metabolism, that was last lecture. What we'll emphasize here is growth, not by way of signals from mom, but growth as experienced by the organism itself by way of stress.

We know the logic once again, running away from the lion, blah, blah, chronic stress. How does this get turned into effects on growth? Because what you get after a while is precisely what seems logical, which is, if you are a young organism and you are chronically stressed, you're not going to grow as fast. This is different from last lecture, chronic stress early in life, and when you're 70, things will be working differently. This is just the plain, straightforward world of lots of stress, and a kid doesn't grow as much. What are some of the mechanisms underlying this? Some very straightforward ones and ones that you could probably construct from Lesson 2, from the second lecture, going over the building blocks of the stress-response, very simple. Those elevated levels of glucocorticoids, that elevated activation of the sympathetic nervous system, the decreased secretion of growth hormone, put those together and that's where you've got problems with growth.

Another one as well, back, remember the cardiovascular stress-response. Not only do you want your blood pressure to go up to deliver energy to those thigh muscles, but in addition, you don't want to deliver blood to unessential areas like your gut. We saw in the previous lecture how one consequence of that is if you are chronically stressed and chronically decreasing blood flow to your gut, it's more prone toward an ulcer, that whole picture. What we see here is if you are a kid and you are chronically decreasing blood flow to your gut, you're not absorbing nutrients as readily. That's another mechanism by which you can disturb growth in kids thanks to chronic stress.

Another question that seems to come up here over and over as we look at some of these adverse outcomes, how big of effects are these? Ooh, thanks to enormous amounts of childhood stress, you're one-eighth of an inch shorter than you would have been otherwise. No, these are not subtle effects, and at an extreme, you get one of the truly bizarre, disturbing outposts of medicine, a disease of kids who are so stressed that they stop growing entirely, termed stress dwarfism, also known as psychosocial dwarfism, psychogenic dwarfism, and this is for real. This is a child where there is no obvious disease. There is no malnutrition. There are no parasites. You look in the bloodstream, and there's no growth hormone. You give them synthetic growth hormone. Nothing happens; the whole system is shut down.

What you have here are the consequences of truly sustained adverse stress. You check around with that kid's background and out comes some appalling psychological stressor. This is standard textbook knowledge. Get some textbook of endocrinology. Look in the chapter on growth, and I guarantee you somewhere in there will be the obligatory picture of the stress dwarfism kid. Those pictures, this is the stunted kid who's naked in front of the growth chart with the rectangle over the eyes, and then I guarantee you turn the page, and you see the consequence of removing that child from that stressful setting. Technical term, you do a parentectomy on them. Get them into a different setting, you turn that page and there's the same kid 2 years later, and they're like 6 foot 14, and they're playing for the NBA, and, they're still naked with a rectangle, but everything else gets better. What we see here is the profound capacity of stress to disrupt growth, and the remarkable capacity to recover from it.

. . .

Here's one dramatic example—and this was a paper that was published a few years ago, about a child with stress dwarfism who wound up in a New York hospital. A child from a severely stressful psychological setting showed, when the child came into this pediatric ward, growth hormone levels were at the floor. Over the next 3 months, he developed this close relationship with this one nurse. This was like the first normal emotional relationship of his life. By the end of those 3 months, he had perfectly normal levels of growth hormone. At that point, the nurse goes on vacation. By the end of the 2-week vacation, the boy is back down to virtually zero. The nurse comes back from vacation, he bounces back up; think about it. Think about it, the rate at which this child was depositing calcium in his bones could be predicted by just how loved and safe he was feeling in the world. You can't ask for a much better example that what's going on here affects every outpost in the body.

We have stress dwarfism. The question then becomes one of magnitude, one of frequency. How common is this disease? If you are shorter than average and you were not obviously malnourished as a kid, are you a victim of stress dwarfism and that's something else your parents did to you? No, this is not conventional stress. This is not, "ooh, when I was a kid, we moved all the time, very stressful." This is not acrimonious divorce; this is nightmare psychopathology. This is the police and the social workers breaking down the door of the apartment and finding the child chained to the radiator smeared in excrement, total nightmare stuff. Remarkably, get the child out of that setting, and there is recovery. The general consensus in the field is this is a remarkably rare disease. This is a once-in-a-career disease to see, extremely rare. Except, it's not so rare. It pops up all over the place. It pops up in areas of—perfectly logically—extreme stress, for example, a whole literature emerging about these poor kids who were raised in the Romanian orphanages shortly after the fall of Communism there. This was just the nightmare settings of kids warehoused in these orphanages with incredible absence of stimulation and contact and affection, all of that major, major impairment of growth.

That's one disturbing realm; but it pops up in other places as well. Here's a great historical factoid. King Frederick II of Sicily, some 13th-century despot who clearly was an early pioneering endocrinologist—I don't know what was going on in their court, but one day they were sitting around there having this argument about what's the natural language of humans. Presumably, there were no villages to pillage and loot or whatever. They were doing philosophy instead that winter, and what's the natural language, and they were holding out one for Greek and another for Latin or classical Hebrew. Presumably, Frederick II of Sicily was holding out for Italian, and he did what was, for the time, a remarkable experiment. He got some children. He commandeered some children in his kingdom, and he had them raised in complete isolation for a number of years, isolation like no one talking to them, like whoever is giving them food runs in silently and leaves food for them, minimal contact with other humans. The notion in this experiment was, at some point they're going to open the door and out will come the child reciting in classical Greek or whatever it is, the natural language of humans. Eventually they opened the door, and the kids did not come out speaking classical Greek, the kids did not come out at all. They had died from the extreme of stress dwarfism.

More examples of that, more examples where this comes up, amid this picture of oh, this was only at the great extremes. What you've got instead are a lot of cases where it does occur. One example, kids who grow up in areas, war zones, areas of civil strife, kids who grow up with all sorts of family dynamics that are highly stressful. Here's one really interesting example. This was a classic study done by a pair of anthropologists in the early '60s looking at kids from different cultures, and asking how physically stressful are the rites of passages in this culture? Rites of passages in some cultures, the scarification, piercing of body parts, tattooing, or putting you out in the desert with poison ants. Then in some cultures you have to play the piano for your grandmother and her friends, whatever is done in your particular tribe. They did like 80 comparisons. They controlled for genetics, they did this perfectly, and what they showed was highly physical, stressful rites of passages between ages 6 to 15 or so, 1 and a half inches shorter as an adult.

Let me tell you about the single creepiest example of stress dwarfism I've ever heard of, and if this doesn't unnerve you, you've got no imagination at all. Here it is: If for some inexcusable reason you find yourself reading chapter after chapter about growth hormone, you're going to find this weird pattern which is a lot of these chapters make reference to Peter Pan. Quotes from Peter Pan, snide comments about Tinker Bell. I had seen this for years. I had no idea what was going on until one day, I'm reading a chapter about stress regulation and growth, and the possibilities for stress dwarfism. It gave the following case history, which is, an 8-year-old boy growing up in Victorian England, perfectly comfortable middle class family in the 1870s. One day he sees his beloved older brother killed in front of him in an accident. This destroys the family. There are no other children. The father was emotionally nonexistent. This was the mother's favorite child. In this Victorian swoon, she takes to her bed with the shades drawn for the next 10 years or so.

Here's this child growing up in this complete emotional vacuum, and there are these terrible scenes where he brings in a tray of food for his mother, and she's saying, "Oh, David, David, is that you? David have you come to me?" David the dead son, and she will go on, "Oh David are you finally—oh, it's only you." Growing up being "only you," apparently one of the only things that the mother ever talked to him about was this crazy idea that she grabbed on to which was if David had to die, he died when he was still my perfect little boy. He never grew up into a man who doesn't need his mother anymore. He'll always be my perfect little boy. He didn't grow up, didn't grow up, didn't grow up. This kid hears this with a vengeance. No evidence of malnutrition, no evidence of disease, stops growing at that point. Lives to 60 years of age under 5 feet tall, dramatic effect, unconsummated marriage, and this winds up being a wild example of stress dwarfism. Then, the chapter concludes by informing us that as an adult, this was the author of the much-beloved children's classic, *Peter Pan*. This was J. M. Barrie, the author of *Peter Pan*. This was one incredibly messed up guy. This was a guy who just cranked out plays after novellas about boys who die and come back as ghosts and marry their mothers and all sorts of stuff like that. His private journals were full of sadomasochistic fantasies with little boys. This guy spent the rest of his life not very effectively dealing with his stress dwarfism.

You may want to think about that the next time you see Johnny Depp up on the screen; but that's a case of one. That's a sample of one. What's the experimental evidence? Here's another remarkable example, a textbook example, where if you were working with lab rats, you could not have designed a better experiment. This was in an orphanage in Germany shortly after World War II, a series of orphanages in fact. What was noted was the children in one of these orphanages had a very stunted growth rate compared to the other ones, and people went and studied. What they thought might have been relevant was the woman running the orphanage who was this cold, berating woman who had zero physical contact with the kids. That's a nice speculation. What was done was the sort of thing that you could not have done any better with rats. The woman was transferred to a different orphanage. Suddenly, the growth rates in that orphanage went down. Remember, everything is controlled for the kids in all these orphanages. They're getting the same diet, the same number of doctor's visits, the same vaccinations, all that was different was this woman in charge. One additional wrinkle, which was, she moved her favorites with her to each orphanage she was assigned to, and those favorites grew at a normal rate. This is a classic example, another one of those that winds up in every textbook.

Based on this, suddenly there are all sorts of possible therapies that come to mind, and a remarkable one was worked out a few decades ago by a psychologist at the University of Miami named Tiffany Field. What she did was notice one of the high points, one of the triumphs of modern medicine with a very major downside, which is you look at kids who wind up in NICUs, neonatal intensive care units. They are taken care of in tubes and tests and monitors and all sorts of things, and in the process of that, there's one thing they don't have which is a whole lot of physical contact with people. Field came up with this idea, how about we go in and physically stimulate these preemies, these severe preemies. How about we go in and massage their backs. Massage their backs, how do you massage the back of a tiny preemie? You're doing it with your thumbs.

They went in, and they did it 3 times a day. They discovered something remarkable, which was there was about a 50% increase in the growth rate in the preemies who were stimulated in this way. The babies were more alert. They were more active, they went home at an earlier stage, and looking at them months later, their growth rates were still enhanced. This was a remarkable effect and Field and the sort of people who followed up on her work have done some estimates that if this were done in every neonatal ward in the country, it would save a huge number of lives. It would save billions of dollars in terms of the long-term adverse consequences of being an extreme preemie.

A remarkable demonstration, get just the right amount of stimulation, and growth is enhanced, just as we've been seeing. Get the wrong amounts into this stressful range, and you disrupt normal growth. All of this is about kids, but somewhere in there, we've got to think about adults, because by now I've noted growth hormone. Growth hormone has popped up a whole bunch of times in this course so far, and growth hormone, you secrete less of it during stress and all of that. What does growth hormone do? It makes you grow, which is what kids are about. But you look at adults, and they've got plenty of growth hormone in their bloodstream, and most of us as adults, we're not growing any more other than wider as the years go by. What's growth hormone doing in the adult? It turns out a very special role that at first was thought to have nothing to do with stress, but where the jury might be no longer out on this which is what you do with growth hormone is remodel your bones.

Most of us view bones as totally boring and nothing is happening there, and they just kind of keep your body together and bipedal and stuff like that. Bones are extremely dynamic parts of the body. You're putting in calcium, you're taking it out, you're remodeling. How else does somebody get bowlegged if you're not constantly remodeling your bones in response to the world around you? What's doing the remodeling? You pull calcium out; you put it in. Growth hormone plays a huge role in depositing new calcium into bones. Along comes chronic stress, and it's not that you're a kid impairing growth, you're an adult, growth hormone levels drop, and what might be the consequence of that? You are now depositing less calcium into your bones. What's that going to set you up for? Brittle bones, prematurely aged bones, osteoporosis, and suddenly in the realm of stress-related disease, there's this possibility that chronic stress can increase the risk of osteoporosis.

What the consensus was in the field until some time ago was, yes, yes, yes, this is possible, but this is not likely to occur. You need such extremes of adult stress and such a collapse in growth hormone secretion that you never actually get overt osteoporosis. You may get the first little baby steps in that direction, but nonetheless, this is not a realm of stress-related diseases you need to worry about. Some years ago, it became clear that this wasn't the case. This was work done by Carol Shively and Jay Kaplan at Bowman Gray Medical School, and they showed that there was a tragic, confused flaw in the whole biomedical literature built around doing this. The flaw was as follows: The tendency of scientists to study male rats and male monkeys and male college students, and they're not all that representative of what animals are about or what humans are about because it's losing half of the equation. Overwhelmingly, the literature was built around studies of males.

106

What happens when you're male, and you're chronically stressed? As we know by now up go glucocorticoid levels, down go growth hormone levels. What does that wind up doing? Up increased glucocorticoid levels, you're pulling a lot of calcium out of your bones. Low growth hormone levels, you're not replacing it, and as we've seen, put those pieces together in the male rats, monkeys, et cetera, and you get just a hint of osteoporosis. Chronically stress females, and something else happens. You have the elevated glucocorticoid levels, you have the suppressed growth hormone levels, but as we are going to find out in the next lecture, something else gets suppressed, which are levels of estrogen. Amid all the controversies of hormone replacement therapy with estrogen postmenopausally, one thing that is absolutely clear is estrogen is very good for the health of your bones. Estrogen promotes calcium uptake. Estrogen is terrific in that regard. It decreases your risk of osteoporosis; that's great. With females with chronic stress, instead of 2 things going wrong that put you within the ballpark of osteoporosis, 3 things, elevated glucocorticoids, low growth hormone, and low estrogen, and suddenly you're more at risk for osteoporosis. At this point, the work of Shively and Kaplan has shown that this is precisely what's going on in lab monkeys and experimental monkeys, females with chronic stress, manipulating estrogen levels. Not quite clear on humans yet, the work is still going on in that area.

We've had this whole range of possible ways in which things can go wrong, prenatal stress, postnatal stress, effects on growth, how long-term are they? How common are these disorders of blunted growth and response to stress? What can be done about it perhaps? The Tiffany Field studies of intervention with extreme preemie kids, lurking around in all of this here is the same sort of theme that was lurking around in the previous lecture, which is parenting style, and how does parenting style wind up influencing the growth rate? For this, one has to get a sense of history, and the history of what sort of parents parents have been advised to be. For a gazillion generations, all of us grew up under the advice of Spock, Dr. Spock. Back around 1900, there was a different person who was the expert, a man named Luther Holt, at Columbia University. Holt was the most influential expert at the time, teaching parents about parenting, and what he had to say was very different from a Dr. Spock scenario. He was the person of the school of "spare the rod, spoil the child."

"Children are meant to be seen and not heard." He even used phrases like, referring to the vicious practice of picking up babies when they were crying and advising parents not to do that. This was an extremely stern view of what parenting should be. This was the dominant model at the time.

A number of decades later, with this remaining as the dominant model, along came a man who absolutely revolutionized this field, a man named Harry Harlow. To appreciate what Harlow accomplished, you have to consider what some of the dominant schools of psychology were at the time. In addition to this whole view of people like Holt, of very stern, detached parenting styles, there was this school of psychology that dominated American psychology in the 20th century, the field of behaviorism best personified by the most famous behaviorist of all time, B. F. Skinner of Harvard. In a totally simplified way, what was behaviorism about? You get rewarded for something, you're more likely to do it later. You get punished for something, you're less likely to do it. It's that positive and negative reinforcement, not exactly comparable to reward and punishment. Nonetheless, in this general world of behaviorism, things that have good outcomes, you're more likely to do afterward, things with bad outcomes, less.

What would behaviorists have to say about this whole maturational process amid Luther Holt-type advice, somewhere up there comes this question: Why do kids wind up getting attached to their mothers? Why do kids bond to their mothers? You're a behaviorist, and you had the exact answer, which is, you get attached to mom because she feeds you. You get positively reinforced. You get reinforcement under those circumstances where you're sitting there saying, my gosh, I'm feeling a little bit hypoglycemic, and here's this breast belonging to mom, and soon I'm not so hypoglycemic. Why, I'll begin to have all sorts of positive feelings about this individual. That was the behaviorist view. Why do we get attached to mothers? Because mothers supply this essential need for nutrients. That was the dominant thinking at the time. All you have to do is combine that with the sort of thinking in the Holt school of parenting style, and you come up with some pretty stern views which are, basically, as long as you provide a kid with food and adequate warmth and things like that, that's all you need to do. Remarkably, this dominated pediatrics at the time, hospital policies, and pediatric wards.

Something that is inconceivable these days, which is your child winds up with some illness and is in a pediatric ward for a few weeks or so, and what was the rule at the time in most of these hospitals? Parents were allowed in for a few minutes a day. Perhaps parents were allowed in only for an hour a week because after all, all parents do is mess up the process with the vicious practice of picking up their kids and coddling them. What we've learned from Skinner, and learned from the likes of Luther Holt is, supply food, supply the right number of blankets, and that's all you need to do if you're doing things correctly.

Here comes the Harlow revolution. Here's where this critical experiment was done that transformed how people think about this subject, one that winds up in every single textbook. I can almost guarantee you've seen one of the pictures from this experiment if you've ever taken Psych 101. This was this classic, brilliant experiment that Harlow did. He takes baby monkeys. Baby monkeys being raised without a mother, a biological mother. What they're raised with instead are 2 different types of surrogate mothers, substitute mothers for a real monkey mother.

First one, the first one was a tube of chicken wire with some Styrofoam monkey head looking thing up on top, and a bottle of milk sticking out of the chicken wire torso, roughly where the breasts are. Second mother, second surrogate has a tube of chicken wire with a monkey head on top and no milk, instead a warm terry cloth wrapped around the torso. You ask the question: Which of these 2 surrogate mothers is a baby monkey going to get attached to? If you're B. F. Skinner, it's completely obvious what the answer is, and you would expect Skinner to very quickly be clutching the chicken wire mom with the baby bottle there because that one supplies nutrients. Of course, you get attached to mom because she supplies you with nutrients.

Look at a real living primate, look at these baby monkeys, and they did something very different instead, which is, sure they were willing to go on the chicken wire mothers with milk when they needed milk. Who were they attached to, though? Who did they spend most of their time on? Who, when something scared them, did they go scampering to for comfort? The warm mother with the terrycloth—it's not that you get attached to mom because she gives you an adequate number of calories. You get attached to mom because she makes you feel safe and makes you feel beloved.

What Harlow did was introduce a word into the technical scientific literature in his papers, the word "love." You get attached to mom because she supplies things that are oh so much more important, fundamental, and interesting than adequate calories and keeping your body at the same temperature that it's supposed to be. Out of Harlow's work came enormously important elaborations. One, a study for example, that showed just how wrong the behaviorists were. Here you've got the cloth mom which a baby monkey is happy to hold on to, and what you've got is in the middle of the torso a little spigot that could blast out, very briefly, a jet of air, unpleasant, and not something you would want to stick around for if you're a behaviorist.

The rule that was set up was when you clutch onto the torso of the mom, you get a blast of air coming out of the torso. Any behaviorist would have predicted at that point that what the baby monkeys are supposed to do is they stop clinging. What they did instead makes perfect sense to anyone who has grown up and attached to anyone. The more they got blasted with the air, the harder they held onto mom. There's no positive or negative reinforcement world there, of oh, you get unattached individuals who blast you with jets of air. What we have here is remarkable insight into things like why do we love people who mistreat us? Why do we make the wrong choices in that realm? It's got to do with what it is we attach to. What Harlow showed was it's not about calories. It's about comfort, safety, and love.

Harlow's work has wound up being enormously controversial, and this was a man who has been just vilified in certain circles of research because he did elaborations on these studies that were brutal: monkeys being raised in complete social isolation, monkey models of severe psychiatric disorders, extremely brutal stuff. When I was a student first reading Harlow's work, I was horrified by some of it, not only the experiments but an extremely callous style that he had in his papers. I was moved to tears by some of these studies because of how awful they were.

Perhaps relevant or perhaps not, Harlow sank into eventually fatal alcoholism amid all this, a very troubled man who did often some very troubling experiments. You look at them, and you ask what seems to be a perfectly obvious question: Didn't they know it worked this way? Didn't they know that baby monkeys, if raised in isolation, would wither away? Wasn't it obvious? Ironically, it took Harlow's work to show how unethical his own work was. You look at a baby monkey, and it's perfectly obvious what would happen if Harlow socially isolated them without a mom. If you prick us, do we not bleed? If you socially isolate us, do we not suffer? The point of Harlow's work was not that it showed the obvious, which is if you socially isolate a monkey in early life, it's going to suffer. What he really showed was if you do the same thing to a human, the same thing happens. That sure wasn't obvious at the time.

Stress and Female Reproduction
Lecture 8

[In] a study of gymnasts ... from the Romanian Olympic gymnastics team—and those are typically those 15-year-olds who weigh 60 pounds and are getting the gold medals—what was the average age at which these kids started menstruating? It was approximately 19. The Western average is 12 1/2 years; this is a huge effect in terms of delaying the onset of puberty.

Female reproduction falls under the auspices of those big, long-term, optimistic projects that the body neglects when faced with chronic stress. A great way to appreciate just how much this is one of those indulgences is to look at how expensive some aspects of female reproduction are. The best estimates are that you spend 50,000 calories over the course of a pregnancy and about 1000 calories a day nursing. This is something that's tough to afford when you're running for your life.

Exercise has wonderful stress-reducing effects, but overexercise can decrease fertility.

What are the hormones involved? At the follicular stage, it's that same axis we've discussed before: brain, pituitary, and peripheral glands. The brain's hypothalamus releases the **luteinizing hormone**, telling your body to prepare for fertilization. Meanwhile, you are releasing **follicle-stimulating hormone** out of your pituitary. These 2 hormones mature eggs and produce estrogen. Once you transition to the luteal phase, progesterone dominates. This hormone prepares the uterus, thickening it for implantation of the fertilized egg.

So what happens during stress? There is decreased brain release of the luteinizing hormone, which in turn tells the pituitary to release less luteinizing hormone and follicle-stimulating hormone. The decreased amount of these hormones makes the ovaries less stimulated to release estrogen. The result is lower estrogen levels and less likelihood of fertilizing an egg. Moreover, stress hormones like glucocorticoids and **beta-endorphin** are also blocking the release of progesterone. Your body doesn't thicken the uterine walls, and it's less likely that the rare fertilized egg is going to implant there.

What other aspects of female reproduction are negatively impacted by chronic stress? Starvation, including the voluntary starvation of anorexia nervosa, can shut down ovulation. This is due to the depletion of fat. That's also the reason why some women who do tons of exercise stop ovulating. For example, runners who run about 50 miles a week begin to see their fat deposits dip below a threshold where they begin to have ovulatory problems.

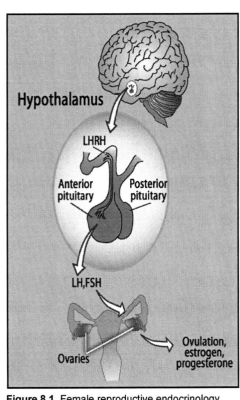

Another domain where stress becomes relevant is high-tech reproduction, in vitro fertilization. This process is enormously stressful: Your lifestyle is dislocated, you are filled up with synthetic hormones that wreak havoc with mood and metabolism, and sex becomes a timed chore.

Figure 8.1. Female reproductive endocrinology.

113

You spend a fortune on it, usually not reimbursed by insurance, and there is a very high failure rate. There hasn't been clear-cut evidence for this yet, but it seems an obvious conclusion that stress makes in vitro fertilization less likely to work.

Another possibility in terms of stress and reproduction is you've gotten a pregnancy to start and chronic stress causes a miscarriage. This is not caused by a horribly stressful event you had one day; this is from stressors stretching out quite a few days. Women who are chronically severely stressed when they're pregnant decrease blood flow to the fetus; if that happens enough, it increases the likelihood of losing the pregnancy.

Lastly, chronic stress decreases your libido. The parts of your body that are sensitive to tactile stimulation are more sensitive when you have high levels of certain reproduction-related hormones in your bloodstream. Those hormones decrease, and sensitivity in those areas is blunted. One additional piece is a brain chemical called dopamine, which has everything to do with pleasure. Sex tends to release dopamine. With chronic stress, you don't have as much dopamine in the pathway, and suddenly sex is less pleasurable. ■

Important Terms

beta-endorphin: A hormone released during stress, predominately from the pituitary gland. It plays a role in stress-induced analgesia and in some of the disruptive effects on reproduction.

follicle-stimulating hormone (FSH): A pituitary hormone that stimulates follicle maturation in females and sperm maturation in males.

luteinizing hormone (LH): A pituitary hormone that stimulates estrogen synthesis in females and testosterone synthesis in males.

prolactin: A hormone released from the pituitary gland in response to stress, exercise, and nursing. It inhibits aspects of reproductive physiology.

Suggested Reading

Sapolsky, *Why Zebras Don't Get Ulcers*, chap. 7.

Tilbrook, Turner, and Clarke, "Effects of Stress on Reproduction in Non-Rodent Mammals."

Questions to Consider

1. What is a consequence for women of excessive amounts of exercise?

2. What, if any, is the link between stress and miscarriage?

Stress and Female Reproduction
Lecture 8—Transcript

We are back again. I have a spanking new set of clothes, courtesy of The Teaching Company, all the way down to new socks, so I am just brimming with manly self-confidence, and thus am willing to tackle the issue of stress and female reproduction. Of course you know the drill by now which is going to be, short-term, running away from the lion, 30 seconds, got better things to do than thicken your uterine walls. Long-term problem, chronic stress, and you begin to impair the reproductive system.

Starting off now, a great way to appreciate just how much this is one of those indulgences, reproduction, one of those ones that fall under the auspices of big, expensive, long-term, optimistic, and this is no time for it, is to appreciate just how expensive some aspects of female reproduction are. Best estimates are 50,000 calories that you go through over the course of a pregnancy, about 1,000 calories a day nursing, and this is simply something that's very tough to afford when you're running for your life. In the face of chronic stress, this is the sort of realm that gets greatly impaired.

Of course you know where we go next with this, which is chronic stress in the form of psychological, psychosocial; it makes no sense at all for your body to say, "Oh, my God. This is too expensive. Let's defer until another period." Once again, you have that same logic that has haunted us in terms of stress-related disease, real physical stressors, the stress-response is wonderfully adaptive. Psychosocial stressors that we humans specialize in, and it makes no sense to turn on the chronic stress-response, and this was one of the realms where you pay a price. To appreciate it, we've got to tackle one of those endocrine axes as talked about in the second lecture. We have to tackle one of those pathways which, as you'll recall, starts with the master gland, your brain, releasing a hormone that has an effect at the pituitary which then, in this case, has an effect on the ovaries.

It's actually 2 different sets of hormones that wind up being relevant here. The first one, for the first half of one's reproductive cycle, is known as the follicular stage. What you're doing there is you're maturing follicles. You're maturing eggs that will be released around day 14 of the cycle, and then you transition to what's called the luteal phase, notion being if conception occurred, right around that 14th day—plus or minus a couple of days—what you now need to do is prepare your body, your uterus, for starting a pregnancy, implanting this fertilized egg.

What are the hormones involved? Follicular stage, that same axis again, as promised: brain, pituitary, peripheral glands. You have starting off, a hormone that lots of people are familiar with coming out of the pituitary, luteinizing hormone. Luteinizing hormone—once again do not write these down. Do not panic if you don't know these terms and don't want to learn these terms—you've got a hormone that comes out of the pituitary, which is going to stimulate egg maturation. Of course, what you know is, the pituitary hasn't a clue when to release luteinizing hormone. Under the control of the brain—the hypothalamus which releases the bizarrely named luteinizing hormone-releasing hormone—out comes this LHRH from the hypothalamus, has an effect on the pituitary, out comes LH, and you are now causing preparation for fertilization. You also are releasing follicle-stimulating hormone out of your pituitary. Collectively what LH and FSH are doing, maturing eggs and producing estrogen coming out of the ovaries, plays a critical role in that.

Once you transition over to the luteal phase, a different hormone dominates, and that's known as progesterone. All you need to do to get a sense of what it's up to is progesterone, progestational, what it does is prepare the uterus, thickening it, preparing it for implantation of the fertilized egg. We've got all the basics of the system under our belts here, and what we now transition to of course is what's occurring during stress. What's occurring with this hypothalamic-pituitary-gonadal axis?

What you see is a very complicated version of exactly what we know by now. First thing that happened, remember that hypothalamic hormone, luteinizing releasing hormone? The first thing that happens during stress is, it releases less of the stuff, and that's occurring within seconds. Which hormones are responsible for that? You remember some of the dread names from earlier on, glucocorticoids. Glucocorticoids work up in the hypothalamus to inhibit the release of LHRH. Another hormone is relevant there, one that was mentioned for 1 and a half seconds in that prior lecture which now begins to be relevant for the first time, that hormone beta-endorphin. Beta-endorphin, about the only thing that registers with most people about beta-endorphin is it's got something to do with blocking pain, a runner's high, an endorphin high. What's it doing, instead, working at the hypothalamus to block LHRH release? Very few hormones do only one thing, so this is another function of beta-endorphin. Don't panic; do not write these down, again, get the general theme.

We've got the first thing that happens, which is, decreased hypothalamic, decreased brain release of this LHRH. By all logic, what that should now do is have a consequence at the pituitary. For lack of that LHRH stimulation, the pituitary is now going to be releasing less LH and FSH. But, that's not enough. Your brain does not trust that things can be solved merely by shutting off LHRH secretion. Another thing that happens is you send signals, hormonal stress signals, you send signals to the pituitary to make it less responsive to whatever LHRH is coming out. You could probably guess the mechanism by now, just like every other hormone, LHRH works by way of its receptor in the pituitary, the pituitary starts making less of these receptors. You've got a double whammy there, less of the signaling hormone is coming out of the brain, and the pituitary is less sensitive to that.

We know the consequence there already. There's going to be less LH, less FSH coming out, and thus, the ovaries are going to be less stimulated to release estrogen. Once again you'll notice the same theme. Just in case the pituitary is screwing up and still releasing some of that LH and FSH, the stress-response, heavily glucocorticoids, are working down at the ovaries to make them less sensitive to LH and FSH; and you guessed it, there are LH receptors in the ovaries, and FSH receptors, and there are fewer receptors. You've got less of the hypothalamic hormone, and the pituitary pays less attention to it. You've got less of the pituitary hormones coming out, and the ovaries pay less attention. The result is lower estrogen levels and less likelihood of fertilizing an egg.

The next thing that kicks in is less progesterone. That's another step in the pathway, those same stress hormones, and the same ones begin to pop up over and over, glucocorticoids, beta-endorphin, they're also blocking the release of progesterone. What you've got at this point is, not only were you not releasing LH, FSH, estrogen, and maturing the eggs, but just in case against all these ridiculous odds you somehow manage to get an egg that matures sufficiently through this follicular stage that it actually gets fertilized. What you've now done is you are making sure the uterus has not matured enough for this fertilized egg to implant. The way you do that is exactly what we were just talking about, you secrete less of that progestational progesterone. You don't thicken the uterine walls, and it's less likely that the rare fertilized egg is actually going to implant there.

One additional hormone that's going to become very relevant soon has a role in that, a hormone called prolactin. We're going to see all sorts of things prolactin does. One of the things it does in this case is it counters the effect of any progesterone that you still manage to dribble out despite the stress signals. What prolactin also does is thin out your uterine walls. What should impress you by now is this is an incredible number of mechanisms for shutting down this reproductive ovarian access at the level of the brain, the level of pituitary sensitivity to the brain, signaling the pituitary, ovarian sensitivity, and all these steps.

There's one really interesting additional step that comes in there, and it's got to do, oddly enough with fat cells in females. It has got to do with a very, very unlikely thing that females do, including human females which is they secrete a certain amount of male sex hormones into the bloodstream, androgenic hormones like testosterone. Where are those coming from? They come from the adrenal glands. Remember what the adrenal glands are up to is making adrenaline, epinephrine, glucocorticoids. In females, bizarrely, they also make adrenal androgens. Not a ton of the stuff, maybe 5% the levels you would see in a male, nonetheless you've got to get rid of the stuff. Unfortunately, as I noted there, fat cells come into play here, which is fat cells have this enzyme that could do like biochemistry 101. They could take the circulating testosterone and convert it to estrogen.

That's great; everybody lives happily ever after. You've turned these bizarre, unlikely circulating androgens into estrogen, and everything is working fine; but what if you're stressed? What if you're stressed like the locusts have come and eaten your crops, and you've been subsisting on 1,000 calories a day. What if you were slowly beginning to starve? What happens, your fat deposits begin to go down. You begin to get depleted of fat. You're starving. What happens is after a while, you have too few active fat cells to do that testosterone-to-estrogen conversion. At that point you are up the creek for 2 reasons. First off, you're putting less estrogen into the bloodstream. That's not that much of a big deal. It's a tiny amount. The biggest consequence though is you're now not breaking down that testosterone. Its levels build up and mess up things at the brain, pituitary, all of that. That's this weird from-out-of-left-field mechanism that's also relevant, this oddity of females making a certain amount of male sex hormones, and when you don't have much fat cells going there for you because of starvation, you don't do that conversion.

That's a major reason why starvation can shut down ovulation. That's also a major reason why voluntary starvation can do the same. Anorexia nervosa, one of its characteristics is that you shut down ovulation very early on. It's the fat depletion. That's also the reason why some women who do tons and tons of exercise stop ovulating as well. Again, the fat deposit is going down. This has actually been widely studied, the ratio of fat to muscle, the amount of fat stores, the readiness with which that conversion is going on. This has been studied in all sorts of cases.

For example, in kids, prepubescent kids, most often studied in terms of girls who are very, very intense athletes, typically gymnasts, ballet dancers, the ones who are doing 6 hours a day, what you will see is a very significant delay with the onset of puberty. This was even shown a few years ago. A study of gymnasts, gymnasts from the Romanian Olympic gymnastics team, and those are typically those 15-year-olds who weigh 60 pounds and are getting the gold medals. What was the average age at which these kids started menstruating? It was approximately 19. The Western average is 12 1/2 years; this is a huge effect in terms of delaying the onset of puberty. Once you've hit puberty, women who do tons of exercise, for example runners, on the average, if you are running about 50 miles a week, that's typically when the fat deposits are getting below that threshold and you begin to have ovulatory problems.

I could be telling you the same exact story with males, men who run that average of 45–50 miles a week, typically there's a little bit of testicular atrophy, sperm count goes down. You are sitting there saying, wait a second, I thought exercise was good for you. Exercise is good for you. In fact, a lot of exercise is very good for you. That doesn't mean, though, that an insane amount of exercise is insanely good for you. At some point, you pass a point of optimal function. You pass a point of homeostatic balance, and too much of a good thing could be just as bad as too little. This winds up being very, very relevant. One of our themes again and again is optimal ranges, homeostatic balance.

What goes on at that point? What happens there is all sorts of problems with trying to make sense of this effect. Trying to make sense of why the body is set up for responding to extreme athleticism, and what you've got is a theme we've had running through here. This is not typical. This is not typical for humans. Let's get a sense of it. Sit down some hunter-gatherer from the Kalahari Desert and explain to them, you know, back where I come from we have so much food and so much free time, that sometimes we'll just go run 26 miles for the sheer pleasure of it. They're going to say, are you out of your mind? This is stressful. I mean throughout hominid history, if you're running 26 miles in a day, you are either very intent on eating somebody or somebody is intent on eating you. This is not normal hominid behavior.

Again, we see the possibility of passing a point of homeostatic balance, a homeostatic ideal. As I mentioned a few minutes ago, a very interesting hormone comes into play here, prolactin. Prolactin, secreted during stress, and it turns out that prolactin works, among other ways, by decreasing pituitary sensitivity to LHRH, it helps block the release of progesterone, all sorts of things like that. As promised, prolactin is not merely a hormone released during stress. It does all sorts of other things.

One interesting circumstance is, if you have nipple stimulation, there's this neural loop going up to the brain and the hypothalamus and you know that whole pattern, and out comes prolactin. Nursing causes prolactin release, and given all the things I just told you, prolactin release should be working as a contraceptive. Nursing is a contraceptive. That's why that works so well. Oh, you are sitting there saying, what does he know? He doesn't even have ovaries. Everybody knows nursing doesn't work very well. Nursing works wonderfully at being a contraceptive. The World Health Organization estimates there are more pregnancies prevented each year by nursing than by all other contraceptives put together. All you need to do is nurse the correct way, which I'm going to show you now. Aren't you folks who went for the audio version regretting it now?

What is human nursing like? Well it depends. If you look at women in Westernized countries, you see the following pattern, typical pattern. You give birth, you nurse your child every couple of hours for 20 minutes or so. Typically, it begins to get lesser amounts of time. In the West, in the United States, women on the average nurse for 6 months. What are you doing if every few hours or so you're nursing for 20 minutes? You begin to nurse, up go prolactin levels; you stop nursing, down they go. Two hours later, up go prolactin levels, down they go. You get this scalloping pattern of prolactin up and down. That's not what humans and other primates normally do with nursing, and thus with their prolactin levels.

To get a sense of that, this was first really studied in a bunch of hunter-gatherers, the folks living in the Kalahari Desert, the Kung Bushmen, living in the Kalahari Desert. They have a very interesting reproductive pattern, which is they have tons of sex. They don't use contraceptives, and despite all of that, women get pregnant about once every 4 years. What is causing that pattern to emerge? The answer was very easy back then when people looked at hunter-gathers, and said, well, what's a hunter-gather lifestyle like? Short, nasty, and brutish, they're all malnourished; they're all depleted of sufficient fat to ovulate. When people actually go and study hunter-gatherers, it becomes clear, agriculture was one of the all-time stupid moves, inventing that. Hunter-gathers live very comfortably, as termed, they were the original affluent society. Folks like these are working 3 or 4 hours a day to get their day's calories. They are not short, nasty, brutish, and starving and depleted of estrogen.

What's actually going on there? What's going on was discovered a number of years ago by 2 anthropologists, Melvin Konner and Carol Worthman. What they did was they noticed the prolactin pattern, the nursing pattern, in women hunter-gathers. What you see there is something very different from in the West. Here's what happens. You give birth, and you nurse your child for 30 seconds. Then 20 minutes later, you nurse your child for 30 seconds, and 20 minutes after that, and you do that around the clock for the next 3 years. You carry your child on a hip sling, and nursing every 20 minutes or so, you nurse throughout the night so that the mother hardly even wakes up. The baby just sort of crawls over and does some nursing. Mom continues to sleep. Oh of course, Konner and Worthman are there, up at night with their infrared goggles and stopwatches, but everybody else is undisturbed. Three years into it or so, your child is still nursing every 20 minutes or so, they come running in from the Little League games to nurse for a little bit. When you have a nursing pattern like that, the first time you nurse for those 30 seconds or so, up go prolactin levels, and they're going to stay up for the next 3 or 4 years. That's the typical human and nonhuman primate pattern of nursing. You do it that way, and you get this huge square away of nonstop of prolactin. You're not going to ovulate. That's what explains that delayed pattern of fertility.

Think about that a second. What's the life history like for one of these women? Here's what you do. You hit puberty maybe when you're about 14 or so, typically a little bit later than in the West, and a year later, you're pregnant, and from what we just saw, 4 years later, you begin to ovulate again. A couple of cycles, you get pregnant again. Four years later, a couple of cycles, eventually you hit menopause, and you suddenly realize, my God, over the life span of these women, they're having maybe a dozen periods. You look at women in the West, and you get 300 or 400. What you realize is the pattern of nursing in the West produces far more—like

10-fold at least—periods, sloughing off of cells from the uterus, than is the typical human and primate pattern. There's lots of reasons to believe that increases the likelihood of a number of diseases in women, one, for example, being endometriosis.

That's another realm of vulnerability. Pushing on, another domain where stress becomes relevant, at least with all sorts of theorizing is the realm of high-tech reproduction, in vitro fertilization. Anyone who has ever gone through this or been near someone who goes through this, this is enormously stressful. Your entire lifestyle is dislocated. You are getting filled up with synthetic hormones that wreak havoc with mood, with metabolism. Sex becomes a timed chore. It's a very high failure rate. You spend a fortune on it, usually not reimbursed by insurance. It's enormously stressful, and thus, there has been an obvious conclusion to reach, which is, stress makes IVF, in vitro fertilization, less likely to actually work. It seems perfectly obvious. At this point, the evidence for it is mixed; it's so-so. It's not one of the more vulnerable realms of female reproduction when it comes to stress. What I can absolutely tell you is the worst consequence of recognizing that stress might have something to do with success rates with high tech reproductive approaches, the worst thing you can do is to have your physician, have your family, have your friends sit you down and say, "Oh, did you know that stress can disrupt reproduction and IVF? Just don't get stressed as you go through all of this." This is ridiculous and one of the worst realms of applying the knowledge coming out of this whole subject.

One additional realm now in terms of stress and reproduction which is you've gotten the fertilization to occur, you've got a pregnancy to start and something that is classically vulnerable here is the possibility of chronic stress causing a miscarriage, a spontaneous abortion. The possibilities of this, the mere fact that stress can cause a miscarriage, that has run through all sorts of classic literature, all sorts of novels where key points of stress, of betrayal, of infidelities cause grief and stress and miscarriage. I could cite the names of those books if I had ever actually read any of them. This is a theme that goes through these, and it fits. It works in lots of nonhuman species. What you will see is lots of stress causes spontaneous miscarriages. In some species, it takes the form of harassment, and often a pattern that you see is a high-ranking female in some social species that's hierarchical, a high-ranking female can harass, can stress fertile, pregnant subordinates to the point where they miscarry. There are even some very elegant versions of this where the stress of the smell, the odor, and the pheromonal signal of a big, scary dominant female can cause miscarriage.

What's going on with humans with that? What's happening there? It can happen. It can happen, but the evidence for it is not very good. It's not good because it relies on what is dreaded in these fields of epidemiology, what's called retrospective data. Something bad happens to someone in terms of a disease, and it may be a disease where people think about stress. They sit you down while the something bad is happening big time, and they say, "Oh, have you been stressed recently?" It's guaranteed that someone is then going to say, "Yes, I've been stressed." When people are in the middle of some awful circumstance, they preferentially remember bad things in their past, and suddenly you come up with all sorts of bits of stressful history there. You can even show this in studies.

This was one classic study where I don't know how they pulled this one off and you couldn't do this with human subject rules anymore, but people were given some sort of drug that made them have this horrible stomachache for weeks afterward. As you can see, this really is not a modern-type experiment, but what happens at that point is the person goes to their doctor, and the doctor is in on the experiment, and says to them, "Oh, this is terrible, you have an ulcer." They don't have an ulcer. They've just taken this medication, this experimental drug, that's making them feel sick, and they don't know they took it. This crazy study, but the doctor at this point says, "Oh, you have an ulcer. Has anything stressful been going on in your life?" Because everyone knows stress and ulcers, stress and ulcers, we saw a few lectures ago how it's more complicated than that. Stress and ulcers, people are suddenly coming up with all sorts of stressors that could explain why they've gotten sick. Same thing in all sorts of retrospective studies where you ask somebody at the time they've gotten bad medical news, so anything stressful going on recently, and people come up with numbers of those events like crazy. It's very hard to trust studies like that.

What you do then is in some cases, prospective studies, when you look at pregnant women, and does stress increase their likelihood of miscarriage. That definitely can occur. One thing that you see, though, is it's a slowly emerging process, so the bias that one would have is, oh, the morning of my miscarriage, I had some horribly stressful event. That probably had nothing to do with it if it is stress related. It's stressors stretching out quite a few days. When that does happen what are the mechanisms for it, and we go straight back to the earlier lectures. You're running for your life; you're shutting off all the optimistic long-term processes. You are delivering blood to wherever it's needed, those exercising thighs, and you're delivering blood at lower rates to parts of the body that are not essential. We saw earlier on one possible consequence of this is by delivering less blood to your gastrointestinal system; in some ways, you set yourself up for an ulcer more readily. You're less able to repair it. Down in this realm, women, female mammals, who are chronically severely stressed when they're pregnant, they decrease blood flow to the fetus. That's triggered by the sympathetic nervous system, and you do enough of that, and you increase the likelihood that you are going to lose the pregnancy.

That is the realm of what stress has to do with fertilization, ovulation, thickening your uterine walls, maintaining a pregnancy, and high-tech in vitro fertilization. One additional area comes in having to do with another feature of sex, one that has long puzzled all sorts of scientist ranging from evolutionary biologists to pscyhoneuroaminoendocrinologists, which is, "Oh, sex feels good." Lots of times we take great pleasure from sex. We have a drive toward sexual behavior pulling out Freud for the first time, a Freudian term, there's libido, sex drive.

Another thing that occurs with chronic stress in both males and females, your libido goes down. You have less interest in sex. What is that one about? You are secreting all sorts of the stress hormones as we know, and 2 general realms where things happen. You've got all sorts of interesting parts of your body that are sensitive to certain types of tactile stimulation, and more sensitive when you have high levels of certain reproductive-related hormones in your bloodstream. It makes all sorts of tactile receptors in your genitals and your earlobes and who knows where else more sensitive, more responsive to tactile information. Down go those reproductive hormones, and sensitivity in those areas are blunted. Things don't feel as good.

One additional piece is a brain chemical called dopamine. Dopamine has everything to do with pleasure. Cocaine works on the dopamine system in the brain to release dopamine, and you feel pleasure or the anticipation of pleasure more frequently. What you wind up seeing then is a very simple fact: Sex, good sex, tends to release dopamine. Nobody has studied this a whole lot in humans. In hamsters, though, when they have good sex, they release lots of dopamine. Lots of dopamine, so what happens with chronic stress, you don't have as much dopamine in that pathway. It tends to get depleted and suddenly, sex is less pleasurable.

Here we have a broad overview of what goes wrong with the system, and remember that piece about dopamine, because that's critical. That is going to come back to haunt us big time when we see what chronic stress has to do with the lack of pleasure of a major clinical depression.

Stress and Male Reproduction
Lecture 9

Apparently it's not fun to be in the Marines. Apparently, it's kind of a drag, in fact, especially during military training. This was this classic study, 1970, *New England Journal of Medicine* looking at military officers' training during this first couple of months. In addition to all the other indignities, these guys had to pee into these little Dixie cups where ... the endocrine people would analyze their hormone levels. Back comes the finding that you look at guys during the first couple of months in the Marines, and they've got the circulating testosterone levels of newborn babies.

L et's switch over to making sense of the male reproductive system and the effects of stress. Short-term, if you're running for your life, it makes sense for your body to decide to make sperm some other time. But do it chronically, and you are going to pay a price. It all revolves around testosterone, this key steroidal hormone that comes out of the testes. The endocrine axis for testosterone goes from the hypothalamus to the pituitary to the testes. This system in males is actually a lot simpler than in females. The female reproductive axis has to have cyclic release, and that takes some very fancy wiring. The male brain, in contrast, just needs to release a certain amount of testosterone on a regular basis.

It turns out the problem during stress is not that testosterone levels go down; the problem is erectile dysfunction.

Nonetheless, amid that simplicity, the male reproductive system is vulnerable to stress in some of the same exact ways. With the onset of stress, testosterone levels go down. Weirdly, it's almost the exact same hormones involved as those in women. From the pituitary, out come follicle-stimulating hormone and luteinizing hormone, which stimulate, respectively, the production of sperm and testosterone. Numerous studies have shown these decreases in testosterone levels in men in circumstances ranging from undergoing surgery to taking final exams to beginning military training.

What are the physiological consequences of testosterone levels going down during stress? There actually is a very surprising finding, which is there are no consequences of testosterone levels going down during stress. Testosterone turns out to be a vastly overrated hormone. It's virtually superfluous. You've got to knock down levels of it enormously in order to impair fertility. It turns out the problem during stress is not that testosterone levels go down; the problem is erectile dysfunction.

What happens during stress? In scenario 1, you can't turn on the parasympathetic nervous system, so you have the problem of stress-induced impotence. In scenario 2, you get anxious and accelerate the transition from the parasympathetic to the sympathetic nervous system, leading to premature ejaculation. This is a world of extraordinary vulnerability, erectile dysfunction. Either you can't get the erection, or you have premature ejaculation. It is incredibly easy for this to occur.

Current estimates are that 60% of the doctors' visits in this country are due not to organic cases of impotency but to psychogenic, stress-related cases. This is a system that is spectacularly vulnerable to stress effects. In circumstance after circumstance, what we see is stress of all sorts, physical or psychogenic, shutting down the reproductive system. ■

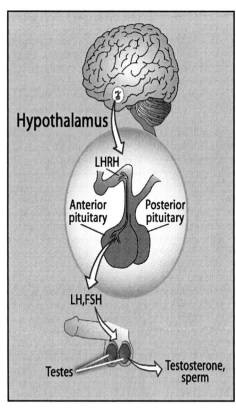

Figure 9.1. Male reproductive endocrinology.

129

Suggested Reading

Sapolsky, *Why Zebras Don't Get Ulcers*, chap. 7.

Questions to Consider

1. What are the effects of stress on testosterone levels, and what are the consequences?

2. What are the effects of stress on erections?

Stress and Male Reproduction
Lecture 9—Transcript

We're here again and it's time for more fun with dysfunctional reproductive systems. Now we move over to the world of males. What were the themes that came through in the previous lecture: the complexity, the cost of the female reproductive axis and the mere fact of that major chronic stress and this is no time for it. As we'll see, there are some of the same exact themes with males. We saw one example of it already in the previous lecture, which was that business about women who do tons of athletics, women who are starving, that business about fat stores dropping down, mentioning that business in passing, males don't do that androgen to estrogen conversion we were talking about. Nonetheless, when males do tons of athletics, as mentioned, on the average, male runners who run 45–50 miles a week—for other mechanisms that we will hear about—sperm count tends to go down, the number of viable sperm as well, testicular size, this theme that we've already recognized.

Switching over to making sense of the male reproductive system and the effects of stress, it's not just pertinent to runners. It's not just pertinent to extreme exercise. It comes up in all sorts of realms, and it's the same exact lesson once again. You can do this one readily and tell the theme. Short-term, you're running for your life; make your sperm some other time. Do it chronically, and you are going to pay a price. What it all revolves around is testosterone. Testosterone, this key hormone, this key steroidal hormone that comes out of the testes, yes, you know the drill by now in terms of an axis. The hypothalamus to pituitary to testes, but the place to start is emphasizing that when you look at this version in males, it's just a lot simpler than in females.

To wit, the male brain is just a whole lot simpler than the female brain at least when it comes to reproductive physiology. Why is this the case? It's because female brains and the female reproductive axis has to do something much fancier than in the male, they have to have cyclic release. They have to have things churning along, and right around day 14, there are massive changes in the levels of this and that, and that takes some very fancy wiring. The male brain, in contrast, all it needs to do is just dribble out a certain amount of testosterone on a regular basis. It's much more of a flat level. This is brought about predominantly during fetal life when fetal brains are either intentionally or inadvertently poisoned with androgens, you wind up with a simpler male brain, one where testosterone release is fairly constant over time. Of course it's not absolutely constant throughout. It responds to experience. You get some guy who's facing off against his worst rival on the whole planet, and he crushes him, defeats him at Chutes and Ladders, and he is going to have this atavistic surge of testosterone. It will make him glow like a baboon on the savanna with sharp canines. Yes, it responds to that, but for the most part, males are these lumpy endocrine creatures. You get a stimulus like that. You get a 3-, 4-, 5-fold difference in testosterone levels. You look at females and there are these massive fluctuations again, so the female reproductive system is much more complex than in the male.

Nonetheless, amid that simplicity, the male reproductive system is vulnerable to stress in some of the same exact ways. As you would guess already, with the onset of stress, down go testosterone levels. It's the same theme as with the reproductive hormones in females like estrogen. Your testes do not know what they are doing. Back to the earlier lectures, they are not autonomous glands, but instead it's that same business, axis starting in the brain to the pituitary to the testes.

Which hormones are relevant? Weirdly, it's almost the exact same hormones as in the female. From the pituitary, out come LH and FSH, follicle-stimulating hormone and luteinizing hormone. Since men don't have follicles, you're not stimulating follicles with FSH; you're stimulating the production of sperm. LH, luteinizing hormone, is predominantly responsible for stimulating testosterone production. Same exact deal as in females, the pituitary doesn't know what it's doing either, so back up in the brain, same hormone again, LHRH, luteinizing hormone releasing hormone, we've got our basic axis here. The simplified male brain in its sort of constant state of hormone release does its LHRH business, LH and FSH from the pituitary, out goes testosterone. The basic theme that runs throughout all of this is, you guessed it, with the onset of stress, down go testosterone levels. You take some guy and you put him through surgery. He's anesthetized, you slice into his belly with a scalpel, and within 10 minutes or so, testosterone levels are going down. You take first-year male medical students during their final exams, and down go testosterone levels, which you may want to take as a cautionary point if any of you males out there are premeds. It doesn't come cheap.

Another realm in which testosterone goes down, take some male baboon who sits there way up on top of the hierarchy and do some vicious manipulative thing so the guy drops in the hierarchy. Down go testosterone levels built around the stress of that circumstance. Here's a stressor which, thank God, I have no personal experience with whatsoever, but apparently it's not fun to be in the Marines. Apparently, it's kind of a drag, in fact, especially during military training. This was this classic study, 1970, *New England Journal of Medicine* looking at military officers' training during this first couple of months. In addition to all the other indignities, these guys had to pee into these little Dixie cups where the psychiatrists would then take over and the endocrine people would analyze their hormone levels. Back comes the finding that you look at guys during the first couple of months in the Marines, and they've got the circulating testosterone levels of newborn babies. You may want to keep that in mind the next time you're in a bar and there's some leatherneck bragging about his androgen levels. Just get him up to date on modern endocrinology, and maybe he'll even buy you a drink. Probably not, and no need to mention my name, but what we see here are all these circumstances where testosterone levels go down.

Of course, as usual, we have to ask the question: What are the mechanisms? Which hormones released during stress mess with this testicular system? It's some of the exact same culprits as with a female system, glucocorticoids working at the level of the brain to decrease the release of that luteinizing hormone-releasing hormone. Glucocorticoids working down at the testes to make those testes less sensitive to whatever pituitary signals are coming out. It's that same theme again, less messenger coming out of the brain and the pituitary, less sensitivity in the pituitary and testes to these signals.

Interesting additional hormone that becomes relevant, and it's one that has now been mentioned a few times, in the last lecture for example, beta-endorphin. Beta-endorphin, another hormone that's released during stress, and we saw that beta-endorphin has some antireproductive effects in females, virtually the same thing in males. Around this point, you begin to try to put some pieces together, beta-endorphin. Beta-endorphin, hormone we haven't mentioned much yet, a hormone that is going to dominate the coming lecture about stress and pain because beta-endorphin is your brain's equivalent, your brain's chemical equivalent, of morphine, the heroin, pain-blocking drugs like opiates, beta-endorphin, endogenous morphine. Of course, there's a whole world of people out there who abuse opioids like that, so you suddenly come up with this wondering question here: Do people who are morphine, heroin, or opium addicts, do they have problems with their reproductive systems? Absolutely, that is absolutely the case in males and females.

We have lots of these steps going on here, doing in sensitivity to the hormone, doing in the release of the relevant hormones, and the net result is less testosterone. At this point, you have to ask a very critical question. This is one that goes through all of physiology. There's a tendency to be very impressed with the change in the levels of some hormone, some brain chemical, activating of some gene, suppressing of some gene, or doing something rather to some enzyme. People consume entire careers being excited about the minutia of this now. Somewhere along the way, you have to ask this very out-of-date question that runs through physiology, which is: What are the consequences of this? What are the physiological consequences? Thus, we must ask the question here, what are the consequences of testosterone levels going down during stress? You could imagine all sorts of things. Males have all sorts of problems, their aggression goes down, and all sorts of things that happen at that point not working very well. When you look at it, there, in fact, is a very surprising finding which is there are no consequences of testosterone levels going down during stress, and just to prove it my voice just cracked in a peripubescent way. There are no consequences. Testosterone turns out to be this vastly overrated hormone. It's virtually superfluous. You need basically a thimbleful of the stuff and a couple of sperm to be in business. Testosterone really is not that interesting. You've got to knock down levels of it enormously in order to impair fertility. What does stress do? It knocks down levels, but typically nowhere near in the range to mess up testosterone and fertility.

The consequences there are pretty clear. There's not much in the way of consequences, so where are the consequences? It turns out the problems during stress are not that testosterone levels go down. The problem is that penises go down. Am I allowed to talk about penises in Fairfax County? I just got the thumbs up from the team of Teaching Company lawyers standing just away from this fine dark wood set. We're all set now finally, so many lectures into this course, to talk about erections. How do erections work? Turns out, in a very complicated way, no surprise, very complicated way, the thing that you have to do for starters is a spinal cord. We heard earlier on, the spinal cord carries information from the brain signaling to voluntary muscles, and that's that boring world of the voluntary nervous system doing the foxtrot, et cetera. That's not the part that's interesting. You can guess immediately what becomes relevant, the autonomic nervous system, all that stuff that we normally can't consciously control: gooseflesh, blushing, all of that. This is where erections come in.

We had a theme in these earlier lectures when first learning about this autonomic nervous system, which is those 2 halves, sympathetic nervous system, parasympathetic—sympathetic arousal, emergency, stress adrenaline; parasympathetic, calm vegetative function. What we saw in these earlier lectures are the extent to which these 2 systems work in opposition. We want to activate the cardiovascular stress-response, increasing blood pressure, increasing heart rate, all that sort of thing, and we saw a great example of the autonomic nervous system working in opposition. What do you do? You activate the sympathetic nervous system, and you inhibit the parasympathetic. In fact, when you look at the systems there in more details, activating the sympathetic sends actively a pathway, a collateral projection that inhibits the parasympathetic. When you activate the parasympathetic, there's a collateral that comes off that inhibits the sympathetic nervous system. What do you see here? This is a mechanism to guarantee that you never inadvertently put your foot on the gas and the brake at the same time, so opposition there.

Heart function, same thing, but with a very different twist. It's the same thing that we saw earlier in terms of gastrointestinal tract. What we saw was with the onset of stress, with the onset of activation of the sympathetic nervous system, you decrease activity in your gastrointestinal system, that whole business, your stomach contracts less, less peristaltic directional contraction in your small intestines. We got that small footnote about the increased activation down there in the large intestines, and getting rid of the dead weight. The main point there is, in this case, the sympathetic nervous system pulls off its stress-response by decreasing activity in the gastrointestinal system. Parasympathetic does exactly this theme again and again of sympathetic and parasympathetic working in opposition.

When you get to the world of erections, things suddenly work differently. This is the first time where there's not a clear opposition, but instead, this amazing choreography that goes on. Here's the deal. In male primates the world over, you need to activate the parasympathetic nervous system in order to get an erection. Very broadly, erections come in 2 different flavors. There's what's called a hemodynamic erection, and what goes on there is you get an erect penis by way of increased blood flow. More blood goes into the penis, you decrease the blood flow out of there, and you got yourself an erect penis. In the other cases, it's a muscular erection, there's this muscle called the levator ani muscle, and what it does when it gets stimulated by the parasympathetic nervous system, it contracts and up goes the penis like pulling up a sail or some such thing. Humans have the hemodynamic. Rodents have the muscular. Muscular happens faster, lasts shorter, humans last longer, take your pick. Nonetheless, in both cases, it's driven by the parasympathetic nervous system.

How do erection and then ejaculation work? Here's what you've got, parasympathetic activity. You've managed to turn on the parasympathetic nervous system. You are calm and vegetative. You got yourself your erection now. What happens next? Maybe it's something having to do with the social context that brought about the erection in the first place. Maybe for some obscure, inexplicable reason, you begin to feel a little less calm and vegetative. Maybe your heart is beginning to beat faster. Maybe you're starting to breathe faster. Maybe you're beginning to exert some muscular exercise/activity thing. What are you doing? You are slowly turning on the sympathetic nervous system. More time goes by, more activation of it, more heart rate, more cardiovascular, and eventually you are blasting with your cardiovascular tone. Your heart is beating fast, blood pressure, you're sweating, your toes are curling, and you're exercising like crazy. Eventually you reach this point where your whole body is screamingly sympathetic except for this one lone outpost where you're desperately holding on to parasympathetic tone as long as possible. Finally, you can't take it anymore.

You turn off the parasympathetic, you turn on the sympathetic, and you ejaculate.

That's how erections work, and what happens during stress? It's perfectly obvious you're not feeling all that calm and vegetative. You can't turn on the parasympathetic nervous system, and suddenly you've got this problem there of stress-induced impotency. There's a second problem that might come in, though. Suppose you manage to pull things off and you've got yourself this erection, and things are starting just fine, and suddenly you think, oh my God, the dollar exchange rate for the euro, and something happens. Suddenly you get all anxious and you accelerate that transition from the parasympathetic to the sympathetic. What happens then is premature ejaculation. You've got this whole world of vulnerability, and this is a world of extraordinary vulnerability, erectile dysfunction. Either you can't get the erection, or you have this problem with premature ejaculation. It is incredibly easy for this to occur.

Current estimates are 60% of the doctors' visits in this country are due to not organic cases of impotency, but to psychogenic, stress related. Mind you, a number like that you've got to take with a certain degree of skepticism. Any time you say stuff like "psychogenic" instead of "organic," at some point or other, all cases of erectile dysfunction were psychogenic in nature. What does that mean? Nobody had discovered an organic explanation yet, and as one gets more and more organic explanations, the incidents of psychogenic go down. Given these caveats, nonetheless, this is a system that is spectacularly vulnerable to stress effects. We now have this challenge, which is, how to tell the difference between an organic case of erectile dysfunction or a psychogenic case. Here's where you finally get something useful out of this damn course where you should take notes. Here's where we see how you make this differential diagnosis.

Some guy comes in and he's complaining about how he hasn't been able to have an erection during sex in the last 6 months, and you think, well, is this organic in basis? Maybe the guy has a pituitary tumor or something wrong with his spinal autonomic projection, some such thing. Or, is it psychogenic? You're trying to distinguish between the two. Here's what you do. You take advantage of a totally weird thing that male primates do, at least as weird as that business about female primates secreting a certain amount of male sex hormones. This weird thing that male primates do, including human males, which is when they go into REM sleep, rapid eye movement sleep, they get erections. I have no idea why. I have talked to Earth's experts, penis experts, and none of them have a good explanation. Nonetheless, males get REM sleep erections. Nothing you can do about it. Here you are, you've got this guy where you can't tell if he has a case of psychogenic or organic erectile dysfunction. Here's what you do. You give him this handy-dandy little penile pressure cuff transducer thingy which he puts down on the base of his penis at night just before he goes to sleep, and he wires it up and satellite relays, and 24-hour operators in Bangalore. The next morning, you've got your answer, which is if this guy hasn't had an erection in sex in the last 6 months, yet does 30 seconds into his first REM stage, this guy doesn't have a brain tumor, it is psychogenic. That's how you distinguish between the two. Do you still get the nocturnal erections? Do you still get the erection during REM sleep? Show that pattern, and it is psychogenic in nature.

That's very easy to differentiate between the two. Actually, it's not so easy to differentiate the two if you really think about it because you got this electronic device on your penis there, it's beeping, has wires, and you're so sure it's going to electrocute you during the night that that's a stressor in and of itself. Here is what you do instead. This is actually what is done most commonly in sexual dysfunction clinics, a wonderfully elegant piece of diagnostic approach. Here's what you do instead. You take a string of postage stamps, and you lick them at one end, and you wrap them around the guy's penis. He goes to sleep and the next morning, if the stamps have been torn loose at one end the guy had an erection during the night. Can you believe how elegant that is? Forget electronic devices and cutting-edge technology. All you need is a bunch of postage stamps. It's wonderful, like 5 bucks and you get a medical diagnosis. It's great, of course, insurance isn't going to pay for it, but someday, someday that will change in this county.

What you see here is a domain of great vulnerability to stress effects in terms of testosterone levels going down. It's not such a big deal as we saw in terms of consequence. Erectile dysfunction, in terms of problems having an erection; once you have it, accelerated transition from parasympathetic to sympathetic, premature ejaculation. That problem there, this challenge of differentiating between when erectile dysfunction, is due to some sort of organic problem and when it is due instead to some sort of psychogenic problem; and the cutting-edge thing that makes one like me proud to be a biomedical researcher, the role of postage stamps in modern medicine.

All of this is great. We have a great deal of insight now into how the male body falls apart during stress. As we saw, probably the most influential piece of that is that business about the sympathetic nervous system has activated during stress, making it very hard to have an erection. Most of the time when you see problems with this, again they appear to be psychogenic in nature. This is a universal. This is how everything works except there is one interesting case where you get exceptions which is, we've got this logic by now running for your life, the predator coming after you, you got better things to do than make sperm. You're in the middle of some socially stressful period. There's one area though where it actually doesn't make sense to inhibit the male testicular system. Suppose you are some male moose or something at the top of the dominance hierarchy. You've just fought your way to the top; it is mating season, there are males challenging you left and right, lots of fighting and butting of heads, and very stressful, very stressful. What a disaster it would be if you have this whole period of fighting like mad, being stressed like mad, in order to come out in a dominant position and get the chance to mate, and you can't get the chance to mate because your whole testicular system is suppressed there. In cases like that, there are mechanisms by which the reproductive system in males are protected from that particular type of stress.

Nonetheless, in circumstance after circumstance what we see is stress of all sorts of forms, physical or psychogenic, shutting down the reproductive system, and again probably the most important step in there is hyperactivation of the sympathetic nervous system, and you're not going to get an erection. This appears to be universal until you suddenly find one species where it doesn't quite work this way, and it is time finally, oh so many lectures into this course, it is time that we finally talked about hyenas. Hyenas, what's the deal with hyenas? Hyenas, spotted hyenas, have horrible public relations problems because of how all of us think about hyenas, to the extent that any of us think about hyenas, and I assume most of us do. Hyenas, what's the scenario? It's one of those Marlin Perkins, *Wild Kingdom*–type scenes there where it's dawn on the savanna. You open up and there's some carcass of something or other and a whole bunch of lions eating on it. You get close-ups of them drooling in excitement, and it is wonderful. Then, and then, you suddenly see right on the edge of those lions there, you see them, those skeevy hyenas, those scavengers looking for a chance to run in there and get a scrap of meat. Hyenas are scavengers. They're not real hunters, and all of us root for hunters instead of scavengers which is pretty odd since what most of us are is scavengers as we go up and down the meat aisle in the supermarket. Not a lot of us have taken down our kills with our canines. Nonetheless, we love those lions, and there are those skeevy hyenas lurking around on the edge looking for a little piece of something dead where they had nothing to do with bringing it down.

This turns out to be nonsense. This turns out to be this horrible bit of urban legend going against our admiration for the hyenas. It turns out hyenas are great hunters. They're extremely organized hunters with high success rates. The reason why people really didn't appreciate it for a long time was looking at lions through rose-colored glasses and the fact that hyenas are nocturnal predators. You have these hyenas, and they've taken down a kill, and it turns out lions are not very good at hunting. They're big; they're conspicuous. They're relatively slow; they have a much lower success rate than you see in hyenas. What lions are really good at is booting hyenas off of their kill. Here you have the hyenas who've brought down the kill. The lions come in and boot them off, the lions who are now the scavengers, and in comes Marlin Perkins with the film crew. No wonder the hyenas are looking all skeevy out on the edge of things. They're the ones who were up all night hunting. Who's having the steaks now? Hopefully, what this has done is pulled out a high degree of sympathy toward the poor, maligned hyena which is a good thing now because what I'm about to tell you may wipe out that sympathy because hyenas are really weird.

Hyenas break all the rules of what boys and girls are supposed to be about for a simple reason—not so simple, but for a very clear reason—hyenas have a sex-reversal dominant system. What do I mean by this? Among hyenas, females have more muscle than males. Females tend to be more aggressive. Amazingly, females have higher levels of one type of androgen, one type of male sex hormone. Females are socially dominant to males. Here's the weirdest thing: Females have genitals that look just like those in males. Something or other gets erect there, they have something or other that looks like a scrotum, and it's totally bizarre. It turns out they really don't have erections and a scrotum. What they have is not a penis but a clitoris, and they get clitoral erections. They don't really have testes; they have these compacted fat cells that kind of look like it. It's all totally bizarre. What it's all about is this weird androgenization of female hyenas. You can't even tell what gender one of them is. As I think I've mentioned, I do research some of the time on baboons in Africa, and over the years I've shared camp with a scientist from Berkeley who is the world's expert on hyena clitorises. Centuries will go by and it will be impossible to talk about the subject without mentioning this man's name. He is as wise on the subject as you can get. You would see these cases there in camp where he's darted and anesthetized some hyena. He drags it into camp, and looks down in there. He's got his binoculars, and it takes him a long time to say, "Well, I think this one is a boy," or "This one is a girl." They've got this bizarre sex reversal system that involves androgenization of the genitals in the female.

Weird, utterly weird, except it turns out it makes sense. Among lots of social carnivores out there, you give birth to a large number of kids, a litter of a dozen lion cubs, and what you've got then is this vicious competition for food where the majority of those cubs don't make it to age one. For a bunch of gynecological reasons, hyenas only have a couple of pups, a pair of pups, and you get that low of a number and you are suddenly under big evolutionary pressure to get those kids to survive. Suddenly, some hyena way back when, got a mutation—probably in the ovaries where they now start pumping out lots of those androgens, not the piddling levels we heard about in the previous lecture. They pump out lots of the androgens, and suddenly, you've got a female who is big, snarly, muscular, and aggressive, and suddenly she is the one who gets to feed her kids. You've got a bunch of hyenas who take down a kill, a bunch of male hyenas, and in come the females and boot them off, and the kids get to eat first. You do that, that food access hierarchy, and your kids do not starve to death. Here's this dominance reversal system.

Where do the weirdo genitals and stress come in? It's as follows: In most species among male primates for example, erections are about social dominance. You get some high-ranking male expression, and he's waving his erection and penis around. Amid hyenas you get just the opposite, which is an erection is a sign of social subordination. You have some poor low-ranking male who is about to be pounded on by a female. What does he do? He gets an erection, he says please don't hurt me. I'm one of those sniveling males. You get a low-ranking female hyena, she does the same thing with her clitoral erection, and suddenly we get to the whole point of this long pointless digression which is amid all those species where activating the sympathetic nervous system wipes out erections, among hyenas, the wiring has to be that the sympathetic nervous system causes erections.

What we've seen here is an example of phylogenetic variability and the wonders of nature and all of that. I would conclude at this point that anybody listening to this has to be overwhelmed with the need to learn more about the subject, so we will stop here and give you a chance to write letters now to The Teaching Company demanding more and more courses about hyenas, so off you go to form those letters.

Stress and Your Immune System
Lecture 10

The evidence that something as bizarre as what's happening in your head can influence your immune system ... in fact goes back quite a few centuries. The first evidence for this was this wonderful study back in the 1800s, and I wish I knew who had the intuition to do this; but you take people back when, with a rose allergy, and you get ... an artificial rose ... and you wave it in front of one of these people's noses. They suddenly start sneezing, not because this was a real rose, but because of psychoneuroimmunology kicking in. Their immune system, their inflammatory system in this case, got tricked into starting to sneeze.

A while back, words like "endocrinology" or "neurobiology" were satisfyingly long. In recent years, though, we have even longer terms: psychoendocrinology, behavioral socioendocrinology, neuroeconomics, and even neuromarketing. There is another multisyllabic term, with some of the most syllables around: a brand new field called psychoneuroimmunology. This field examines what's going on in your head and how it impacts your immune system.

How does the immune system work, and how is it affected by stress? The immune system is unbelievably complicated, but in a nutshell, it protects you from pathogens—invasive things that don't belong in your body and could make you sick (most broadly, bacteria and viruses). This is done in wildly complicated ways. For one thing, all sorts of subtypes of immune cells activate the system, suppress the system, activate the suppressors, and suppress the activators. New immune cells are made in various places: in your bone marrow, in your thymus gland, in your spleen, and in your lymph nodes. Broadly, there are 2 categories of immune cells, or lymphocytes: T cells and B cells. T cells originate in the thymus; B cells originate and mature in the bone marrow. That's a very simplified version here for our purposes.

T cells and B cells do very different things. B cells are constantly surveying your body to look for pathogens. When they encounter a pathogen, they have the brilliant capacity to recognize that it doesn't belong there, and they start to make antibodies specific to this pathogen. Naturally, pathogens aren't just sitting there passively getting blown over by the immune system, and just as the immune system has evolved to be fancier, pathogens have evolved to have fancier defenses. T cells and B cells are the 2 basic features

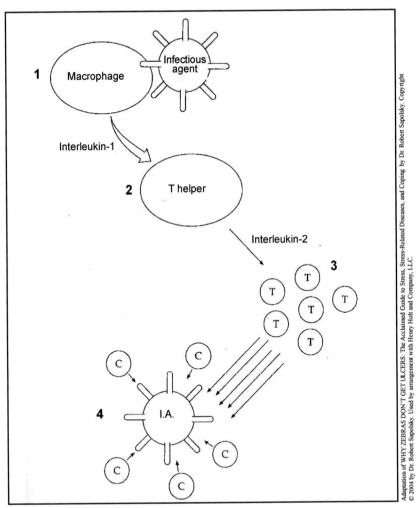

Figure 10.1. Cell-mediated immunity.

of the adaptive immune system, the fancy stuff. Then there is this ancient part of the immune system called innate immunity. Innate immunity is all about inflammation. It just kicks in with any sort of infection, any sort of injury. You get a cut, and you have inflammation there, set to attack any bugs that get in through your injury.

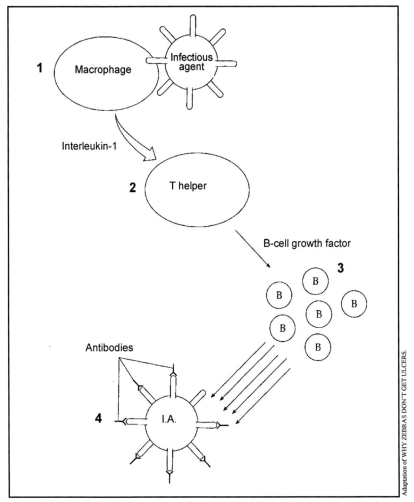

Figure 10.2. Antibody-mediated immunity.

What can go wrong when stress is introduced? The first thing that happens has to do with that short-term stress-response and its short-term effects on immunity. You begin to see an increased risk of autoimmune diseases. These are diseases that cause your immune system to decide that a part of you that is normal and should be there is, in fact, some invasive pathogen. There's a whole array of autoimmune diseases. We've begun to see a hint in the literature that with the onset of lots of stressors, where you activate the immune system over and over, you increase the likelihood of the immune system overactivating into autoimmunity. So we see a relationship between chronic stress and flare-ups of autoimmune diseases. What you see with excessive stress is something very different. Not only with each stressor do glucocorticoids get secreted and bring the immune system back to baseline, but with enough stress, you have the immune system not only going back to baseline but being suppressed below where it normally is, leading to the grave phenomenon of immunosuppression. ∎

Suggested Reading

Sapolsky, *Why Zebras Don't Get Ulcers*, chap. 8.

Sternberg, *The Balance Within*.

Questions to Consider

1. Why does chronic stress suppress immunity?

2. What is the link between stress and the likelihood of getting certain infectious diseases?

Stress and Your Immune System
Lecture 10—Transcript

I have just been dry cleaned, and I've got a new fuzzy sweater. It's time for a little Jimmy Carter–esque fireside chat about our next topic, stress and the immune system. If you hang out with scientists, you'll notice they have a very irritating tendency which is they like big words. They like complicated words. They like multisyllabic words. They like them to substitute for much easier concepts. For example, there is a stress-related disease called idiopathic alopecia areata. It means you lose your hair for some mysterious reason, idiopathic, instead of just saying we don't know.

There are all sorts of these fancy terms. Back in those ancient days for which you feel nostalgia, words like "endocrinology" or "neurobiology" counted as those satisfyingly long words. In recent years, though, it hasn't been enough. You get even longer terms, and suddenly this is this word of psychoendocrinology, behavioral socioendocrinology, neuroeconomics, or I kid you not, something called neuromarketing. Amid all of that, there has been another multisyllabic term, a brand new field, which has emerged somewhere since the 1980s. This one will dominate this lecture. This one has some of the most syllables around. This one is called psychoneuroimmunology, and the basic premise here is what's going on in your head, what your psychological state is, has something to do with how your immune system functions, how you fight off infectious diseases.

The evidence that something as bizarre as what's happening in your head can influence your immune system, something like that, in fact goes back quite a few centuries. The first evidence for this was this wonderful study back in the 1800s, and I wish I knew who had the intuition to do this; but you take people back when, with a rose allergy, and you get an 1800s version of an artificial rose, probably not plastic, and you wave it in front of one of these people's noses. They suddenly start sneezing, not because this was a real rose, but because of psychoneuroimmunology kicking in. Their immune system, their inflammatory system in this case, got tricked into starting to sneeze. Another more recent study, another wonderful example of how this system works, this was a study done with professional actors, and what they did was spend a day reading through a scene, practicing a scene that had some sort of horrible, catastrophic event in it. A few days later, they spent the day reading through a scene that had some wonderful buoyant news in it. What do the scientists observe? Spend the day pretending that you are in the middle of some horrible distressing disastrous scene, and by the end of the day, your immune system is not working quite as well. Sit there and spend the day reading about some euphoric scene that you're acting your way through, and by the end of the day, your immune system is working a little bit better.

Not surprisingly at all, this was carried out at UCLA sitting there in Los Angeles, no shortage of actors who are willing to have their immune systems futzed with, but this is the sort of informal evidence that this field, this psychoneuroimmunology is for real. How does this work? Especially how does stress impact the system? To appreciate this, we have to have a little bit of an overview of how the immune system works, and I know in this day and age, it's very important to do something confessional. I will confess here. I am terrified of the immune system. I have felt that way since kindergarten because it is unbelievably complicated. If you don't panic, I will try not to as well as we go over the basics of the immune system.

What the immune system does is protect you from pathogens, invasive thingies that don't belong in your body that could make you sick, most broadly, bacteria and viruses. Viruses that are especially clever, what they can do is insert into your DNA, insert their viral DNA and use that to take over your cells for their own nefarious purposes. The immune system's job is to constantly be on the lookout for bacteria and viruses, and when they spot them, to quick, mount an attack. The immune system is also built around attacking cancerous cells, the starts of tumors, but the main thing they're about is going after invasive pathogens.

This is done in wildly complicated ways. What you see is, for one thing, all sorts of subtypes of immune cells that activate the system, suppress the system, activate the suppressors, and suppress the activator. They come with all sorts of names. There's even like tough-guy immune cells called natural killer cells, this whole array of different types of immune cells. Broadly, there are 2 categories of immune cells, white blood cells, lymphocytes—broadly, there are 2 categories having to do with 2 different functions, 2 different origins. The immune system, new cells are made in various places, new immune cells. They're made in your bone marrow, some are made in your thymus gland. Others are made in your spleen and your lymph nodes. Broadly, there are these 2 classes, T cells and B cells. T cells originate in the thymus. B cells originate and mature in the bone marrow. That's a very simplified version here for our purposes.

What T cells and B cells do are very different things. What does a B cell do? It is constantly surveying your body to look for those pathogens. What happens when it encounters one of them? It has this brilliant capacity to recognize what doesn't belong there, and when encountering one of these things, it starts to make antibodies that are specific to this pathogen, antibodies that will recognize this pathogen. What those antibodies do is help to activate the T-cell immune response, which is a whole bunch of these T cells to home in on whatever this pathogen is and blow it to smithereens. Naturally, pathogens aren't just sitting there passively getting blown in by the immune system, and just as the immune system evolved to be fancier, pathogens evolved to have fancier defenses against the fancy immune system, what might be termed coevolution. You see all sorts of vicious tricks. There's this bacteria, this tropical one, called trypanosome; it's a parasite. What trypanosomes are able to do is they keep switching proteins on their surface, the sort of proteins that B cells would home in on to make antibodies. You've got some trypanosome protein on the surface there. B cells spot it. It doesn't belong there, start making antibodies, and just in time to attack those trypanosomes, the trypanosomes have put in new, different proteins, and the immune system can't find it. They're very complicated coevolutionary battles.

What you find are the 2 basic features of what's called the adaptive immune system, the fancy stuff, T cells and B cells. Then there is this ancient, ancient part of the immune system which refers to innate immunity. This is ancient-like bits and pieces of innate immunity have been found in insects of that sort. What B cells and T cells are about is specifying, going after some specific pathogen. What innate immunity is about, innate immunity is all about inflammation. It just kicks in any sort of infection, any sort of injury, and you just kick into action there with your innate immunity, and this is not 2 weeks later making your antibodies. This is you get a cut, and you get inflammation there being all set to attack any bugs that get in there through your injury.

We've got the fancy, top-of-the-line, adaptive immunity, T cells and B cells. Then we've got these simplistic first ones in there, inflammatory response, innate immunity. What does stress do superimposed on this? The first thing that happens, which was brought up in the very first lecture, is with the onset of stress, you activate the immune system. Particularly, you begin to activate that adaptive immunity. How do you do this? Not surprisingly, you take advantage of the fastest part of your immune system, the adaptive stress-response, and you take advantage of one of the fastest features of the stress-response, the sympathetic nervous system.

In addition, glucocorticoids in the very early phase of the stress-response help to activate the immune system, and by now, we see the perfect logic of it. You have had a tense meeting. Your boss has ripped your innards open, dragging in the dust, blah, blah, and this is a good time to activate the immune system. This is what happens. Naturally, it is enormously complicated, and part of what you see is not only sympathetic nervous system and glucocorticoids activating the immune system, glucocorticoids also swoop in and do things like kill some of your old immune cells so you sculpt out your immune response so that the ones that are on the scene are really critical.

Some really nice work by Fertos Darbar at Stanford University showing another thing that happens during that time is the immune response takes circulating immune cells and rushes them over to wherever the injury is, what he has termed, moving the soldiers from the barracks to the battlefront as quickly as possible, all of this highly, highly adaptive. What happens, of course, with the problem of stress when it goes wrong? The first thing that happens has to do with that short-term stress-response and its short-term effects on immunity. What you begin to see is sometimes an increased risk of autoimmune diseases.

What is an autoimmune disease? As already noted, what's going on is your immune system is going throughout your body and looking for things that shouldn't be there: pathogens, bacteria, viruses all of that. Thus, what the immune system is brilliant at is telling the difference between—here's the jargon—self and nonself. Self, it belongs there, nonself, you activate an immune attack, and it's going around and it says, hemoglobin, part of us, good thing. Virus, bad thing, nose, good thing, and what happens is it then attacks the stuff that isn't supposed to be there. What an autoimmune disease is about is your immune system screws up and decides that a part of you that absolutely is normal and should be there is, in fact, some invasive pathogen and attacks that part of your body. There's a whole array of autoimmune diseases, and what you begin to see is a hint in the literature, with the onset of stress you activate the immune system. With the onset of lots of stressors, where you activate the immune system over and over, you increase the likelihood of the immune system activating to the point of overactivating into autoimmunity.

Thus what you see is a relationship between lots of stress and flare-ups of autoimmune diseases. Where this has been seen most often in the literature is flare-ups, stress-related flare-ups of multiple sclerosis, which is a disease where your immune system is attacking part of your nervous system. Where you have this autoimmune disease rheumatoid arthritis where it's attacking your joints. Autoimmune disease, Graves' disease where your immune system is attacking your thyroid gland, other ones as well, and what you have in all these cases is with lots of stress, you increase the likelihood of spiraling into autoimmunity.

What you see is very little evidence that stress can actually cause these diseases, but what you see instead is that they increase the likelihood of a flare-up after you've gotten it. Not huge effects, but nonetheless, it's there in the literature. What's going on with that and what becomes relevant are of course glucocorticoids since they come in everywhere, glucocorticoids playing a very special role here. We've already heard they work with the sympathetic nervous system to cause a very rapid activation, but what they mostly do is something that takes a lot more time. You've had this acute stressor, and you activate your immune system. Stressor is over with and what you've got to do is coast the immune system back to where it came from, recovery. What glucocorticoids play a large role in is the recovery process, just like in that earlier lecture, glucocorticoids during the recovery phase after a stressor increasing appetite. In this realm, glucocorticoids have something to do with mediating the immune stress-response. They've got more to do with recovery from it.

That's great, but what if you've got a disease problem where you don't secrete glucocorticoids at that time. This is an important transition, because ad nauseam now, we've been considering the circumstances where there's too much glucocorticoids. What if there's not enough now? What you've got is, what if you don't get that recovery going on quite as well. What you would immediately predict is you may be getting into trouble there with an increased risk of autoimmunity. A number of years back, an endocrinologist named Allan Munck of Dartmouth University, a titan in the field and a man who I deeply, deeply respect, came up with a fascinating theory which was if you see disorders where you don't secrete enough glucocorticoids during stress, you see an increased risk of autoimmune disease. This was viewed as wildly nutty and theoretical and implausible at the beginning. Research since then has shown, both in humans and in experimental subjects and animal subjects, that there are all sorts of circumstances where if you don't have the normal rise of glucocorticoids during stressors, the normal rise that will coast the system back to baseline, you increase the risk of the immune system spiraling out of control into the realm of autoimmune disease.

We're suddenly in a very different realm here after the endless cases where you get in trouble because of an excess of glucocorticoid. Here for the first time we're dealing with what if you don't have enough glucocorticoids, enough of a stress-response. You are prone toward autoimmunity. You are prone toward too much inflammation. Just to mention a disease that I don't really want to go anywhere near, or where there's hints that this might be going on, fibromyalgia, all sorts of inflammatory pain throughout the body. Nobody really knows what's going on, but one important thing that has popped up, there tend to be lower than normal glucocorticoid levels in people with fibromyalgia. I'm not going anywhere closer to that. This is a very, very confused, unclear controversial subject at this point.

We've got this picture here now of with the onset of stress, you activate the immune system, wonderfully adaptive. Not only are you generically activating innate immunity, that inflammatory stuff, but it's fancy, you're sculpting out old, grotty white blood cells, immune cells that aren't doing you much good under the circumstance. You're really focusing in on what's needed. You're mobilizing these cells to the injury site. All of that is great. As we've just seen, if you don't secrete enough glucocorticoids, you're in danger of spiraling into autoimmunity. We've got a vastly confusing point here because what we've just seen is not enough glucocorticoids, more at risk for autoimmunity. A few minutes ago, though, we have lots of stress (probably lots of glucocorticoids), and you're more at risk for autoimmune problems, autoimmune flare-ups. This seems rather contradictory and paradoxical. Too much glucocorticoids or too little and you've got autoimmune problems. Here's a very, very, very rough solution, and this has to do with that same point we had in the lecture about appetite. You say, I am chronically stressed 24-7, and as we saw, that's not chronic stress. Whole body burns are chronic stress. What we are saying when we say "oh, chronic stress" is a lot of those episodes of transient stressors, intermittent stressors, and what we saw with the appetite realm is that problem of you've got a lot of transient stressors, and you've got a lot of periods of recovery.

What you wind up seeing is with just the right amount of these transient stressors, what you are beginning to bias toward is eventually not having the glucocorticoids doing exactly what they should be doing, and perfectly, and mediating that recovery period. You are in danger of spiraling into autoimmunity. What you also see is, get just the right pattern of an excess of glucocorticoids, and you can get into the same trouble. It's an immensely complicated field, and relevant to that, Hans Selye—that guy I discussed in the second lecture and the first lecture, the guy who's one of the founders of the whole field—Selye got as confused as everybody else as to what glucocorticoids are doing to the immune system. He made a massive mistake in the 1950s predicting how something was going to work with glucocorticoids and immunity, and it's generally acknowledged that the sheer visibility of that massive mistake had a lot to do with the fact that he never got a Nobel Prize. This is tremendously complicated terrain.

What you see with excessive stress, not lots of the intermittent stressors, but major league chronic stress is something very different. Not only do glucocorticoids with each stressor get secreted and bring the immune system back to baseline, but with enough stress, you now have the immune system not only going back to baseline, but being suppressed below where it normally is, and you have this grave phenomenon of immunosuppression. Short-term stress, you enhance immunity. In more sustained stress-response, after enhancing immunity, you return to baseline. Major league, chronic stress and you actually suppress the immune system.

This goes back to, in fact, Selye in the 1930s once again. One of the first signs of stress-related disease. We heard the main, most famous one earlier on which is stress increases the risk of ulcers. We now know how much more complicated that is, but stress and ulceration. You saw a second indication, or rather Selye spotted a second classical sign, which was chronically stressed animals got adrenal glands that were bigger. How come? Because they are working like crazy pumping out epinephrine and pumping out glucocorticoids. They're working more, they get bigger. But he noticed a third sign that was part of this trio of stress-related disease back in the founding years which was that immune glands, like the thymus gland, shrink. The immune glands atrophy. We have that first triad, ulcers, adrenal hyperplasia/hypertrophy, and atrophy/shrinking of immune glands.

That absolutely reflects this whole phenomenon of chronic stress. You are going to massively suppress the immune system. You get things like that thymus; this is not a subtle effect. Just to give you a sense of this, have yourself a really awful stressful 3-day weekend, you're going to come back at the end of it, and your thymus gland is going to be a quarter of the size it was on Friday. This is not subtle. This is like saying, oh, psychosocial stress, and I wipe out 3 out of the 4 chambers of my heart. These are big effects, and a lot of attention has gone into figuring out how this occurs.

It's glucocorticoids with chronic major-league stress, they do all sorts of interesting things. One of the things they do, incredibly hot subject in this field, one that seems quite bizarre, is glucocorticoids kill some cells of the immune system How they do it is they turn on genes called suicide genes. They get the cells to do themselves in. There's a painfully fancy term for this process of cells committing suicide, it's called apoptosis—don't write that down—but it's very, very trendy at this point. But we've got this general theme here. Acute stressor, you activate the immune system. More sustained you go into the recovery phase of glucocorticoids bringing you back down to baseline. More sustained, major league stressor, and now suddenly, forget going back to baseline, and you get profoundly immunosuppressed. This begins to explain a very, very major piece of clinical medicine which is when you've got an autoimmune disease, when you have an inflammatory disease, you want to give somebody glucocorticoids, not some piddley amount to kind of coast it back down to where you started from. Remember what an autoimmune disease is about is massive overactivity of the immune system. The notion there is throw in boatloads of glucocorticoids so it's coming out the wazoo of this person, and what you take is this way overshoot of immune activity into autoimmunity, and you coast it back down. In other words, give somebody synthetic glucocorticoids, and you may be able to do very helpful things for their autoimmune disease, their inflammatory disease.

What are we talking about here? We're talking about synthetic glucocorticoids, also known as corticosteroids. In the everyday sense when somebody is "put on steroids" because of their MS or their rheumatoid arthritis, they're being given glucocorticoids. We know some of these synthetic ones, hydrocortisone, prednisone, dexamethasone. What you're doing there is taking advantage of a sledgehammer of a glucocorticoid dose, and you take this disease of overactive immunity, hyperinflammation, autoimmunity, and you coast things back down to baseline.

Just as a qualifier here, as a caveat, when talking about steroids in this case, these are not the androgenic steroids that get you thrown out of the Olympics. That's the world of testosterone. In this case, steroidal hormones—glucocorticoids are also steroidal—when somebody is taking steroids for their rheumatoid arthritis, they're taking synthetic glucocorticoid, huge doses that are bringing you back to baseline when things are too active. We see this world where a little bit of glucocorticoids activates. This is what you get with transient stressors. A ton of the stuff, way more than your body ever generates during stress, and you can take an overactive immune system and bring it back down to baseline. Think about all the lectures that came before this and all the bad things that glucocorticoids can do when they're in excess. What you wind up seeing is take these high doses of these synthetic glucocorticoids, and you begin to get a lot of the problems that we've heard about in the prior lectures. You get a lot of side effects.

This is a very complicated world of stress and autoimmunity and immune suppression and the therapeutic use of synthetic glucocorticoids. Somewhere in there, though, you focus on that fact that major stressors—not synthetic glucocorticoids, but major stressors—and you can get your immune system to the point of being suppressed below normal, and suddenly you have the cornerstone concept of psychoneuroimmunology which is insofar as lots of stress can suppress immunity, lots of stress should impair your immune defenses. There are all sorts of infectious diseases that should mow you over, and what's known now a few decades into this field of psychoneuroimmunology is that's exactly how it works for the relatively boring stuff. For example, with chronic stress, the common cold becomes more common. We all learned that anecdotally back in college where enough all-nighters right before exams and 30 seconds after you come out of your final, you come down with some horrible cold. Chronic stress, increasing your risk of a cold, impairing your immune defenses against rhinoviruses, that's how you get nose colds. This has been well studied in experimental settings in studying immune defenses against rhinovirus infection and the effects of stress on it.

One of the most charming examples of how people have studied this was what used to be this research unit in England, their famed Cold Unit where volunteers would come and spend a couple of weeks at this idyllic country club research facility where you can either wind up being a control or an experimental. No one would tell you which you were. At some critical point, they would spritz up your nose either some placebo or some spray full of rhinovirus. Then they look at various manipulations involving stress, involving stimulation, involving sociality, or whatever, and see who gets the nose colds. They would do, for the most part, very simple things and were wonderfully relaxing. Some of the folks got the lousy experiments where they had to, for example, test the hypothesis does getting really cold—your body cold—impair your defenses against rhinovirus? They would make subjects stand out there and dump cold water on them while they're standing in their skivvies. It turns out the stressor of hypothermia increases the risk of a cold. Wonderfully insightful studies getting at the mechanisms by which chronic stress can increase your chances of a cold. This facility, this Cold Unit, was apparently wonderful. People would have a great time at them unless they got the horrible nose cold standing there in the ice bucket. People would fight to get invited back there. More than one couple emerged from people being there at the same time where they came back and honeymooned at the Cold Unit. People get some very surprising realms of pleasure out there.

Chronic stress and the cold, other realms, chronic stress and another world of viruses, viruses that infect us and then go latent, for example, herpes viruses. You get a herpes infection and you get a flare-up and then it goes latent for a month, for 50 years, and what's known is one of the things that triggers herpes reactivation, sustained stress. Remarkably, this covers all sorts of realms in rats, social stress, radiation in humans, bereavement, all sorts of things like that, and you activate herpes viruses out of latency. This is brilliant on the part of herpes because what you want to do if you're herpes is take advantage of when the immune system is suppressed by stress. Quick, make a run for it, come out of latency, make lots of copies of yourself and then go hide again. Remarkably, viruses like herpes virus, it has been discovered, can actually measure your glucocorticoid levels. That's amazing.

We've got stuff like chronic stress with psychoneuroimmunological conical knowledge there, and it can increase your risk of a nose cold. It can increase your risk of a viral reactivation. How about some bigger stuff? How about, for example, an HIV infection? Somebody who's infected with HIV, and it has now transitioned to overt AIDS. What's AIDS about? It's about declining immune function. If you are majorly stressed, does the immune system decline faster or more severely? The jury is out on that one. It looks as if certain personality types, when crossed with major stress, you get an acceleration of them. Now we come to what is absolutely the biggest subject in this whole field of stress and psychoneuroimmunology. The biggest subject, the most important one, the most controversial, the one that really, really dominates some folk wisdom about psychoneuroimmunology: What does stress have to do with cancer? That will be the subject of the next lecture.

Stress and Cancer
Lecture 11

In people with AIDS, one of the things you see is an increased risk of certain types of cancers, one called Kaposi's sarcoma. Severe immune suppression increases the risk of cancer. All things considered is the fact that the immune system is just ground down to nothing in HIV, and only a relatively small subset of AIDS patients come down with this cancer. Making that same point again, you've got to absolutely push the immune system down to the floor, and on the simplest level, stressors just don't do that.

The most challenging topic in this whole field is what does stress have to do with cancer? Cancer is a problem of uncontrolled growth: cells that are growing much faster than they should. During fetal and childhood development, your body is all about things growing, and when a particular type of growth has gotten to where it's supposed to be, the relevant genes switch off and ideally are switched off for the rest of time. Cancer is an accidental reactivation of those growth genes, called oncogenes.

So what is the relation between stress and cancer? Everybody knows that stress causes cancer, or at least increases the risk of getting cancer. And once you have cancer, stress makes tumors grow faster and makes relapse more likely. This is one of the most commonly held beliefs about how cancer biology works and how stress-related disease works. Not so fast—it is time for us to start dissecting this belief.

First let's look at the laboratory. What is found there? Lots of stress and lots of glucocorticoids increase the risk of cancer in laboratory animals. And once they have cancer, stress accelerates the progression of the tumor. But how does this translate to humans? Right off the bat, we have lots of reasons to pay no attention to those laboratory studies. Because scientists can't sit around and wait for 10% of their rats to come down with spontaneous cancer, they inject cancerous cells into the lab rat to see whether they take off as a tumor. Because human cancers are not due to being injected with tumorous cells, there's the disturbing issue of whether lab rat studies are in fact pertinent to human cancer.

This is a particularly tough field because lots of folks go into it with the belief that there is a causal relationship between stress and cancer. It has taken some enormously obsessive, aggressively detail-oriented research to try to pick apart this issue in humans. What do we know in humans about stress increasing the incidence of cancer? At first glance, this appears pretty straightforward: Studies show that people with a stress history have a higher likelihood of coming down with cancer. But there's a problem with a

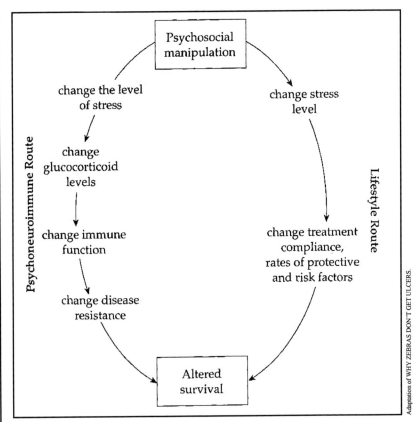

Figure 11.1. The link between chronic stress and disease risk.

number of these studies, which is that they are retrospective. In other words, somebody comes down with cancer, and you then find out what stressors they had in their life, sometimes by asking them. This problem is that when something bad is going on, our memory is preferentially focused on bad things. When someone has a cancer diagnosis and you ask them about stress in their life in recent years, they tend to remember the bad stuff. When you control for stress, cancer patients have a higher rate of remembering stressors than noncancer patients, as do patients with severe cancer over people with less severe cancer. Retrospective data are very shaky for those reasons. Prospective studies, on the other hand, are considered the gold standard. These involve following a healthy population of people over the years and seeing if they come down with cancer. A number of these studies have suggested that lots of stressors in life increase the risk of cancer, but even these studies often have confounds, making them hard to evaluate.

What seemed to be one of the strongest links between stress and cancer is instead probably a compliance issue.

How about a next realm of stress—the notion that certain personalities increase the risk of cancer? This has been a wildly controversial field. In general, the literature showing on this has been pretty unimpressive. How about the next step in the progression? You've had a successful treatment, and your cancer has gone into remission. Does stress have anything to do with the likelihood of a relapse? There is minimal evidence on this at best. What about the rate of progression, the rate at which the cancer grows? This one is controversial as well. Roughly half of the studies support the idea that supportive group therapy and other psychotherapeutic interventions slow cancer progression, but about half do not. What might actually be going on? In the context of supportive therapy, patients tend to support each other's compliance with treatment plans. What seemed to be one of the strongest links between stress and cancer is instead probably a compliance issue.

Why is this such an important topic? Because there are highly credentialed charlatans out there who take advantage of it. These are often very influential and credentialed medical experts, pushing their brand of stress management to slow down or reverse your cancer. But the science simply isn't there. If you push the view that there is a causal relationship, that is bad science, bad medicine, and ultimately bad ethics. ■

Suggested Reading

Cohen, Janicki-Deverts, and Miller, "Psychological Stress and Disease."

Sapolsky, *Why Zebras Don't Get Ulcers*, chap. 8.

Questions to Consider

1. What is the evidence that stress can directly increase the likelihood of cancer occurring and of it progressing more quickly?

2. How might stress play a very indirect route in cancer progression?

Stress and Cancer
Lecture 11—Transcript

We're roughly halfway through this course, and at this juncture, we come to the topic which in some ways is the most difficult, I think, emotionally the most difficult. A subject that is very complicated, very ultimately sad, which is what does stress have to do with cancer? What we saw in the last lecture, this whole world of psychoneuroimmunology, was a very simple prediction. Insofar as chronic stress can chronically suppress the immune system, if you are chronically stressed, there are all sorts of infectious diseases that you should now be more at risk of. As we saw, that's absolutely the case for things like nose colds, for things like viral reactivation, herpes cold-sore flare-ups.

What we approach in this talk is the most challenging one in this whole field: What does stress have to do with cancer? In order to approach it, we need to spend a couple of minutes at the beginning here looking over what cancer is in order to see where stress impacts it. Cancer, in the broadest possible terms, is a problem of uncontrolled growth, cells that are growing much faster than they should, growing as tumors, cells that are growing at the wrong time, uncontrolled, inappropriate growth.

When in life do you have perfectly controlled, appropriate growth? That's during development. All you're about then is things growing, things developing, and there are all sorts of genes that regulate growth at different points during fetal life, childhood, and all of that. If everything goes right, somewhere around the points where a particular type of growth has gotten to where it's supposed to be, the relevant genes switch off. Ideally, they are now switched off for the rest of time.

What is cancer? Cancer is when there is accidental reactivation of those growth genes. Many years later in adulthood, cancer is activation of genes that have no business being active anymore. A technical term, and ignore it if you want, these genes, these growth genes that can reactivate and then cause cancer are called oncogenes. The main point is that what cancer is about is accidental activation, turning the switch on at a point in life where the switch should not be on, resulting in uncontrolled growth in the worst places at the most inappropriate times.

What are the causes of cancers in humans? A whole bunch of the leading causes, one is radiation, one is carcinogens, xenobiotics which are things out in the world that shouldn't be out there, various toxins, food that is carcinogenic, for example food that has lots of oxygen radicals. Another major source of cancer is when you have mutations in those oncogenes where they turn on again when they're not supposed to. Another one is there are certain viruses that can cause cancers. These happen to be rather rare, and what you see is, best evidence, one of those viruses isn't enough. You have to have multiple hits. One oncogene mutation isn't enough. You have to have multiple hits.

That's the basic picture of what cancer is about, uncontrolled growth. What you get is an interesting transition in what the biology of cancer is which is you have this early phase of uncontrolled growth, and that's all about those oncogene things that will determine if a cancer is growing successfully, successfully from the cancer's standpoint. After a while, they're transitioned into a second stage which is these tumors, by definition, are growing like mad at an abnormal rate at an abnormal time. They're hungry. They have very high metabolic rates, and after a while, as cancer progresses, the challenge for the cancer is not so much to activate growth, but to feed the cells. Highly, highly elevated metabolic rates, so one of the things you see with cancer as it progresses is this wild phenomenon which is cancer cells, tumors, can give out signals which trigger the ingrowth of blood vessels, of capillaries, to supply more nutrients to the tumor, a process called angiogenesis.

A very exciting field of cancer therapeutics these days is the notion of finding angiogenesis inhibitors. If you've got a growing tumor and you make it impossible for it to get a new source of energy, you're going to starve it away. What are some of the classic defenses against cancer? Early phases are immune defenses. We heard in the last lecture, one class of immune cells, natural killer cells, which can go after cancerous cells. There are factors released by immune cells, tumor necrosis factor, and things of that sort. With any luck, they can spot a tumor when it's just beginning to be tumorous and wipe it out. The early stage of defenses against cancer are these immune defenses. As the cancer transitions to that more mature stage, the one as just talked about where the main thing the cancer is about is getting enough food to grow like crazy, some of the body's defenses are built around trying to starve that tumor.

That's a general, of course, highly simplified picture of what cancer is about. Now we transition to what stress does to the system. All we have to do is have stayed awake during the last lecture, and you know the answer. We have the early phases of cancer defenses built around the immune system being active and doing what it's supposed to do, so if chronic stress is dramatically inhibiting the immune system, chronic stress should impair your defenses against cancer. QED, case closed, and it's not hard to construct a sequence there that seems irrefutable which is, lots of stress, thus you suppress the immune system, thus your defenses against cancer are impaired, thus you're more at risk for cancer and tumors grow faster. An absolutely clear sequence, stress to bad immune system to bad defenses against cancer to uncontrolled cancer, it's perfectly straightforward.

Of course it's going to turn out to be wildly unstraightforward as we begin to consider the subject. What's going on? What's going on in terms of cancer progression, in terms of this simple prediction that lots of stress puts you more at risk for cancer? It's obvious how it works. It's very straightforward. Everybody knows how this works. Everybody knows that stress causes cancer, stress causes cancer, stress increases the risk of getting cancer. Stress, once you have cancer, makes tumors grow faster. Stress is more likely to cause cancer relapse. Everybody knows this. It's one of the most commonly held beliefs about how cancer biology works and how stress-related disease works; sufficiently so that some years ago, there was a paper published in the journal *Psycho-Oncology* on the interactions between psychology and the cancer process. In this paper, in 2001, a bunch of women who had just gotten a very serious breast cancer diagnosis were asked something simple. What do you think caused your cancer? We saw a few minutes ago all sorts of possibilities: radiation, carcinogens, mutations, all of that. By a wide margin, what was the most common answer? Stress, stress caused my cancer.

We've got this deeply held belief here that stress can cause cancer. It's now time for us, amid that picture, to start dissecting this belief. First off, what's going on with animals, experimental animals? The world in which you can understand cancer in its greatest detail, the experimental setting in the laboratory. What is found there? Yes indeed, lots of stress, lots of glucocorticoids, they of course were inevitably going to come in on the scene. Lots of stress, lots of glucocorticoids increase the risk of cancer in laboratory animals. Once they have the cancer, what stress does is accelerate the progression of the tumor, and it's reasonably well understood how this works involving immune defenses being impaired, involving some of those metabolic defenses being impaired. It's reasonably well understood. My lab, in fact, did some of that work some years ago, perfectly straightforward.

We appear to have this slam-dunk in the world of experimental laboratory research, stress and cancer, stress and cancer. They seem interlinked. What about humans, what about humans in a broad way, and what we've got right off the bat here inevitably is a really complicated picture. Right off the bat, what we have is lots of reasons to pay no attention to those laboratory studies for a very simple reason, what causes the cancer in these animal studies? For the most part, you can't sit around and have the 10% of your rats, as they get older, come down with spontaneous cancer. It's really hard to study that. What you do is you experimentally induce the cancer. What you do is take some cancerous cells and inject them into the lab rat, and cancer occurrence, what that's about is whether those cancerous cells take off as a tumor. What cancer progression is about is how fast that tumor grows then. Human cancers are, no surprise, not due to being injected with tumorous cells, as we heard already, viruses, pathogens, radiation, all of that. Immediately, there's this disturbing issue as to whether any of the laboratory stuff with lab rats are in fact pertinent to human cancer.

What we now need to do is very carefully dissect what's actually going on. This is a particularly tough field because, as noted already, lots of folks go into it with some beliefs about how things work. It has taken some enormously obsessive, aggressively detail-oriented research to try to pick apart this issue in humans, some really hard work calling into play epidemiologists who look at patterns of disease in people, statisticians—God help us—who play a critical role figuring out were data analyzed the correct way, very, very challenging field.

What do we know? First off, what do we know in humans about stress increasing the incidence of cancer? This appears to be pretty straightforward, which is there is indeed an increased incidence of people with a stress history having a higher likelihood of coming down with cancer. Probably the major stressor that has been studied most frequently is major depression, and as we will see in a few lectures, you cannot begin to understand what's going on in depression outside the context of severe stress. Depression, other stressors, increasing the risk of cancer seems absolutely straightforward from "the cancer in me is due to stress," to all the other ways in which people believe there is a connection. This appears to indeed be the case when you look at the data.

There's a problem though. There's a problem that has already popped up in a number of these studies and a number of these disciplines that we've heard about which is these studies are mostly retrospective. In other words, somebody comes down with cancer, and you then find out what stressors did they have in their life? Even more shaky, they come down with cancer and you ask them, what stressors have they had in their life. What we saw in the previous lecture is there's this problem. There's this problem which is when something bad is going on, our memory is preferentially focused on bad things. When something as awful as a cancer diagnosis is going on and you ask people, just say, well have you had a lot of stress in your life in recent years, people will preferentially remember the bad stuff. We saw that in the previous lecture that wildly unlikely, who-approved-this-experiment where people were made to have chronic stomach problems experimentally. The doctor tells them, not truthfully, they've got an ulcer. Was anything stressful going on? Suddenly you remember all sorts of stressors.

Retrospective data are very, very shaky for those reasons. Even retrospectively like going back through medical records. What you see is when you look at cancer patients versus people without cancer, cancer patients remember more stressors prior in life when you control for did these 2 groups actually have the same amount of stress. Cancer patients have a higher rate of remembering stressors than noncancer patients. Patients with severe cancer at a higher rate than people with less severe ones, there are huge problems with this retrospective literature.

Then we switch over to what's the gold standard of these sorts of studies, vastly more difficult, what are called prospective studies, which is you sit down with a bunch of people who don't have cancer. Who, in order to qualify for these studies, in fact, appear to be perfectly healthy, and now you follow them over the years and see if they come down with cancer, prospective. You need vast numbers of people in these studies because the incidence of cancer in the time span of these studies tends to be rather low. You need an enormous amount of resources to do these studies. This is the gold standard doing a prospective study. When they are done, what has come out of that literature? A number of studies suggesting that, yes indeed, prospectively lots of stressors in life increase the risk of cancer. These studies though often have some problems in them. For example, there's this classic one that everybody learned about as this field first emerged, a study of a large number of people working in a Western Electric plant, I believe in Buffalo in New York, where in a prospective study what they showed was focusing in on a classic stressor as we've already heard, major depression. What they showed was major depression as you prospectively go through this study, major depression caused a 2-fold increase in cancer risk, not good. Seemingly an absolutely clear, irrefutable connection here between stressors and cancer risk.

That one is the iconic demonstration of the classic one. Some years after it was carried out, a very subtle energetically detailed focusing, statistically wise guy went and analyzed the hell out of these data. He discovered a very interesting confound in there, which was the people who were working in this Western Electric plant who were getting depressed were mostly getting depressed because they had an awful boss who had them working under unsafe working conditions with lots of exposure to carcinogens. Oh, well that's kind of a confound. That's kind of hard to evaluate then. This classic study is down the drain then in terms of showing a cancer connection.

What else might come out of these prospective studies? You might ask, well do people who have stressors, do you begin to see changes in immune function—what we know is change is suppression of immune function—in a way that now puts you more at risk for cancer. In general what these studies have shown is you don't get enormous decreases in immune function. Yes, in the last lecture we heard chronic stress, you can suppress immunity enough that you're now more at risk for a nose cold. Seemingly, the stressors that we think of as increasing the risk of cancer, they don't suppress the immune system anywhere far enough because the finding and the reality is you need to absolutely flatten the immune system to seriously increase your risk of cancer. This is seen, for example, in HIV, people with AIDS. In people with AIDS one of the things you see is an increased risk of certain types of cancers, one called Kaposi's sarcoma. This used to be a cancer you would see in 80-year-olds once in a career, and suddenly it's popping up in a lot of 30-year-olds with AIDS. Severe immune suppression increases the risk of cancer. All things considered is the fact that the immune system is just ground down to nothing in HIV, and only a relatively small subset of AIDS patients come down with this cancer. Making that same point again, you've got to absolutely push the immune system down to the floor, and on the simplest level, stressors just don't do that.

We now have a greatly weakened viewpoint of stress, including the likelihood of getting the cancer. How about a next realm of stress? How about the notion that certain personalities increase the risk of cancer? This has been a wildly controversial field. There has been a long-standing view that there is a certain personality type that increases cancer risk. These are individuals who are introverted and repressive and especially repressive about anger, and there's minimal evidence for this, minimal evidence. One of the big problems is that that literature has relied very heavily on retrospective evidence. Furthermore, you see no evidence that these folks with these repressive cancer-prone personalities have anything screwy about their immune systems. In general, the literature showing a link between certain personality styles and cancer risk has been pretty unimpressive.

What we've seen now is there's not a ton of evidence for cancer, the likelihood of getting cancer, the incidence of cancer being stress related. How about the next step in the progression? You've had cancer. There's been a successful treatment. The cancer has gone into remission. Does stress have anything to do with the likelihood of a relapse, the cancer coming out of remission, and what you see is minimal evidence at best.

We now move over to what, in lots of ways, is the most controversial issue in the field. Not what does stress have to do with getting cancer, not does it have to do with a relapse, but what does stress have to do with the rate of progression, the rate at which the cancer grows, the rate at which things get worse. Can stress accelerate cancer progression? This one is wildly controversial, except, on first pass it doesn't appear to be very controversial at all in that there seems to be some fairly good evidence showing that stress can accelerate cancer progression.

The best evidence for that, the one that most caught the public attention and seemed to just reify stress–cancer, stress–cancer, is to go in with a certain experimental style which is intervene with cancer patients. Do something or other that decreases their levels of stress, and does that slow down the cancer progression? Some studies have looked at this. There's one classic one carried out by a colleague of mine at Stanford named David Spiegel who did the study which was published in the late '80s in the *New England Journal of Medicine*, and before it was over with it was front-page news all over the country.

Here's what he did. Women, who had just gotten a metastatic breast cancer diagnosis, and Spiegel had these women randomized into 2 different groups. The first group got standard medical treatment for the cancer. The second group got standard medical treatment plus they joined a cancer support group that had intensive group therapy a number of times a week. When he broke the code, out came the finding that the women who went into the cancer support setting had an average of 18 months longer survival than the other group. This was a huge finding. This was a dramatic effect. This was amazing news, and this was immensely exciting. Part of what was immensely exciting was it was absolutely clear how the underlying biology of this would work. We've already heard this. A nice supportive group setting of therapy with other cancer patients makes you feel less stress, thus your immune system works better, thus you're better at fighting the cancer, thus you live 18 months longer on the average—amazing finding, one that just had a huge impact in the field.

What has happened since then? Roughly half the studies that have been carried out since then support the finding showing that supportive group therapy, various psychotherapeutic interventions, slow down cancer progression, about half the studies haven't replicated it. What's going on there in the cases where, yes, indeed you are slowing down the cancer progression? What's going on there? Obvious sort of pathway again, better immune defenses thanks to less stress, all of that. Spiegel and his group have looked at whether there are indeed changes in immune function in women with these supportive settings, and there are some changes, but they don't particularly correlate with the cancer outcome. That has been less clear.

What's actually going on here? What's happening? What we have here is something extraordinarily subtle and very tough to get at, and this is something where Spiegel has been one of the leading thinkers in this area. This is a man who has a wonderful research integrity in terms of not getting pulled in by the easy explanations. What might actually be going on? Here we get into what is one of the dirty secrets in cancer therapeutics. You have cancer, and you're going through treatments, chemotherapy, radiation therapy, it is absolutely clear this is your best chance, go through it, power through there. It turns out an awful lot of people with types of cancer seriously diverge from what their treatment is supposed to be like. They are not as compliant as they are supposed to be. They fail to take their medications. They miss doctors' appointments. Something like a quarter of cancer patients seriously diverge from their treatment regime.

Why is this a dirty secret in the field? It's obvious. You've got cancer. There's this whole sort of structure in the field, type C personality, people with cancer who are going to fight, fight, fight, and not let the cancer do them in. If there's a treatment that might help, do it twice as much and just power through there. Suddenly you've got people with cancer who aren't taking their medications as much. Ooh, this looks really bad. Secret, dark secret, very rarely dealt with, why does this happen? It's obvious why it happens, because most of the cancer treatments make you feel so sick and so awful that it's hard to comply entirely. What happens in this cancerous supportive therapy context? What you've got there is you're sitting around with a bunch of other people going through the same hell you're going through, and they all support each other. They support each other in terms of compliance, sitting there saying, "Did you take your meds today? I know; I hate them too. They make me totally nauseous, but you know what, we're both going to take them right now. Have you eaten today? Yes, I have no appetite either, but we are going to eat. Right after this you are going to the doctor. You're not going to skip that appointment." When people are in that supportive setting, of other cancer suffers where they're cheering each other on, people become more compliant. In lots of ways, this might be what's going on in this literature. Again, this is not a stress reduction, better immunity, less cancer, this is a completely roundabout way. What seems to have been one of the strongest links between stress and cancer, it's instead probably a compliance issue.

Of all the classes, all the topics we've had so far, this is the one where I've probably spent the most time going after an individual subject, going after it in detail. Why is this important? Why is this such an important topic to go after? Remember that 2001 study, remember that one where the women with breast cancer asked to attribute their cancer to something or other, and the most common answer was stress, was stress. Somewhere in this urban legend, this folk psychology, somewhere in there with this erroneous connection between stress and cancer, something very dangerous and damaging occurs, something which, frankly, there are all sorts of highly credentialed charlatans out there who take advantage of it. We know this world, people who flog the notion that here's my brand of stress management—credit cards accepted—that will slow down the progression of your cancer, that will stop your cancer from growing, that will completely reverse it. What we have here is very little, if any, scientific evidence linking this. These are not crackpots off in the periphery; these are often some very influential and credentialed medical/biomedical experts.

There's one particular one I want to focus on. I will bypass his name, just out of sort of legalistic prudence here. This is an individual, a Yale-trained physician, who in the late 1980s had a wildly successful bestselling book looking at this notion advocating the notion that stress causes cancer; and thus stress reduction can slow down cancer progression. Just to be really careful about this, as I read some quotes from this man's book, I am going to actually have them here just so I get them right. Here are some of the quotes in thinking about the causes of disease, the causes of cancer. Quote number 1, "The fundamental problem most patients face is an inability to love themselves." Next quote, "She chose the path of life, and as she grew, her cancer shrank." Next quote, "Patient: 'I decided to live to be 100 and leave my troubles to God.' I really could end the book here because this piece of mind can heal anything." In other words, if you have cancer and it's out of control, and it's doing you in, and it's killing you, why is that happening? Maybe because you're unable to love yourself, maybe because you didn't choose the path of life, maybe because you didn't grow in the face of adversity, maybe because you decided that you weren't going to leave your troubles to God, maybe because you really didn't want to live to be 100, all of these attributions here. All these are blaming the victim.

In lots of ways, this person's philosophy is most aptly summed up in, once again, a direct quote, and one of the sort of main ones in this book, quote, "There are no incurable diseases, only incurable people." What are you teaching someone when this is happening? You've got somebody on their deathbed with their terminal cancer that has resisted the treatments and progressed. What this viewpoint teaches is, while you're lying on your deathbed, ooh, too bad I didn't have different priorities in life, too bad I didn't control my stress, too bad I didn't choose life, too bad I couldn't love myself sufficiently, this is where you wind up. Would that it be so that these sorts of interventions could cure cancer, if only cancer could be stopped if we were sufficiently brave and sufficiently tenacious and sufficiently filled with love.

It doesn't work that way. This view, being flogged by folks who are not crackpots out in left field, but again often highly credentialed experts, the science simply isn't there. Amid all the diseases that we've had to think about in this course so far, all of these diseases where stress plays an adverse role, this is a domain where it doesn't count. If you really push the view that it does, ultimately, bad science, bad medicine, ultimately bad ethics, shame on anyone who would profit from this.

Stress and Pain
Lecture 12

You're eating wildly spicy food to the point where it hurts. You've got sweat running down your nose, and you're taking great pleasure in this. ... People long wondered why spicy food at an extreme can hurt, why spicy food tastes hot. Remarkably, it turns out that this capsaicin, this chemical found in hot peppers, actually activates some of those hot receptor neurons. Spicy food that is hot is literally activating the hot pain system.

P ain is utterly intertwined with stress: Pain constitutes a stressor, and stress can cause you to change your sensitivity to pain. In other topics in this course, the pattern has been that in the short term, stress-response is good, but in the long term, it is bad. The biology of pain is the one exception to this rule. Pain is wonderful when it comes at the right time, allowing you to change your behavior and decrease the source of damage. But when there's nothing you can do, pain can be a misery.

Pain starts off with sensors all over your body that pick up when something is going wrong. These are on the level of your skin, your muscles, your organs, and so on. These sensors respond to pain signals by sending that information to your spinal cord and up to your brain. You have pain sensors, for example, that are sensitive to heat, to cold, to pressure, and to when you've cut your skin.

How is the pain signal processed in your spinal cord and up to your brain? The Wall-Melzack model (see below) is the dominant model in the field and gives wonderful insight as to how this system works. It is highly schematic; your neurons don't actually look like this. In part A, we have a neuron in the middle, marked X, that sends a projection to the brain. This neuron is sitting in your spinal cord, and when it is stimulated, it sends a signal telling your brain that something painful is happening. The projections above and below neuron X are coming from pain sentinels somewhere to the left of the diagram. There are 2 types of pathways that could stimulate neuron X, those for sudden pain and those for slow pain.

Part B shows a bit more detail. There is a second neuron, neuron Y, in your spinal cord. Neuron Y sends a projection to neuron X, making it less excitable. So, for instance, your sudden-pain receptors respond to your getting a cut. They send that signal to neuron X and stimulate it, and you feel pain. At the same time, that same sudden-pain neuron has a cable that sends a projection to neuron Y and stimulates it. So with a slight delay, neuron Y turns off neuron X. This is why you get a sharp pain that subsides shortly afterward. When it is the slow-pain pathway that activates neuron X, this time that collateral cable inhibits the activity of neuron Y. So something painful occurs and activates neuron X, but neuron Y is shut down, making it unable to blunt neuron X. What happens then? The pain keeps going: chronic, throbbing pain.

In part C, we see the possibility of projections coming down the spine from the brain, which can stimulate or inhibit neuron X. Your brain is influencing how sensitive those neurons are to a painful input. One positive effect of stress can be the blunting of pain perception, which is known as stress-induced **analgesia**. This is shown in part C, via the bottom projection

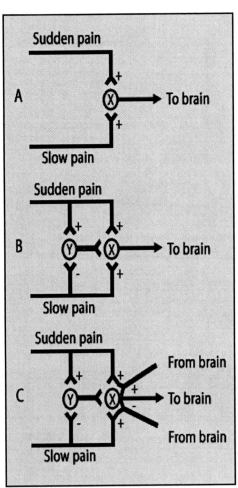

Figure 12.1. The Wall-Melzack model.

coming from the brain. It inhibits neuron X and blunts pain perception, generally with endorphins.

But how does massive, chronic stress impact the pain "wiring" system? Here is the bad news. Major, sustained stimulation of pain pathways makes them more sensitive and more responsive, so that pain begets pain, leading to **hyperalgesia**. You get depleted of beta-endorphin, the hormone that protects you from the stressor. So it is not the case that you eventually turn off the pathways; the pain comes back and just keeps going. ∎

Important Terms

analgesia: The blocking of pain perception. Stress-induced analgesia is the phenomenon where extreme, acute stress blocks pain perception.

hyperalgesia: Exaggerated pain sensitivity.

Suggested Reading

Sapolsky, *Why Zebras Don't Get Ulcers*, chap. 9.

Questions to Consider

1. How can stress blunt pain perception (as in stress-induced analgesia)?

2. Why can pain perception be highly subjective?

Stress and Pain
Lecture 12—Transcript

In this lecture, we're going to look at a subject that's utterly intertwined with stress, which is pain. This is bidirectional. Stress can cause you to change your sensitivity to pain. Pain constitutes a stressor. We're going to look at the interaction between the two.

By now you know the drill sufficiently so that they could come in here and deflate me and put me in a storage closet, and you could leap right in and go through the dichotomy. Short term, stress-response is good news. Long term, it's bad news. As we're going to see in the biology of pain, this is the one exception.

We start off with pain. We all hate pain. Pain is a great thing to get rid of. Pain is bad news. Pain is remarkably good news and remarkably helpful when it's occurring at the right time. You generally want some sort of signal coming from the periphery, saying, "Ooh, my big toe is in the fire there. This might be a good time to move it backwards." You need pain signaling you in circumstances where you can fix the situation. There is a terrible disease where people are born, a rare one, without the ability to feel pain. What you get is all sorts of things go wrong, even to the extent of these are people who damage their legs, damage their knees because they don't get the pain feedback telling how much force you should be descending a flight of stairs with.

Pain is wonderful when it's occurring in a circumstance where you can actually change your behavior and decrease the source of damage. As we would well know, when it's circumstances where there's nothing you can do, pain is a misery. Pain is a nightmare. How does it work? Shifting over to the biology of pain so that we could then appreciate what it is that stress does. Pain is actually quite well understood. It starts off with all sorts of outposts in your body, all sorts of sentinels, all sorts of sensors that pick up when something is going wrong, and this could be on the level of your skin. It could be on the level of muscles, when you have muscle pain. It could be in various organs when suddenly you have a stomachache when suddenly something else feels more serious. In all these cases, what you have to have is something that is responsive to a pain signal out there, and it is then able to send that information to your spinal cord and up to your brain, and there you go. What you have to have are pain sensors, and pain comes in all sorts of different forms. You have sensors, for example, that are sensitive to extreme heat. They will pick up a signal of heat somewhere on your skin wherever it's relevant, and these receptors, these neurons, these brain cells—wait these are brain cells out in your skin. This is your nervous system sending projections everywhere—you have these specialized heat sensitive neurons that pick up that heat, activate, and send the signal on down.

Meanwhile, not surprisingly, you have other receptive neurons that do just the opposite. They're sensitive to cold. Meanwhile, there are other ones that are sensitive to pressure, extreme pressure. Ouch, somebody is squeezing your hand so pressure-transducing neurons there which take that sort of signal and turn that into a different sort of pain perception. There are even pain neurons that respond to things like you've just gotten cut, and this is really a weird one when you think about it. There are certain chemicals that are found inside your cells, and as a general rule, if they're found outside the cells, that's a bad sign because something has sliced that cell open. As a result of the innards of that cell spilling out, that particular chemical binds to a receptor in another cell nearby and sends a signal, we've been cut. Why is that bizarre? Because what that winds up meaning is when you accidentally, for instance, get a paper cut and it hurts, you literally are slicing some cells in there in half where they are spilling out their guts, so different types of pain. Very interestingly, there turns out to be an additional type of pain, and this is one that initially seems metaphorical, and turns out to be much more literal. You're eating wildly spicy food to the point where it hurts. You've got sweat running down your nose, and you're taking great pleasure in this. Very spicy food hurts; and spice is mediated by a chemical found in spicy food called capsaicin. People long wondered why spicy food at an extreme can hurt, why spicy food tastes hot. Remarkably it turns out that this capsaicin, this chemical found in hot peppers, actually activates some of those hot receptor neurons. Spicy food that is hot is literally activating the hot pain system.

How does this work once you've gotten past these receptors, once you've gotten past that first phase? How is it now processed in your spinal cord on up to your brain? To appreciate this, we need to shift over to a diagram that's in your Guidebook, one that is the dominating model in the field. It's wonderful, wonderful insight as to how this system works. In this diagram, we start with part A, up on top. What we've got are projections of neurons talking to other neurons. Do not panic, this is highly schematic. None of your neurons look this way. What we have is a neuron sitting there in the middle, the one marked X which sends a projection to the brain. This neuron is sitting in your spinal cord, and when it is stimulated, it sends a signal telling your brain that there's something painful happening.

When does it get stimulated? You see there are the projections above and below neuron X, those lines coming from a neuron somewhere to left of this diagram. What sort of neurons are those? Those are the pain sentinels; those are the cold responsive, hot responsive, and pressure responsive. There are 2 different types of pathways that could wind up stimulating that neuron X. The first one, shown up on top, mediates sudden pain. We see that projection coming from the imaginary neuron on top to the left, its cell body, projecting sending this cable-like projection to neuron X, and what it does there is it stimulates neuron X. When the neuron that mediates sudden pain gets activated, it stimulates and activates neuron X. Meanwhile, down below in the same diagram, you've got a slow-pain pathway, and that's coming from a different type of pain-receptive neuron which activates in response to a painful stimulus, activates that pathway, which stimulates neuron X also. Soon your brain gets information that something painful has occurred. This doesn't explain much. Where the subtlety, where the beautiful elegance of this model comes in is right now we transition over to the B part of the diagram because it's a little more complicated than what I showed you. We've now got a second neuron on the scene, neuron Y, also found in your spinal cord. Neuron Y sends a projection to neuron X. What neuron Y does is it inhibits the activity of neuron X. It makes neuron X less excitable.

Look at what's happening, back to the sudden-pain pathway up on top. Your sudden-pain-oriented receptors responding to things like a cut, get activated, and as we just saw, send that signal to neuron X and stimulate it, and you feel pain. At the same time though, that same sudden-pain neuron up on top has a collateral, a cable that comes off which also sends a projection to neuron Y and stimulates it. What happens here? The pain receptive neuron up on top gets stimulated by something painful and stimulates neurons Y and X at the same time. Then with a slight delay, neuron Y turns off neuron X. What have you just explained? Why you get a sharp piercing pain which then goes away shortly afterward. You touch a pot that's hot and you pull your finger back, you get a paper cut and it suddenly hurts and then it goes away. That's all due to the fact that with a delay, neuron Y is turning off neuron X after that excitation.

Meanwhile, still in diagram B, underneath, you've got that slow-pain pathway when some pain-invoking stimulus that we tend to subjectively feel as being slow activates that neuron as we saw before. The projection comes in and stimulates neuron X, you're feeling pain. Just like before, that same neuron has a branch, a collateral going off to neuron Y, but this time what that collateral does is it inhibits the activity of neuron Y. What happens, something painful occurs, activates neuron X, which gets excited sending a pain signal. What you're also doing there is you're shutting down neuron Y which makes it impossible for neuron Y to shut down neuron X. What happens then? The pain keeps going. It throbs. This is what chronic thobbing pain is about. Two very different pathways are pulled out of this diagram.

This begins to explain a couple of really interesting things. What this tells you is, suppose you've got a throbbing chronic pain, which is neuron X is activated, and neuron Y doesn't have the means to silence neuron X. What would you love to do? Let's stimulate Y so it kicks in and shuts off X. When is that going on? You have a chronic pain which is what itching is. In some circumstances, you've got some horrible itchy mosquito bite, and what do we often do? Don't scratch the mosquito bite, it will get infected. What you do instead is you scratch on either side of it, and what you're doing is you're stimulating that sudden-pain pathway, which stimulates Y, which silences X, and the itchiness goes away for a little bit.

Another example of this: Suppose you have a chronic pain, throbbing, coming from that lower slow-pain pathway, and you want to make it go away, some throbbing pain in your muscles. What do you do? You go get somebody to pound on your back hard, give you a massage because what is done with really aggressive massaging is you stimulate those acute pain pathways which activates Y to silence X. Even more examples, you've got a condition where somebody has a lot of trouble delivering energy to cells throughout the body. We heard about that earlier. That's what juvenile diabetes is about. As a result of that energy depletion, some of your cells begin to die, and for very complex reasons in a pathway like this, it's the sudden-pain pathway neurons that die. What's the consequence of this? You turn on a slow-pain pathway, and Y shuts down and X keeps screaming its head off for long afterward, and it just keeps going and going because you can never shut down that signal with a sharp input. What have you got but diabetic neuropathy. In fact, that pain there just goes on and on.

Here we've seen the basic wiring of the system. How does it begin to play out? There's all sorts of interesting things that happen that underlie an important fact there, which is pain is not that objective of a state. There's a lot of subjectivity that comes into pain perception. For example, you can have a circumstance where you feel pain and there's not even a stimulus, a painful stimulus happening. A lot of us feel that pain which is when you're in the dentist chair, and the person so much as walks in the room and your teeth are aching. There was no stimulus there. If you're really hypersensitive, you feel throbbing pain in your gums there simply by hearing the Muzak going on in the office. That could be a source where, with no actual stimulus, you're feeling pain. Some of those neurons are sending messages up to your brain when there was nothing that stimulated them.

Another example: You sit there and instead of experiencing some pure, overt, realistic pain stimulus, hot/cold whatever, you sit there and you watch the same thing being done to a loved one, and you feel their pain. On a certain level, the feeling of pain is an empathetic response that taps into the same wiring here. As we'll see in a coming lecture, there's another example of this. Clinical depression appears to involve overactivation of a couple of these pain pathways. In other words, psychic pain even has some reality in terms of wiring. Some of the time, you can turn on a pain response when there's absolutely no stimulus. Some of the time, there can be a pain stimulus and you won't even notice it. Let me give you a highly technical example. Suppose somebody takes some really rough sandpaper and unexpectedly sandpapers your rear end over and over, abrading it. This is likely to seem unpleasant. Suppose instead, in some rare abstract scenario, you are abrading your rear end exactly the same way having enthusiastic sex while on a carpet, and you don't even notice it. Context makes this huge difference.

Then there are some settings where you not only don't notice the pain where you actually give a subjective interpretation that the pain is good news.

Here are some very poignant examples. The first one, you have some soldier in battle, a battle that is utterly terrifying, people getting killed left and right. The person gets shot in their leg. It hurts. This is not a fatal wound. It hurts, and why could this be good news? This means they're injured. They're out of this war. They're being sent to the back lines. This hurts like crazy, but here's the wonderful news, I'm going to survive. Another example that is quite poignant as well, and this is someone I happen to know with a very serious type of cancer, and at some point they tried an experimental drug. It wasn't quite clear if it was going to work, and if it did work, if this drug started killing some of the tumorous cells, things were going to hurt like crazy as those cells died. A few weeks into it, yes indeed, fortunately this therapy was working. In talking to this friend, saying, well how does this feel, the response being, it hurts like hell, and that's the greatest news I could possibly get. This is the sign that it's working. There's this tremendous element of subjectivity going on in there. How might that subjectivity work? We will see the wiring for that shortly, but what you know is going on in there is your brain isn't just getting signals from your spinal cord, your brain is sending signals down to your spinal cord.

A bit more about the wiring; you hit one of those painful stimuli, and it is activating the sudden, acute-pain pathway, or the throbbing, dull one. Part of what happens then is exclusively in your spinal cord. You've got reflexes where a pain signal comes in and an instant later, the spinal cord is sending a message to the relevant muscles to get your foot out of that fire. You are not sitting there consciously saying, "Well, my, that sure feels adversive, and in fact, my toe is roasting, this might be a good time to send a message. Let's see, was it my left toe, big toe, or my right—right one, let's send a message there telling it to retract." It's purely spinal reflex, so that's a first level of analysis of a painful input.

The next is going on in the brain, and it's a level of the brain, a very ancient part of the brain that's telling you objective information about the source of pain. It's telling you how painful the pain is. It's telling you where the pain is coming from; this is your painometer telling you how many units of ouchness you've gotten there. This is one that is sending up information saying it's your foot not your hand that's gotten injured. This is a bad one. This is a moderate one, whatever. This activates parts of the brain which, in turn, tell other parts to make you start breathing faster, your heart to speed up, maybe to whimper, and some of your blood vessels there to constrict. All sorts of autonomic nervous system stuff. That's a bit of wiring that's in common to all sorts of species out there including us. Then there's a level on top of it. This is not the painometer ancient part of your brain measuring how many of your toes feel miserable, this is forebrain, more recently evolved parts of the brain, your cortex, in particular an area called the frontal cortex. What that one plays a role in is evaluating the pain, telling you what you think about it, how you feel about it. As soon as you're in a world of people who, where being in great amounts of pain is wonderful news because they're out of the war, where looking at their loved one feels painful, when you're up there, this is not the painometer part of the brain. This is that forebrain, that frontal cortex doing evaluative stuff. What does this pain information mean?

In order for that to work, we have to return to that diagram which is in the Guidebook and now we see a very important elaboration. What we've just gone through are circumstances where pain, those parts of the brain that give the subjective evaluative notion of what the pain's about, changes your pain perception. In other words, not only as promised is the brain getting pain information coming from the periphery, the brain is sending information back out to the periphery. As you can see in the diagram here, part C, we've now added in an additional element. We've got the sudden-pain inputs, the slow-pain inputs, neuron Y, neuron X. Neuron X when activated sending information up to the brain, and stuff we all know. Now what we also see is the possibility of projections coming down the spine from the brain, some of which stimulates neuron X. Suddenly the Muzak in the dentist's office is making you feel miserable. Some of it coming down inhibiting neuron X, the evaluative stuff, this is great news; I'm out of the war now. What we have here is this bidirectionality: Your brain is influencing how sensitive those neurons are to a painful input.

This is the basic wiring about how pain works. What does stress do on top of it? We've already heard a bit about this in the very first lecture. Massive, painful, stressful stimulus, and this is our zebra with its innards ripped out by the predator, and one of the things that happens is blessedly, pain perception gets blunted somewhat, stress-induced analgesia. Analgesia, the inability to feel pain, severe stress can block some pain perception. This pops up, this has been documented in all sorts of fascinating ways. For example, you get people who are involved in a serious car accident, and what the literature shows is, above a certain degree of seriousness, 80% of them need morphine as a painkiller.

Meanwhile, you look at soldiers in the middle of a battle who get the exact same severity of injury, and the rates of the percentage that need the morphine is vastly lower. What's that about? You have a car accident that comes from out of nowhere, excruciating pain. You get the same injury in the middle of a battle, and the stress of that battle has been producing a roaringly effective case of stress-induced analgesia. There are much more commonplace circumstances where the same thing happens. You're in the middle of the annual company volleyball game, and you come down and you twist your ankle, and you don't feel it quite as much. That's because in this case, the stress of the physical activity has induced a certain degree of stress-induced analgesia. That's a mighty useful thing if you are running away from that lion, and you've got that bad injury. How does it work? What are the mechanisms underlying that? It's actually quite well understood, and a big piece of it has to do with the stress hormone we've heard about, a lot in some recent lectures, beta-endorphins. Remember I brought up that point, beta-endorphins have something to do with pain, but weirdly, here's yet another hormone chemical messenger that does more than one thing. It's got something to do with reproduction and all that. Now we get to the central arena of what beta-endorphin does. Again, going back to its name, what the source of it is, endorphin, endogenous morphine, beta-endorphin is the drug that blocks the pain perception, the chemical messenger.

We can once again go back to that diagram, to part C, and you look at those projections coming down from the brain. Look at the bottom one, the one that inhibits neuron X, the one that makes neuron X less likely to activate, the one that blunts pain perception. Almost certainly, in a lot of these circuits, that projection from the brain makes use of endorphins to block the pain perception. That's great. That begins to account for the reason why most people who know what beta-endorphin is about understand what it does which is the famed runner's high, your endorphin high. You go out and you decide to run some long distance. It hurts, you're miserable, you're dizzy, and you're ready to keel over. Somewhere around 10–20 minutes into it, suddenly you get this wonderful gauzy sense of well-being. It's great, and that's when the endorphins kick in. Mind you the next day you're going to be miserably sore, but for the moment at least, that's where it's coming from. There's also evidence that acupuncture, when it blocks pain perception, is doing so by stimulating endorphin release. There's also evidence of placebo effects, when one is faked into thinking that you've blocked pain. You're putting a painful stimulus, maybe something hot on your fingertip, and the subjects are told that they're putting on a cream which blocks pain perception, but it actually doesn't really do that. It just causes a placebo effect, and you feel less pain there. What that placebo effect appears to be about in a lot of cases is activating those descending beta-endorphin pathways. This finger is screaming with the exact same painful hot stimulus, and your brain is saying, hey that doesn't really hurt because after all we've got this new analgesic cream on our fingertip. That's the brain sending that message down to the neuron X, almost certainly using beta-endorphin as the pathway.

We now come into, instead of the realm of acute stress and the activation of beta-endorphin and that whole sort of pathway, and the acute tapping into that circuit, now what about chronic stress. What about massive chronic stress? What we get to is truly bad news. Let us return to that diagram yet again. What happens with sustained stress, major stress, is really unpleasant. A lot of stimulation of pain pathways make pain pathways more sensitive, more responsive so that pain begets pain, and you have the phenomenon of hyperalgesia, which is where you have enhanced pain sensitivity. There are some horrible clinical disorders where there are problems in the nervous system and the sort of wiring we've been looking at where those neurons just fire spontaneously. Thus, you are constantly in pain, the hyperalgesia. One of the things that chronic stress can do, though, is increase the excitability of those neurons. At an extreme, what you wind up getting is a neuron that actually keeps stimulating itself. Let's look once again at neuron X, and we've already seen the possibility that a neuron sends its primary projection and then has one of those collateral things that come off. What you can sometimes see is something like a neuron X forms a collateral that loops back on itself, and every time neuron X gets stimulated, it stimulates itself more, more and more hyperalgesia. Where stress appears to come in making this possible is what we've heard about already, the capacity of acute stressors to activate innate immune response. You remember that from a few lectures ago, to cause inflammation. Inflammation makes pain-mediating neurons more excitable and more likely to get into this vicious circle of pain activation, causing pain activation, causing pain activation.

Back to where this lecture started which was going through our usual dichotomy, short-term/good news, long-term/bad news. Also going back to the very first lecture, going through that notion of Selye's which turned out to be wrong. Why is it that chronic stress makes you sick? He came up with that completely incorrect idea that with chronic stress you go into the exhaustion phase. You run out of the hormones of the stress-response. You are depleted of adrenalin, epinephrine. You're depleted of this or that hormone related to stress, and you were pummeled there, and as we saw, this doesn't happen. There is no organism on Earth that has been so stressed that it runs out of adrenaline. It simply doesn't happen. This is the one domain where it appears to happen, because what you get is with enough pain, with severe enough of pain, with long-lasting enough of pain and stress, what do you do? You get depleted of beta-endorphin. The beta-endorphin that comes out of the pituitary, as it turns out, and works on the spine, you get depleted of beta-endorphin for a very simple reason. Those cells that are making the beta-endorphin, they're dumping so much of the stuff out, and they get just a little bit behind, and they can't quite keep up with demand. The problem in this case is not the one we've been seeing over and over in lectures which is the stress-response just keeps going for too long, too much prolactin, too much glucocorticoids. The problem here is this rare case of Selye being right in this regard.

You run out of the hormone that protects you from the stressor. What does that mean? That means something really sad and really awful, which is you get that person with a horrendous injury, you get that soldier who has just been shot, you get the woman with a terminal painful cancer, and it's not the case that eventually you turn off the pathways. What eventually happens is you run out of stuff like beta-endorphin and the pain comes back and just keeps going.

Stress, Learning, and Memory
Lecture 13

> There are a number of different types of [implicit memory]. One
> example is what would be called fear conditioning, a type of association
> ... a type of memory, if you will, that your body learns—that you learn
> implicitly, unconsciously. Let me give you an example of this. I was
> in the 1989 earthquake in San Francisco, and it was not fun. It left
> a lasting impression and implicit memory that I often find, which is
> I might be sitting some place and some large truck rumbles past ...
> and the ground vibrates a little bit. I stop in my tracks wondering is
> this another earthquake. What that is is implicit fear conditioning
> because what occurred during the earthquake was 15 seconds or so
> of the stimulus, 15 seconds that has taught my implicit pathways
> something indelible.

How does memory work? There are many different types of memory, and the most relevant to the area of stress and learning is the dichotomy between explicit and implicit memory. Explicit (or declarative) memory is where you know a fact, and you know that you know the fact: I have a birthday in April; I am a mammal. You know the facts sufficiently so that you can actively, consciously behave with that knowledge. In contrast, implicit memory involves things that have been internalized by your body and do not require conscious thought.

What parts of the brain are involved in learning and memory? The hippocampus is intensely involved in memory formation. The **hippocampus** and the associated cortex do the declarative memory type of learning, whereas the cerebellum is involved in implicit memory. What's going on at the level of individual cells? A memory isn't about a new neuron or about a new connection, as previously believed. It's about strengthening preexisting connections, making those connections more excitable, potentiating those connections, and potentiating them so that they last long term. This is called **long-term potentiation** and is the dominant model in the field.

A level that has come to be really interesting to researchers in the field is the notion of networks of neurons storing memory. The whole notion of these networks is that information is diffusely distributed. Information of memory is not contained in any single neuron or any single connection; it is contained in patterns of activation. When you are at a party, and you are trying to remember someone's name, you try to pull out that memory by association. How many syllables does that person's name have? I remember it started with a B sound. Where was I when I learned that person's name? Who was I with? You are tapping into associations, and somewhere at the intersection of all those networks, that name will suddenly pop out.

> **In the short term, stress does great things for your learning and memory.**

What then happens with stress? In the short term, stress does great things for your learning and memory. You increase your heart rate, you loosen up blood vessels in critical areas of the brain, you deliver more oxygen and glucose to the brain, and your brain starts working better. Also with the onset of stress, connections between neurons become more excitable in the hippocampus, and long-term potentiation happens more readily. Studies show that stressors make it easier to remember certain things.

With more chronic stress, we begin to see memory disruption. Once stress goes on for a few hours, you are no longer delivering more glucose and oxygen to the brain; you're delivering less. You are no longer enhancing long-term potentiation; you're disrupting it, and in the worst place, the hippocampus. Perhaps most remarkable, with more sustained stress, you change the structure of neurons in the hippocampus; you cause them to atrophy. This makes it harder for neurons in the hippocampus to survive things like a stroke or a seizure. So chronic stress can potentially worsen neurological outcomes. ∎

Important Terms

hippocampus: A part of the brain's limbic system that is centrally involved in learning and memory and highly sensitive to the effects of stress.

long-term potentiation (LTP): An increase in the ease with which neurons communicate with each other across synapses; this increase in excitability is thought to be a cellular building block of memory formation.

neurogenesis: The generation of new neurons. The fact that this can occur in the adult brain has been a revolution in neurobiology.

Suggested Reading

Sapolsky, *Why Zebras Don't Get Ulcers*, chap. 10.

Questions to Consider

1. On the level of individual cells and synapses, how does short-term stress enhance learning and memory?

2. On the same level, how does chronic stress do exactly the opposite?

Stress, Learning, and Memory
Lecture 13—Transcript

No doubt everybody out there is still reeling from the distressing digression we had in the last lecture away from our usual dichotomy, short-term/good news, long-term stress/bad news, and discovering that chronic activation of pain systems in fact don't occur, you run out of beta-endorphin, that whole fact that we finished with last time. What we do now in this lecture is get back on wonderful, comfortable ground. We're dealing once again with this dichotomy of ours, short-term activation of the stress-response doing a good thing; in this case, the theme of this lecture, enhancing learning and memory, chronic stress doing just the opposite.

As with a lot of the other lectures, what we first need to do here is go over the basic workings of the system we're going to talk about. How does memory work? What we'll do is first look at memory as a behavioral phenomenon, then how memory works at the level of whole sections of the brain, how it works at the level of individual cells, and how it works at the level of networks. The first important point here in looking at memory as a behavioral phenomenon is memory is not monolithic. There's not just one type of memory. If you will, there's a whole taxonomy of different types of memory, short versus long-term versus remote memory and other subcategories. There's one that's going to be quite important here, a dichotomy between what is called explicit or declarative memory and implicit memory.

Explicit, declarative memory, you know a fact and you know that you know the fact. I have a birthday in April. I am a mammal. I have a doctor's appointment next Tuesday. You know the facts sufficiently so that you can actively, consciously behave with that knowledge, explicit, declarative memory. You can declare that piece of information. In contrast, you have the implicit memory, and there are a number of different types of it. One example is what would be called fear conditioning, a type of association, a type of memory that you learn without being conscious.

A type of memory, if you will, that your body learns, that you learn implicitly unconsciously. Let me give you an example of this. I was in the 1989 earthquake in San Francisco, and it was not fun. It left a lasting impression and implicit memory that I often find which is I might be sitting some place and some large truck rumbles past wherever I'm in, whatever building, and the ground vibrates a little bit. I stop in my tracks wondering is this another earthquake. What that is is implicit fear conditioning because what occurred during the earthquake was 15 seconds or so of the stimulus, 15 seconds that have taught my implicit pathways something indelible.

Other types of implicit memory and one that becomes very, very important in all sorts of realms, memory, once again where your body almost knows better than your head does. Just a metaphor, but where it's the memory of how to do things, how to do procedures, how to carry things off, how to do things that are adept, dexterous, where you don't have to think about it. What procedural memory is about is learning to do something automatic. Procedural memory comes in all sorts of domains, for example, learning some sort of motoric task. What you initially do is have to deal with it as an explicit declarative piece of information which then, with practice, transitions over into implicit memory.

For example, you are learning some new part of a piece of music on the piano. There's this difficult trill, and every time you're coming up to it a few measures before, you have this explicit, declarative thought which is, here it comes, remember tuck in my elbow, lead with my thumb underneath, some such thing, this very explicit process. Then one day you're playing it, and you suddenly realize I'm 3 measures past that trill, and I didn't have to think consciously about it. That's the day that information got moved from an explicit pathway into an implicit one. That's the first time where in effect, your hands know it better than your head does. The process of learning some motoric pathway typically takes the route of moving from explicit information to implicit. Something that's interesting is the system is lousy going in the opposite direction, going from implicit knowledge, information, procedural information that you've got to the point your body knows it better than you do, and forcing it back into a declarative channel.

We can see this with a very, very simple experiment, one that you should not carry out alone, which is to walk down a flight of stairs, and right near the bottom, maybe 3 steps from the bottom, think in this declarative, explicit way: What exactly am I doing when I'm going down a flight of stairs? Am I beginning to shift my weight over to my right knee at this point or am I still holding something on my left? What's going to happen is you're going to fall down those stairs because we have not done stairs in an explicit, declarative way since we were about 3 years old. Often the process of getting new, automatic information, going from explicit into implicit pathways, forcing it in the opposite direction is real clunky and doesn't work very well.

Now we transition to the actual brain, what parts of the brain are involved. Take Intro Neuro 101 any time in the last millennium and you start off with a part of the brain called the hippocampus. The hippocampus is intensely involved in memory formation. *Hippokampos*, some Latin name, *hippokampos* means seahorse, which shows you how pathetic neuroanatomists are because they never get outside the lab because a hippocampus doesn't look like a seahorse at all. It actually looks like a jellyroll, but I guess nobody knows Latin for jellyroll. Hippocampus is this part of the brain that does an aspect of learning for you of a certain type, of the declarative memory type. You can see this specialization in a number of different settings. You, for example, can see patterns of brain activation. You put somebody in one of those scanners where you can see what part of the brain is being metabolically active. Deal with a new fact, trying to learn it in a declarative way, and it's the hippocampus that activates. Look at something that's already in an implicit—your hands know it better than your head does—procedural way, it's a different part of the brain, the cerebellum that typically activates.

The hippocampus is about declarative knowledge. You can also see this in a much sadder circumstance. You look at somebody with Alzheimer's disease. Alzheimer's disease predominantly damages parts of the cortex and the hippocampus, demolishes the hippocampus in lots of ways, and what you see with people with early-stage Alzheimer's, it's the declarative memory that's shot. The procedural is still good. That's where you have somebody where he could not tell you what decade it is and where he is, but this retired plumber can still fix a sink trap without even thinking, because that's procedural.

The hippocampus and the associated cortex, specializes in declarative memory. This has also been shown in one of the most remarkable incidents and sort of remarkable chapters in all of neurobiology. It's the story of a man, the only person in all of history where scientists, where doctors, intentionally took out his hippocampus. This was a man who was only known to the literature as H. M., by his initials. He is in every textbook. H. M., in the 1950s had a rare, horribly intractable form of epilepsy that was running amok through his hippocampus. The drugs available at the time weren't controlling it. It was clearly going to kill him, and the very desperate decision was made to go in surgically and remove his hippocampus. That was done by a very famous neurosurgeon, and in the aftermath of it, the seizures predominantly went away.

It officially worked, and in the aftermath of that, H. M.'s ability to learn new, declarative information was very, very much impaired, virtually entirely impaired. Everything he had learned before the surgery, everything filed away, was still intact. He remembered his childhood. He remembered the name of his mother, things of that sort; everything was there because it was stored someplace other than the hippocampus. It was acquiring new information where things didn't work. There was say, a 30-second memory span. There wasn't this transition from very fragile, short-term memory into more permanent long-term memory, because there wasn't a hippocampus.

This was absolutely remarkable to see. I actually met H. M. once. Of course, he never remembered me. I met H. M. once. It was when I was doing research in the laboratory at MIT and he happened to be most intensively studied by some neuroscientists at MIT. It was one of those dream moments where you're sitting there in lab and somebody runs in and says, "Guess who's out in the hallway, H. M. H. M., oh my God, let's go meet H. M." This is like taking Pavlov's dogs for a walk. You run out in the hallway, and there's H. M., who is this perfectly gregarious man. He introduces himself, and you shake hands. He's saying, "Hi, my name is Henry," and that's great. Somebody slams a door down the hall, and you glance over. You look back, and he says, "Oh, hi. I don't believe we've met. My name is Henry." You could stand there doing that all day long, utter damage to his declarative memory processes.

It was H. M. that first got people attuned to the fact that there are more than one type of memory. There's this explicit, and there's also this procedural. H. M. could continue to learn procedural tasks. He could learn how to do things with his hands at least as well as any control subject. He simply didn't know he had learned it. You would give him some puzzle, task kind of thing, and because of has explicit memory problem, he had no memory he had done it. He would say, "Well, I've never seen this before, but I'll try. I'll do my best." Then he whips through it incredibly fast because he has the procedural memory stored elsewhere.

What about H. M.? In 2009 H. M. died in his 80s, and people who had been waiting to study his brain for decades moved in at that point. Early in 2010 a virtual religious rite ran through the neuroscience community. The neuroanatomists and neuropathologists who were going to study his brain went through the first step, slicing his brain and mounting the slides to begin to examine the brain tissue microscopically. In a remarkable event, all of this was broadcast live, streaming video online, where tens of thousands of scientists watched this, and there was something intensely moving about sitting there watching the brain of H. M. and the involuntary sacrifice of this man for science, watching the brain being sliced.

That was H. M., teaching us tons about the hippocampus. Shifting down at this point to the level of individual cells, what's going on with cells and memory? People used to know just what was going on around 1900, which was this view every time you make a new memory, you make a new brain cell, and that memory is contained in that brain cell, that neuron. That one fell by the wayside very quickly. Then there was a new view there, there are these connections between neurons, technical term, synapse—don't worry about it. There's these connections, those cables that we've now seen in the diagram in the last lecture, and the notion there was learn something new, and you form a new connection.

That dominated for a while. Except that went by the wayside because that didn't seem to be happening much. What happened by the 1950s is what came to be the dominant view. A scientist named Donald Hebb—and when talking about memory, if you don't mention Hebb's name, they take away your neurobiology license—had the most wonderful, dominating insight, the notion that a memory isn't about a new neuron or about a new connection. It's about strengthening preexisting connections, making those connections more excitable, potentiating those connections, making them more excitable, and potentiating them so that they last long-term. The jargon in the field winds up being LTP: long-term potentiation. That has wound up being sort of the dominant model, and an enormous amount of work has gone into figuring out what that LTP, that long-term potentiation is about. Some sense on the cellular level now.

A level that has come to be really interesting to lots of researchers in the field is the notion of networks of neurons storing memory. That Donald Hebb view that memory is about you stimulate a pathway over and over, you learn something, you then change the excitability of this synapse, and that's where the memory is. A single memory is not stored in a single connection between neurons. Instead, it's stored in networks. The whole notion of these networks is information is diffusely distributed. Information of memory is not contained in any single neuron or any single connection. It's contained in patterns of activation. What you see is a characteristic of memory which absolutely proves how it's contained in networks.

You're sitting there at a party, and you're trying to remember the name of that person sitting across from you and you can't remember their name. What you begin to do is try to pull out that memory by association. How many syllables does that person's name have? I'm remembering it starting with a B sound. Let's see, where was I when I learned that person's name. Who was I with? You're tapping into associations. You're tapping into the people with this number of syllables in their name network, and people who have their names starting with B. People who I met in this setting, and somewhere at the intersection of all those networks, that name will suddenly pop out. That's what memory, that's what pulling out something, is often about in terms of these networks.

196

What that begins to explain is something remarkable you could see with Alzheimer's disease, which is early on in the disease, it's not that memories are lost, it's harder to pull them out. It's harder to evoke them. You can see this in all sorts of ways. You get somebody where, for example, you are trying to tap into their orientation to space and time. You have an Alzheimer's patient, and you will give them an orientation test. You will say, "Do you know what the date is? Do you know where you are? Do you know how many children you have, the name of your spouse," some such thing. Then you will ask them a question, one which is pertinent right now when this is being taped, which is to ask them, "Oh, and do you know the name of the former president?" Not there, completely gone, they can't evoke it. Now what you do is prove that that information is not contained in a single neuron that died, that the information is in a network. You begin to tap into the intersection between that network and other ones. You prime the person. You say, "OK, let me help you out a little bit. The name was one syllable." Nothing, doesn't come out. Then you give them a little stronger priming, tapping into yet another network, saying "OK, it's a one-syllable word and it's something you might encounter in a park." Nope, it doesn't come out. Then you give them the strongest type of priming; you actually force them to choose, you say, "OK, so was it President Bench, President Tree, President Shrub, President Bush?" Bush, that's right, the kid, the son, Bush, President Bush, and out it pops showing this characteristic early on in Alzheimer's. It's not that the memory is lost, it has taken more work to pull it out of the networks, because the networks have lost neurons; the networks have weakened.

That gives a sense about how memory works at the level of whole regions of the brain, the hippocampus, and it's not just the hippocampus, but hippocampus being very notable for this declarative memory. What's going on down at the cellular level? Memory does not consist of making new neurons. It does not consist of making new connections, but strengthening preexisting ones, and how those strengthened connections play out over the course of lots of neurons, networks of neurons, making those connections with each other.

Ironic-ending department: It turns out, oh, that ancient, laughable notion that memory consists of making new neurons or even memory consists of making new connections, that's ridiculous. That's medieval neuroscience. In the last few years, there's increasing evidence that that actually does occur some of the time. A huge revolution in neurobiology has occurred. For the last centuries, if you're learning basic neurobiology, one of the facts that gets hammered in immediately is the adult brain doesn't make new neurons. You're stuck with whatever number you got early on and all that happens from there is you go downhill with fewer of them. This revolution being that it turns out the adult brain, even in humans, does make new neurons, adult neurogenesis.

Remarkably, the place in the brain where it happens the most is in, you guessed it, the hippocampus. At this stage, there's beginning to be evidence that certain types of memory acquisition require the formation of new neurons. Here we have both learning the lessons of history and having it repeat on you. Here we are back again, the notion that some of memory formation actually involves forming new neurons or forming new connections as it turns out. Nonetheless, the bulk of what goes on appears to be that strengthening of preexisting neurons.

We've got basic memoryology under our belt here at the systems level, and networks, individual cells. What then happens with stress? What happens? You know exactly what happens which is short-term, you have memory enhanced. Short-term, stress does great things for your learning and memory. We saw that starting in the very first lecture, short-term, what do you do? You increase the delivery of oxygen to the brain. You increase the delivery of glucose. Those are exactly the sorts of things that make for a perkier brain that is more able to do the very energetically costly process of all that excitation business. What's that due to? That's the increased heart rate, blood pressure, you dilate, you loosen up some of the blood vessels in critical areas of the brain, deliver the oxygen and glucose up there, and suddenly you've got a brain that works better.

What else? With the onset of stress, you suddenly have those neurons that undergo that long-term potentiation business, that business about these connections becoming more excitable in the hippocampus, and suddenly LTP happens more readily. This could then be shown on the level of actual learning and memory, the sort of thing where you look at does a stressor make it easier to remember certain things?

This was shown in a magnificently elegant study carried out by 2 scientists, Larry Cahill and James McGaugh, University of California, Irvine. McGaugh, one of the senior figures in the field, and here's the study they did, totally elegant. You take a bunch of control volunteers, and what you do is you tell them this 12-sentence story. Boy and his mother go walking through town. They pass the grocery store. They pass the hardware store. They cross the street. They go into the hospital where the mother works. The mother shows the boy how the X-ray machine works, and on and on. The first 4 sentences being they cross the street, up to that point. Then in the hospital, so that's the first version. The second version, the experimental subjects, what happens with them is, one part of the story is different. A boy and his mother are walking through town. They pass the grocery store. They pass the hardware store. They begin to cross the street when the boy is struck by a huge truck. The boy is rushed to the hospital where they rush him to the X-ray room and X-ray him and this big—you'll notice the first 4 sentences are the same, and then it goes into a much more emotionally arousing, a much more stressful story.

What Cahill and McGaugh showed was come back a couple of weeks later, and see what people remember about the story. The people who got the first boring version, and the mother goes and shows the kid the X-ray machine, they don't remember it very well. You get the people who got the much more stressful, emotionally arousing version, and they remember it better. The part they remember better is starting when the child is hit by the truck. That's the arousing, stressful part. That's the part that gets filed away, and suddenly the oxygen and the glucose is coursing up into the brain. What causes this to happen? This has some responsiveness, some involvement of glucocorticoids, some involvement of the sympathetic nervous system predominantly.

In the final elegant touch to this study, they showed exactly how this sympathetic nervous system plays that role, which was they gave these volunteer experimental subjects a little bit of a drug which blocks activation of the sympathetic nervous system, a drug which blocks a certain type of receptor for epinephrine (adrenaline). This is a drug a lot of people have heard of and used, it's called a beta-blocker. Beta-blockers tone down sympathetic tone, drugs like propranolol. What they did at this point is they either had people get a placebo and hear the horrifying, really distressing, stressful version of the story, or people were given a beta-blocker and heard the same story. In other words, they went into hearing the really upsetting part of the story with their sympathetic nervous system damped down. Those folks didn't have preferential memory of that event. What that's telling you is, this short-term enhancement of memory driven by the sympathetic nervous systems is, number 1, specific to the more arousing parts of the memory, and as just shown with that experiment, yes, indeed involves the sympathetic nervous system.

We've got our short-term response to stress, a 30-second story. Now we switch over to our more chronic scenario of stress. More chronic and what you begin to see as we would absolutely guess is a more sustained stressor disrupts memory. A more sustained stressor, how would you show that in lab rats? They have to learn some sort of maze, that kind of thing. How do you show it in humans? All sorts of experimental settings, you force somebody to go through a stressor, like giving a public speech, and then afterward you see how well they remember something from beforehand. That might be viewed as stressful in this case, but fortunately, I'm a computer-generated image. For most people, though, doing something like this, you would begin to disrupt memory because it's stressful. What do you see? Once stress is going on for a few hours or so, no longer are you delivering more glucose and oxygen to the brain; you're delivering less. No longer are you enhancing LTP, that long-term potentiation; you're disrupting LTP and exactly where you don't want to have it disrupted, in the hippocampus.

Next, you actually, with more sustained stress, begin to do something remarkable, which is, you change the structure of neurons in the hippocampus. You cause them to atrophy. You cause them to atrophy, those long processes we've been hearing all about. Those long processes with which a neuron talks to another neuron. What are you doing there? You're disconnecting circuits. Suddenly, what circuits there are, are not very excitable, disrupting that long-term potentiation, and you're making for fewer connections because you're disconnecting, you're atrophying these neurons. That's not enough. More things go wrong.

Back to that revolution in neurobiology, back to that finding that the adult brain, the adult hippocampus, can make new neurons. When does that occur? It occurs in response to all the logical things, learning something new, environmental stimulation, exercise, and very interestingly, estrogen as well, a whole bunch of things that stimulate neurogenesis. The 2 surest ways to shut down neurogenesis, lots of glucocorticoids and lots of stress. That's another domain in which you pay a price.

Moving on to the next realm, what you have with sustained stress—and glucocorticoids play this role—is you endanger neurons in the hippocampus. You take hippocampal neurons, and you make them a little fragile, a little bit wimpy, a little bit nauseous, and green around the gills. What you do is you take a hippocampal neuron and you put it right on the edge of a cliff during sustained stress. At that point, if nothing else happens, the neuron recovers. Everyone lives happily ever after. If at that point, though, you push the neuron with something else, it's that much more likely to go over the edge. What this endangerment translates into is stress, and glucocorticoids make it harder for neurons in the hippocampus to survive things like a stroke, a seizure, things of that sort. You suddenly have chronic stress potentially worsening neurological outcomes. This is actually an area of research that my lab has spent the last 25 years on trying to understand what this endangerment is about.

Finally, at the greatest extreme, with massive amounts of exposure to stress or glucocorticoids, you apparently are able to actually kill neurons in the hippocampus. This was originally shown in rodents—and again, I was involved in some of this work—and subsequent to that, shown to be involved in nonhuman primates, and thus we moved to the critical, disturbing question: What about humans? Can sustained stress disrupt LTP? Can sustained stress in humans cause atrophy of neurons? Can sustained stress make neurons in the human hippocampus more fragile, more likely to be done in by insults? Does sustained stress actually kill hippocampal neurons in humans? This is where we're going to pick up in the next lecture. All I can leave you with at this point is the news is not good.

Stress, Judgment, and Impulse Control
Lecture 14

What does the frontal cortex do? It does all sorts of complicated things, regulating executive behaviors and strategizing. ... It makes you do the harder thing when it's the right thing to do. It makes you do something that is difficult when that's what you should be doing. ... For example, the frontal cortex makes you, at a party, do the right thing even though it's harder. You have been served the most horrendous meal you can ever imagine, and it's your frontal cortex that kicks in and says, "Whoa, this is delicious. I've got to have the recipe." It keeps you constrained. It keeps you in line.

It has been demonstrated in rodents and nonhuman primates that massive amounts of exposure to stress or glucocorticoids can actually kill neurons in the hippocampus. But what about in humans? Can sustained stress make neurons in the human hippocampus more fragile, or even kill them? Much of this is impossible to study in humans, because you can't tell if individual neurons are atrophying or whether there is long-term potentiation. But we can use brain-imaging techniques to see the size and level of activity of different structures of the brain. These studies have begun to provide some pretty disturbing conclusions.

This first domain of humans who have excessive exposure to glucocorticoids is those who take synthetic glucocorticoids to control medical problems like lupus or rheumatoid arthritis. The first hints of the literature are showing that these individuals have memory problems that increase with the level of glucocorticoid exposure. The next area of relevance to humans is **Cushing's syndrome**, a number of diseases whose commonality is the secretion of high levels of glucocorticoids. This leads to atrophy of the hippocampus and resultant memory problems. This is almost certainly the atrophy of individual neurons, because laboratory studies show that with the abatement of stress, the processes grow back.

There is emerging literature showing that chronic major depression can be associated with hippocampal atrophy. **Post-traumatic stress disorder** has also been shown to cause a loss of volume of the hippocampus—and the more severe the traumatic history, the greater the memory problems. What about more everyday stressors, such as chronic occupational stressors? There was a remarkable study done some years ago in which, controlling for all other variables, those folks with more stressful jobs tended to have a smaller hippocampus and greater memory problems. So this is some initial evidence that occupational stress can have some of the same consequences.

Your brain is not just good for learning and memory. Your brain is also good for judgment, for impulse control, for executive decisions— and all of this involves a part of the brain called the **frontal cortex**. The frontal cortex is arguably the most human part of the brain. It does all sorts of complicated things, like regulating executive behaviors and strategizing. The frontal cortex is the last part of the brain to fully develop, a process that takes until around age 25. That

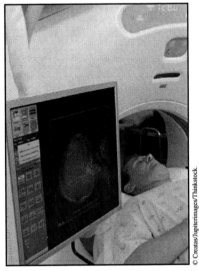

Brain-imaging technology has allowed us greater understanding of the function of different brain regions.

explains an awful lot of college campus behavior. It also motivated the U.S. Supreme Court decision that a person cannot be executed for a crime they committed under age 18. There's another realm in which brains don't have much frontal function: brains that have been damaged. A substantial percentage of people on death row in the United States have a history of major concussive trauma to the front of the brain.

What does stress do to the frontal cortex? A lot. The hippocampus and the frontal cortex have glucocorticoid **receptors** at far higher levels than elsewhere in the brain, and sufficient amounts of stress and glucocorticoid excess begin to interfere with how the brain works. It is a very new literature that's just emerging, but it tends to show atrophy of neurons in the frontal cortex and the layers of the frontal cortex thinning out. What happens after the stress is over with? What's known at this point is that with stress glucocorticoids, there is atrophy of the neurons. After stress subsides, they grow back, but with different sorts of connections. We don't know yet the full significance of these findings. ∎

Important Terms

Cushing's syndrome: A collection of diseases involving pathologically elevated levels of glucocorticoids.

frontal cortex: The brain region involved in decision making, impulse control, long-term planning, and gratification postponement.

post-traumatic stress disorder (**PTSD**): A psychiatric disorder comprising a constellation of symptoms (e.g., sleep disruption, flashbacks, and hypersensitivity to stimuli) caused by severe trauma (e.g., combat trauma, childhood abuse, or rape).

receptor: A hormone or neurotransmitter carrying messages from one cell to another. Each type of hormone or neurotransmitter binds to a specific receptor on a target cell and exerts its actions through that route (e.g., estrogen stimulates uterine growth by binding to estrogen receptors in uterine cells).

Suggested Reading

Sapolsky, *Why Zebras Don't Get Ulcers*, chap. 10.

Questions to Consider

1. What psychiatric disorders are associated with atrophy of the hippocampus, and why might that be?

2. What does the frontal cortex have to do with stress making you more impulsive?

Stress, Judgment, and Impulse Control
Lecture 14—Transcript

We now continue the previous lecture, the lecture about stress and memory, and we finished that lecture with a very disturbing, provocative question. You'll recall in the final minutes of that lecture what we focused on was the consequences of major long-term stress for the brain, for the memory systems in the brain, and we saw lots of bad news, chronic stress, and the declarative memory that the hippocampus specializes in is disrupted. Chronic stress, less oxygen, less glucose delivery to the brain, you begin to disrupt long-term potentiation, and that increase in excitability. You begin to cause atrophy of neurons in the hippocampus. You suppress neurogenesis, that wonderful new phenomenon. You make it harder for neurons to survive all sorts of insults, and at an extreme, you can actually kill neurons.

The question we were left with there is: What about humans? How much of this applies to the human brain? Much of this is impossible to study in humans, not like you could study in laboratory animals as described before because you can't tell if individual neurons are atrophying in the human brain. You can't detect whether there is long-term potentiation, in particular, connections between neurons. But one thing you can do that's quite pertinent is to take advantage of brain-imaging techniques, ones where you put somebody in a scanner and you can see the size of different structures of the brain, the level of activity, CAT scans, MRIs, things of that sort. What you can do with those approaches is look at the size of the hippocampus. What those studies have provided are the starts of some pretty disturbing conclusions. What we know by now is what's going on—an awful lot of those sources, chronic stress causing atrophy, neuronal damage, all this stuff from the lab animals—is a function of the excessive exposure to glucocorticoids.

We start off with the first domain of humans where there is excessive exposure to glucocorticoids. Back to the immunology lecture, that whole business about what glucocorticoids can do is suppress immunity, and that business that when you have an immune system that spirals out of control into autoimmunity, glucocorticoids are good for coasting you back again. As a result, there are hundreds of thousands of people out there taking high-dose glucocorticoids, synthetic versions, long-term to control their lupus, another autoimmune disease, and their rheumatoid arthritis, whatever. Suddenly you come up with the inevitable question: Do folks like these begin to have the sort of memory problems that are associated with hippocampal dysfunction?

These are extremely tough studies to do because by definition, if you are marinating somebody in synthetic glucocorticoids, it's because they've got a serious disease. If there are cognitive problems, is it due to the disease? Is it due to the steroids? It has taken some very subtle difficult studies, case control studies, where you match 2 people for age, education, gender, all of that, and the severity of the disease, and you take ones where it has been treated over the years with nonglucocorticoid, nonsteroidal, anti-inflammatory drugs, versus steroidal glucocorticoid ones. Then look at memory, and just the first hints of the literature are showing the more glucocorticoid exposure, the more problems you have with hippocampal-type memory, so that's not good.

Moving to the next version, that of relevance to humans, a disease—in fact a syndrome of diseases—called Cushing's disease, Cushing's syndrome, any of a number of different types of tumors where the commonality is you secrete boatloads of glucocorticoids. You've got all of the side effects that are associated by now, diabetes, hypertension, all that sort of thing, and inevitably, one then has to ask what's going on up in the brain. Do you get the sorts of memory problems associated with a hippocampus that is not doing its best? Yes, indeed, it's often called Cushingoid dementia.

What about the hippocampus in terms of structure? First brain-imaging studies some years ago showing that long-term chronic people with Cushing's disease—typically people have Cushing's for about 2 years before it's diagnosed—major long-term cushingoid bathing in glucocorticoids and you get atrophy of the hippocampus. The more prolonged, the more severe the glucocorticoid excess, and the more hippocampal atrophy. Is this due to dead neurons, almost certainly not because equally interesting studies have shown if you then go in and surgically correct the tumor, get rid of the excess glucocorticoids, over the next year or so, the hippocampus comes back to normal volume. What's this about? This is almost certainly that atrophy of individual neurons, because what the laboratory studies show is with the abatement of stress, with the abatement of glucocorticoid exposure, the processes grow back. The hippocampus, able to shrink, and seemingly some capacity to recover, and the memory processes come back to normal.

The next human version is truly profoundly troubling which is, emerging literature, well-replicated studies, showing that chronic major-league depression can be associated with hippocampal atrophy. As already alluded to and as what will fill up 2 different lectures, depression has much to do with stress. Depression is intertwined in many cases with glucocorticoid excess, and what these studies have shown is atrophy of the hippocampus, the more prolonged the depression history, the more atrophy, the more memory problems. Is this reversible? To date, the majority of studies have shown that it's not. With the abatement of the depression, when it has gotten under control with the correct antidepressants, when the depression goes away, you don't necessarily get full recovery of hippocampal volume. Caveat, fine print here, have a depression, have a depressive period, do not get into a fraught state here of worry. No evidence yet that everyday clinical depression can cause this. This is horrendous, massive serious depression associated with this.

Here's the next version that might be relevant, a human disease, a disease of people with horrible exposure to stress, some traumatic incident producing PTSD, post-traumatic stress disorder. What is seen there in a large number of studies from recent years is, once again, atrophy, loss of volume of the hippocampus, preferentially the hippocampus, and the more severe the traumatic history, the more atrophy, the more memory problems. This happens to be a wildly controversial incendiary subject built around this confusing issue. Depression, very often elevated glucocorticoid levels; Cushing's disease, by definition, elevated glucocorticoid levels; give somebody synthetic glucocorticoids, and you raise their glucocorticoid levels. It remains very controversial whether PTSD is associated with elevated glucocorticoid levels, or remarkably, lower than normal levels, and mixed results are in the literature. It's not entirely clear what's going on. Nonetheless, in the cases where it's below normal levels what you see is enhanced sensitivity to the glucocorticoids. The PTSD story is quite confused at this point, but what is far clearer is the evidence that lots of synthetic glucocorticoids, excess glucocorticoids in Cushing's disease, excess glucocorticoids in the severe cases of depression, you get loss of volume of the hippocampus. The more severe the insult, the more volume loss, and the more problems there are with the sort of memory that the hippocampus specializes in.

Disturbing bad news, but this is disturbing bad news at some of the extremes of things that can go wrong, tumors, major depression, all of that. What about more everyday stressors though? What about, for example, chronic occupational stressors? There was a remarkable, fascinating study that was done some years ago published in the journal *Nature* which is probably the most prestigious journal in the world.

What this was about was looking at people with a certain occupational stress. These were flight attendants for 2 different airlines. Both of them that do intercontinental flights, and the 2 airlines happen to differ after you do an intercontinental flight with a massive switch of circadian cycle, inducing dramatic jet lag. How many days do you get off from intercontinental flights in order to recover? There was the nice airline where you had 15 days to recover, and then there was the mean stepmother airline where you had 5 days to recover. What the study showed—and it was perfectly done, controlling for the total number of time shifts that somebody had done professionally as a flight attendant. It's not that one group had more of these shifts. The 2 groups merely differed in recovery time. What was shown was those folks working for the airline that gave you only the 5 days to recover, smaller hippocampus and more memory problems.

What I thought was very interesting—actually 2 things—one was that the paper carefully went about not mentioning the names of these airlines because I assume if they had mentioned the 5-day one they would have gotten their keisters sued off for this. The other was, which struck me somewhere in there, that also undergoing all of those time shift stressors are the pilots, and they were unmentioned in this study. It seems kind of disturbing. It's bad enough to get the memory problems where you can't remember if the person wants ice cubes in the milk or not, but if you're getting problems like you can't remember if this little old switch goes up or down in the cockpit there, this is not a good thing. Nonetheless, first evidence that occupation stress can have some of the same consequences.

Finally, the realm of normative aging, and this is wonderful work done by a neuroscientist, Sonia Lupien at the University of Montreal. What she has done is look at what glucocorticoids might have to do with successful aging, a subject that will come in an entire lecture. Just briefly foreshadowing here, in this study of hers she took 70-year-old individuals and characterized them at that point, the size of their hippocampus, brain imaging, their glucocorticoid levels, and then came back 5 years later. What she saw was for those people whose glucocorticoid levels have risen over those 5 years, they tended to loose hippocampal volume and tended to get more memory problems. At this point, this is a very preliminary literature. Nonetheless, it suggests all the bad news of the last lecture in terms of what chronic stress, chronic glucocorticoids can do to memory processes might very well apply to our own brains.

Now we transition to the other topic in this lecture, which is the fact that your brain is not just good for playing the piano and going down flights of stairs. Your brain is not just good for learning and memory. Your brain is also good for judgment, for impulse control, for executive decisions, and all of this involves a part of the brain briefly mentioned, a part of the brain that is so interesting called the frontal cortex. The frontal cortex is absolutely fascinating, "cortex," the surface of the brain, "frontal cortex," the surface in the front of the brain. The frontal cortex is such an interesting part of the brain. I have spent the last 25 years of my life studying the hippocampus. The hippocampus has been good to me. I love the hippocampus, but I have become badly infatuated with the frontal cortex in recent years because it does such interesting stuff. Yes, learning and memory is cool. The frontal cortex, though, is amazing.

The frontal cortex is arguably the most human part of the brain. Proportionately, we've got more complex frontal cortices than any other species out there. It's the most recently evolved part of the brain. Frontal cortex, a big-time frontal cortex is virtually a primate invention where humans are really running with it. What does the frontal cortex do? It does all sorts of complicated things, regulating executive behaviors and strategizing. On the very simplest level, what does the frontal cortex do? It makes you do the harder thing when it's the right thing to do. It makes you do something that is difficult when that's what you should be doing.

The frontal cortex, you want some terrible utterly inapplicable metaphor, the frontal cortex is the nearest thing we've got to a superego, the nearest thing to a part of the brain saying, "I wouldn't do that if I were you. You are going to regret it." The frontal cortex has this role manifested in all sorts of domains. For example, the frontal cortex makes you, at a party, do the right thing even though it's harder. You have been served the most horrendous meal you can ever imagine, and it's your frontal cortex that kicks in and says, "Whoa, this is delicious. I've got to have the recipe." The frontal cortex is what gets you to compliment somebody's hideous new hairdo. The frontal cortex keeps you from being a serial murderer. It keeps you constrained. It keeps you in line. The frontal cortex is also something that kicks in in a very dramatic way during early development. Most of us, way back when, had to suddenly get a lot of frontal function when we learned to be toilet trained. That is something that soon moved from frontal executive control to implicit pathways. Most of us don't have to think consciously anymore about being toilet trained, but early on, that was one of the big, initial frontal tasks that we had to master.

Frontal cortex has all sorts of fascinating other features of it, and this just became clear. Part of development, child development, is your frontal cortex maturing. You can show the fact that kids don't have a whole lot in the way of a frontal cortex by brain imaging, things of that sort, and you find out something absolutely astonishing. The frontal cortex is the last part of the brain to fully develop. Your frontal cortex is not fully developed until around age 25. That is astonishing. That explains an awful lot of behavior in freshmen dorms. That explains all sorts of things. The frontal cortex takes forever to develop, and thus childhood is filled with a frontal cortex that doesn't work very well yet. You can show this, this wonderful study, this wonderful experimental paradigm, where you take kids, and what you do is you put the child in a room. You put a marshmallow in front of them. "You say, OK, here's the deal. I'm going out of the room. I'm going to come back in a while, and if you want, while I'm out of the room, you can have that marshmallow. On the other hand, if you don't eat it, when I come back, you can have 2 marshmallows." In other words, can you regulate your behavior, regulate this impulsive desire to grab that marshmallow. Kids very early on are awfully, awfully challenged in order to hold on and not grab the marshmallow early on. In fact, there is a literature by now showing, you take, like, 4-year-olds, and the longer they can hold on not taking the marshmallow, the more frontal regulation they have of their behavior, and that is in part predictive of things like SAT scores a decade later in high school. This is the mark of a frontal cortex that is developing in a very impressive manner.

Although, as a parent, what I've discovered is there's a much easier way of measuring the degree of frontal development which is play Hide and Seek with the child. Here's what happens. You're playing Hide and Seek, and the kid is hiding and you count up to 10, and you come into the room, and you say, "Ready or not, here I come. Ooh, where are you?" Suddenly the kid says, "I'm right here under the piano," because they can't stop themselves from saying where they are because they've got no frontal cortex. Or you now switch and now you're the one who hides, and they're over there counting up to 10. They go 1, 2, 3, 4, 5, 6, 7, 8, 9, 10, 11, 12, 13, 14 because they've just learned all these numbers and all these numbers are so exciting, and they can't stop themselves at number 10. This is exactly what a brain without a whole lot of frontal function looks like.

There's another realm in which you can get brains without a whole lot of frontal function, brains that have been damaged. A remarkable finding which is, a substantial percentage of people on death row in this country have a history of major concussive head trauma to the front of the brain. This will come back to haunt us in a few minutes, the implications of that. The other version of a frontal cortex that's not working very well is when you get a wildly violent criminal act by someone who is young enough that their frontal cortex has not developed all that much yet. The possibility of this is what motivated a Supreme Court decision a number of years ago saying that you cannot execute somebody for a crime they did under age 18. The decision explicitly talked about how some parts of the brain were not fully developed at that point, that there was some degree of impairment of frontal regulation of behavior.

As I mentioned, humans have the biggest, most dramatic frontal cortices out there, recently evolved. Other species have frontal cortices too. Rodents have them; primates have them. They don't have a whole lot. Take, for example, monkeys, like baboons, and baboons are schemy, competitive, backstabbing animals, but they're not very strategic about it because at all sorts of critical points, they blow it because they're wildly impulsive animals. For example, baboons can form cooperative coalitions. If 2 males help each other out in a fight, what you wind up seeing is this should be a brilliant strategy because 4 hands are better than 2, or 2 tails are better than one or whatever. A stable cooperative coalition should be unstoppable; but with an astonishing frequency, the fight finally breaks out and the guy spins around and attacks his coalition partner because how could he resist because he's only got like 7 and a half frontal neurons. I remember some years ago sitting at a primatology conference looking at a film about primates that have really good frontal function, apes. Apes like chimps and such, and we were watching a film that was called *Chimpanzee Politics*, looking at chimpanzee political power grabbing strategizing which they're really good at. I was sitting next to another baboonologist, and at some point, we turned to each other after some amazing chess move that one of these chimps had just pulled off. We turned to each other and said, "My God. That's what a baboon would love to be like if had a shred of self-discipline or gratification postponement." They don't because they don't have much in the way of a frontal cortex.

Transition to apes, chimps, for example, and they've got a lot more frontal cortex, a lot better regulation of impulsivity, but they're still not in the range of a human. You can show this with a study that looks something like as follows: Here you have in this hand you've got one M&M, in this hand you have 5 M&Ms. The chimp has a choice as to which hand to reach for. The rule is if it reaches for the one M&M, you quickly pull your hand away, and the chimp gets a reward of 5 M&Ms. If the chimp reaches for the 5 M&Ms,

you quickly pull your hand away, and the chimp gets a reward of one. In other words, if the chimp is disciplined and ignores the 5 M&Ms right there and instead is going for the tougher decision, going for the one M&M, it gets the much bigger reward. Chimps cannot do that. They are ready to reach for the one M&M to do the more disciplined thing. They just can't stop themselves. They reach over for the 5 because the chocolate is right there in their face, and it smells so good. They don't have enough frontal neurons to make them do the right strategic thing, go for the one M&M because you get the bigger reward. Now you make a very important elaboration in the experiment. Now this hand has one little chip of wood, this hand has 5 chips of wood. Reach for the 5 chips, pull the hand away, and the chimp gets one M&M. Reach for the one chip, pull the hand away, and the chimp gets 5 M&Ms. The same sort of deal if you are more disciplined and reach for the one piece of wood, you get a bigger reward. Now chimps can do this before the stimulus because the stimulus is less salient; it's less in their face. "The chocolate, I can't stop myself." Wood chips, the chimp has enough frontal function to go for the single piece of wood, and thus get the bigger reward.

As alluded to in talking about people who have come into the criminal justice system with a history of concussive head trauma in the front, history of frontal damage, there is a whole challenging world out there of what happens when people get frontal damage. In terms of organic impairment, a problem with the brain that the courts generally recognize—there is the gold standard out there—which is when somebody is so organically impaired, so neuropsychiatrically troubled that, as the standard goes, they can't tell the difference between right or wrong. Trivia fans, this is something called a McNaughton rule in criminality, and it often goes with people with severe schizophrenia where they can't tell the difference between right and wrong. Get somebody with frontal damage, and they can tell the difference between right and wrong, they simply can't regulate their behavior. They don't have volitional control. These are often people in fact who can verbalize what the appropriate rules are, can verbalize what the strategy should be, could verbalize saying, "I know, I should reach for the one M&M because I get a bigger reward that way." Then they go for the 5 because they can't control their behavior. This is a huge challenge in the criminal justice system. This is not McNaughton—you can't tell the difference between right and wrong— this is you can tell the difference, but because of an organic impairment, you can't regulate your behavior. In my view, there are way too few states out there that recognize this is as much of an impairment as the right and wrong dichotomy.

We've now got a pretty good sense about how the frontal cortex works, how it evolved, how it develops during growth, during childhood, what happens when it's damaged. What does stress do to frontal functioning? What does stress do to the frontal cortex? What you wind up seeing is ... lots. Once again, the usual suspect, it's mediated by glucocorticoids. Back to our endless theme here, hormones, brain chemical messengers, et cetera. They work by way of binding to their specialized receptor. Thus, glucocorticoids work by way of glucocorticoid receptors. If you look in the brain, there are 2 areas that have glucocorticoid receptors at far higher levels than elsewhere in rodents and nonhuman primates and humans. What are the 2 areas? You guessed it, from the last lecture, the hippocampus; from this lecture, the frontal cortex. These are the 2 hotspots in the brain when there is sufficient amounts of stress and glucocorticoid excess that you're beginning to mess with how the brain works, it's the hippocampus and frontal cortex that go first.

The last lecture, dribbling over into this one, really look in great detail as to what happens in the hippocampus with chronic stress, chronic glucocorticoids. That's that whole picture of atrophy, potential recovery, dead neurons, no more neurogenesis, that kind of thing. What's going on in the frontal cortex with chronic stress and glucocorticoid excess? Far less studied, a very new literature that's just emerging, but what you tend to see is atrophy of neurons in the frontal cortex. Atrophy in terms of processes retracting, same deal as in the hippocampus. The frontal cortex, again the surface of the brain, and it comes with a number of layers, tends to thin out. You've got less complex connectiveness there which thus is not surprising if you're having neurons disconnecting, very similar picture to in the hippocampus. What's an extremely challenging finding at this point is: What happens after the stress is over with? We heard in the hippocampus relevant to Cushing's disease is after you've got the atrophy of the hippocampal neurons, they can regrow, they can reform their connections, and things go back to normal. What's known at this point—very, very recent studies, showing in the frontal cortex—yes, stress glucocorticoids you get atrophy of these neurons. After it's over with, yes, they grow back, but they grow back with different sorts of connections.

What does that mean? Nobody knows at this point. All that's known is lots of stress, lots of glucocorticoids, and the frontal cortex thins out, atrophies, almost certainly isn't working as well. In the aftermath of it, it's going to work differently than it did before without anybody having a good sense yet of what "differently" means. Many lectures, oh so many ago, we were looking at the consequences of sustained stress during child development, everything about growth, prenatal stress, et cetera. Back to that point about the frontal cortex being the last part of the brain to mature, what happens with stress during childhood. What does that do to the frontal cortex? There is such a disturbing, such a depressing literature emerging out there having to do with childhood development of the frontal cortex and socioeconomic status, your degree of poverty, education, the wealth of the neighborhood you live in, that sort of thing, socioeconomic status. A literature has been emerging for some years suggesting by some appallingly young stage, by around kindergarten, there are already differences in socioeconomic status in terms of how well kids have their frontal cortex working, how well they do emotional regulation, gratification, postponement. The first studies are coming out now showing that those correlate with differences in metabolic rates in the frontal cortex. Mind you, the usual caveats, this is a statistical phenomenon. This is on the average what you see. There are huge amounts of variability. Nonetheless, a totally disturbing suggestion that by an extremely young age, your socioeconomic status, the sheer, utter, damn blind luck you've had in terms of which household you got yourself born into, is already having an impact on your developing brain, how readily you control your impulses, how readily you control your behavior. This is a theme that will come back in a whole lecture later on having to do with stress, health, and socioeconomic status.

Lurking in here is a very important subtle point which is, there's huge excitement these days about what genes have to do with behavior, that sort of thing, resequencing the human genome. Keep this in mind, interesting implication, if the frontal cortex is the last part of the brain to fully mature, by definition the frontal cortex is the part of the brain least constrained by genes and most shaped by environment. What we've seen here now are all sorts of circumstances with chronic stress and chronic glucocorticoids where the frontal cortex doesn't work as well. What is it that we've explained here? This oh-too-familiar circumstance where during the period of stress you make some decision that is just asinine which at the time seems utterly brilliant and insightful, and you spend an awful long time afterward dealing with the adverse consequences. You really do need to have a nice functional frontal cortex, and chronic stress doesn't do good things to it.

Stress, Sleep, and Lack of Sleep
Lecture 15

We all know this phenomenon, which is you study something right before you go to sleep, you practice a piece of music, or whatever, and the next morning, it's magically in there to a much greater extent than if you had done that same learning in the morning and tested it toward late afternoon. There's consolidation of memory that goes on in the brain during that time.

Sleep is a weird thing to have happen to your body and your brain. Not only is sleep this weird suspended state, but it's very structured, with many different sleep stages. What is going on in your brain when you are sleeping? It depends on which of the sleep stages you are in. Typically when you are sliding into a good night's sleep, the first thing that kicks in is **slow-wave sleep**, so called because the brain has very slow cycles of activation. Most of your brain has much less activity going on, which allows for restoration of energy in your nervous system. Then comes **rapid eye movement (REM) sleep**, during which some parts of your brain become completely silent while others become more active than usual.

Which areas of the brain become more active than usual during REM sleep? One interesting one is the secondary sensory cortex. When you look at

Sleep is an important factor in combating stress.

© Pixland/Jupiterimages/Thinkstock.

something, the information goes into your primary visual cortex. It gets processed there, you extract some information about what's going on, and then you kick that up to your secondary and tertiary visual cortices, which do all sorts of processing. Something different happens during REM sleep: The primary sensory cortex goes silent, and the secondary and tertiary become extremely active. In other words, those parts of the brain are processing things without any actual visual or auditory information coming in: This is dreaming.

Why is it that we dream anyway? Why is it that we have any of these sleep stages? And most broadly, why do we need to sleep at all? The answer is somewhat obvious in that sleep restores energy, particularly to your brain. The brain constitutes about 3% of your body weight, but it uses 20%–25% of your body's energy, and brain cells (neurons) have virtually no capacity to store energy. So sleep is especially about restoring energy to the brain. It's only in recent years that people have figured out there's an additional function: You consolidate memories during your sleep. As for why we dream, there have been innumerable theories over the years. One of the more convincing explanations is that it's a chance to use circuits in your brain that you may have underused during the day. It's not quite clear exactly why we dream, but what is clear is that sleep in general is good for consolidating memory, and REM sleep appears to be particularly useful. If you disrupt REM sleep, you interfere with cognition: You don't remember things as well, and you generally don't learn things as well.

> **The brain constitutes about 3% of your body weight, but it uses 20%–25% of your body's energy.**

Let's superimpose stress on top of this. Very simply, sleep deprivation is a stressor. If you don't get enough sleep, your levels of glucocorticoids go up. There's a hormone called corticotropin-inhibiting hormone that seems to inhibit activation of glucocorticoids. In other words, it's a hormone that helps the onset of sleep. The very chemical messenger that transitions you into sleep is the same one that decreases glucocorticoid levels. If you don't get enough sleep, your glucocorticoid levels go up, and elevated glucocorticoid levels disrupt sleep. But don't panic—this cycle is not as vicious as it seems. When you are sleep deprived, glucocorticoid levels go up, but not that much. And no matter how high your glucocorticoid levels are, if you're exhausted enough, you're eventually going to sleep. All sorts of other regulatory factors have some input as to how much sleep you get, and they can eventually override the effects of stress. What about the impact of stress on the quality of sleep? Here there is some particularly disturbing news. You can get lots of sleep, but if there's not a predominance of slow-wave sleep, you don't get the energy restoration that you need. ∎

Important Terms

rapid eye movement (REM) sleep: The sleep state during which dreaming occurs. It unexpectedly involves higher levels of activity in some brain regions than during normal waking.

slow-wave sleep: The deepest stage of sleep, in which the most energy restoration occurs. This is the sleep stage most disrupted by stress.

Suggested Reading

Dement, *The Promise of Sleep*.

Sapolsky, *Why Zebras Don't Get Ulcers*, chap. 11.

Questions to Consider

1. Vicious cycle part 1: How do elevated stress hormone levels make it difficult to sleep?

2. Vicious cycle part 2: How does sleep deprivation elevate stress hormone levels?

Stress, Sleep, and Lack of Sleep
Lecture 15—Transcript

All things considered, there is hopefully a lot of useful advice that has been coming out of this course so far, things you might want to do more of in your life, things you might want to do less of. I've even taken some of these points to heart. Never once have I taken a bubble bath just spiked with glucocorticoids. In college I wouldn't go out with my buddies and chug down sort of mixtures of prolactin and glucagon. You know, there's a lot of useful stuff that can come out of paying attention to these things.

However, this is a lecture where I just have to put all sorts of fine print up front. In this lecture, I am an utter hypocrite because what this lecture is about is how you need to get enough sleep. I personally don't get enough sleep. In fact, there's a researcher at my university, a man named William Dement who's like the dean of sleep research. Basically, I live in terror of running into this guy when I'm really looking moth-eaten in the morning, because the whole theme here is you really do need a lot of sleep because it is highly intertwined with how your body deals with stress. This is one of those lectures that I plan to pay no attention to as I'm giving it. Thus, we've got the main theme of this lecture, this is one of those "do as I say, not as I do."

We start off thinking about sleep, and the very first thing to deal with in terms of sleep is it's a totally weird thing to have happen to your body and your brain. There are all sorts of diseases of abnormal amounts of sleep. As we're going to see in a few lectures when you have severe clinical depression, your sleep pattern changes in all sorts of ways. There's this disease, narcolepsy, where you can fall asleep suddenly, no warning, and often in response to emotion arousal. How's this for a weird disease? There's this disease called Ondine's curse, which is due to a certain type of tumor in your brain stem. What you've got there is your brain stem isn't working very well, and what you have is a deep problem now. Apparently, Ondine was some nymph or something that Zeus was hitting on and she was not willing to go along with this. He placed Ondine's curse on her, and what he did was take away her ability to breathe automatically, where she had to breathe consciously.

I'm not quite sure how much the legend got into the physiology of this, but nonetheless, Ondine's curse is when, thanks to this tumor, you cannot breathe involuntarily; you have to think about it. What does this disease kill you from? From lack of sleep because you go to sleep and 30 seconds later you wake up gasping because you need to be awake to remind yourself to breathe now and then, totally creepy stuff.

That doesn't even begin to scratch the surface when you really think about sleep and you twitch, your eyelids do things, you sleepwalk at times, which is totally creepy. You drool, and you get penile and clitoral erections, and that doesn't even deal with species that have very odd things going on with sleep. For example, there are species out there that sleep with one half of their brain at a time. Often what that's about is some species that better be on the lookout for predators 24-7, one-half of your brain sleeps. There are bird species that are able to sleep while they're flying. There are fish that sleep, and the whole notion of fish sleeping is just weird in and of itself. There are even fruit flies that sleep.

Not only is there sleep, this weird suspended state, it's very structured. There are all these different sleep stages, slow-wave sleep, deep rapid eye movement sleep. It's just a very weird thing to have going on in you. Nonetheless, it does. What we have to start off with right off the bat is what's going on in your brain when you are sleeping, and it turns out it's got to do with which of those sleep stages you are in, whether it's your slow-wave sleep, or whether it's this rapid eye movement stuff. Typically when you are sliding into a good night's sleep, the first thing that kicks in is this slow-wave sleep. It's termed that from when they stick electrodes on your head and monitor your electrophysiological activity up there, and this is a pattern where you've got very slow cycles of activation. Not surprisingly when you stick somebody into one of those brain scanners at the same time—which we've already heard about, one of the ones that tells you which part of the brain is metabolically active—what you see is with the onset of slow-wave sleep, everything is less active. Of course, this makes sense because you've slipped into deep sleep. Most of your brain has much less activity going on. That makes perfect sense. We'll see exactly why that makes wonderful sense, given a lot of what sleep is about, restoration of energy in your nervous system. Then along comes REM sleep which is really quite different. REM sleep, and suddenly some parts of your brain become completely silent, and other parts become even more active than usual.

Which parts become completely silent? Most of the areas do, except one particular part of your brain as we'll see as an exception. Which areas become more active than usual? One very interesting one is known as secondary sensory cortex. What's that about? You look at something and the information gets into what's termed your primary visual cortex. It gets processed there, and you extract some information about what's going on, and then you kick that up to your secondary visual cortex and tertiary and it's doing all sorts of processing. Meanwhile, you've got your primary auditory cortex, that sort of thing, so when you're looking at things that are vivid, when you're hearing a lot of sounds, you get activation of those brain areas, primary, secondary, and tertiary cortex. Something different happens during REM sleep which is the primary sensory cortex goes silent, and the secondary and tertiary activate like crazy. In other words, those parts of the brains are processing things as if you were having visual information and auditory information without the primary layers activating, without any actual visual auditory information coming in.

What's this about? This is dreaming. This is dreaming, active processing of sensory information that simply is not there. This is instead of activation of these layers from your eyes, your ears, it's from whatever parts of your brain are running the dreaming process. That's one striking thing. Meanwhile, another area of your brain becomes more active than usual, and this is one we remember from oh-so-many lectures ago, and this is the limbic system. Limbic system, because suddenly you've got all sorts of emotions ripping around your head. There are not a whole lot of us who have dreams about contrapuntal music or calculus. Instead we have dreams that are just frothy with emotional content unless you're the sort of person for whom calculus is frothingly emotional. For the most part, this winds up being a realm of limbic activation, highly emotive content to dreams. Where's the limbic system getting off becoming more active than usual during dream stage? When you think of this, everything in your brain should be going offline, but you've got these secondary and tertiary parts of your sensory system hallucinating away with information that isn't there, dreaming. You've got the limbic system all activated, the emotional content of dreaming.

One additional area, very interestingly, shows not just that pattern of slow-wave sleep becoming less active than usual. This one area just hits the basement, turns off entirely. Which area is that? This is straight out of the previous lecture. What area is this? It's the prefrontal cortex. What does the prefrontal cortex spend a whole lot of time doing? As we heard previously, it makes you do the harder thing when the easier thing is tempting, when the harder thing is the right thing to do. A lot of what your prefrontal cortex does when it's pulling that off is it's inhibiting the limbic system, saying, "Oh, no, no don't actually try to butt heads with that moose because that's a particularly scary one." A lot of what the frontal cortex does is rein in limbic function. Thus, what you suddenly have during REM sleep when you are dreaming, the frontal cortex goes silent. That's why your limbic system runs amuck. That's why in dreams you do all sorts of imprudent things at all sorts of junctures where you don't do the hard or right thing, and instead you do—with greatly interesting consequences—the easier thing. You've got this pattern. Frontal cortex goes down. We've got this odd picture, perfect sense during slow-wave sleep. The brain is using much less energy during dream stage, REM sleep. This very interesting pattern, more of a decrease in energy consumption through most of the brain, but cortical activation processing imaginary sensory information, the limbic system supplying the weirdo emotive content to it, and your frontal cortex going into a deep, deep sleep where it's got nothing to say, nothing to say that's inhibitory in nature to your limbic system. This is a profile in terms of the energetics and what's happening there.

Of course when you begin to think about this, up comes the inevitable question of why is it that we dream anyway? Why is it that we have any of these sleep stages? Most broadly, as the initial question, why do we sleep? Why do we need to sleep at all? The answer is somewhat obvious in that sleep restores energy. What sleep onset is usually about is fatigue, all of that makes perfect sense. You get tired, and thus you go to sleep. You get exhausted by increased activity, and you go to sleep earlier and are in more need of it. It's about restoration of energy. What's become clear is what is particularly focused on with energy restoration is in your brain. That has to do with one of the great factoids—you are not allowed to teach Introductory Neuro anything or other without pulling this one out in terms of impressing everybody with what a tough, impressive organ the brain is compared to those dumb old kidneys or a liver or something—the brain constitutes about 3% of your body weight, and it uses 20, 25% of the energy. The brain is incredibly expensive, and that gives you some insight into why your epididymis, if you happen to have one of those, why it's not the one solving problems for you, why the brain does this fancy stuff. It consumes enormous amounts of energy. You need to replace those enormous amounts. Just to make things even messier, there are all sorts of cells that store a lot of energy, back so many lectures ago, storing energy in your fat cells, your liver, your muscle. It turns out brain cells, neurons, are terrible at storing energy. They have virtually no capacity to do it. You get an energy crisis like a stroke, and your neurons have about 30 seconds worth of energy available to them before they crash. There's another cell type in the brain called glial cells, and they're a bit better at storing energy. But nonetheless, your brain uses a ton of it, doesn't store it very well, so a lot of what sleep is about is restoring energy throughout the body, and especially in your brain. That's one of the things it's useful for, and that's the traditional explanation for what sleep is about.

It's only in recent years that people have figured out there's an additional thing that's really, really interesting, which is you consolidate memories during your sleep. We all know this phenomenon which is you study something right before you go to sleep, you practice a piece of music, or whatever, and the next morning, it's magically in there to a much greater extent than if you had done that same learning in the morning and tested it toward late afternoon. There's consolidation of memory that goes on in the brain during that time. There's at least one hint as to how that might work when you have onset of sleep. What decreases in your bloodstream? Glucocorticoid levels do, and we know, oh-so-well by now that high levels of glucocorticoids can disrupt aspects of cognition. Sleep is the perfect time to get rid of those glucocorticoids and do a whole lot of memory consolidation. What does this look like, this pattern of you learn a bunch of factoids and it's being consolidated during your sleep, those factoids instead of something else.

Some wonderful work by a scientist named Bruce McNaughton has shown that in the brains—in this case, in rats—if you show certain patterns of activation in a rat when it's learning some new task, some maze or whatever, right before it goes to sleep, if you study the brain while the animal is sleeping, it preferentially activates the same pathway. It's running it again and again, getting that information in there. One of the other things you do during sleep is you sleep on it. You do all sorts of things with judgment. Lots of the time, we do indeed sleep on it. We come up with some assessment, some insight, some gut feeling, some intuition. In that regard, you don't make a judgment about whether or not the final digit of some phone number was 6 or 7 kind of thing. You're making judgment about a complex sort of circumstances. That comes into it also.

At some point, we then have to deal with the even bigger, more mysterious issue, which is, why do we dream? If sleep is about energy restoration, what's the deal with dreaming? There have been a gazillion theories over the years. The purpose of dreaming is to work out the troubled, ambivalent aspects of your relationship with your mother, or you dream in order to keep surrealists on the dole and working away there. Then there's that whole world where you have one of those totally bizarre sex dreams with somebody you never even thought about before, and the next day you act all weird about them around the water cooler.

What's in a lot of ways one of the more convincing explanations as to what dreaming is about is it's a chance to use circuits in your brain that you may have underused during the day. This is usually summed up in the notion of a "use it or lose it" kind of model. If you think about it, this is both perfectly reasonable and utterly contradictory with something I talked about earlier. Think about this here. You need to use a circuit that's underutilized. Suppose for example, you are thinking far too infrequently about William Seward, secretary of state in the Lincoln first administration and your brain really needs more of this because you are not utilizing that William Seward neuron. You know from so many lectures ago that's a gross simplification. There is not a William Seward neuron. There is instead a William Seward network, and it's the intersection, the network of secretaries of states and the network of stud muffins from the 19th century, and out pops William Seward's name. You're not thinking about that enough during waking hours, so a notion of what dreams are about is exercising pathways that don't get enough stimulation during the day. Why is that contradictory? Why that's contradictory is due to something we just heard about. The argument from the work of someone like McNaughton is the very pathways, the very patterns you activate during the day as you learn something, those are the patterns you run again and again at night to consolidate some sort of new information. With this argument that what dreaming is about is activating pathways that otherwise atrophy away, the very pathways that are least active during the day are the ones that get activated at night.

It's not quite clear what the resolution to that one is, but nonetheless, what you've got are some very intriguing array of possibilities for what dreaming is about. What is clear, though, is not only insofar as sleep in general is a good point for consolidating memory, REM sleep appears to be a particularly good one. Preferentially disrupt that and you screw up cognition, part of this larger theme of, disrupt sleep as a whole, and you get cognitive problems. You don't remember stuff as well.

You don't learn things as well with one very interesting exception. This was work done by, in fact, an ex–graduate student of mine, Ilana Hairston, and what she did was show that there's one domain in which sleep deprivation improves your memory. It works as follows: It involves something called a reversal task which is a fiendishly challenging thing for your brain. Suppose you learn some process that you need to do if you're a rat, for example, it may not be particularly fancy, which is whenever this little light comes on, you've got to hit this lever. If you do it correctly, you get a food pellet as a reward. You spend all day learning this to the point that every time that light comes on, you are lunging for that lever. You have learned this association. You have learned this task. Now they hit you with a reversal task which is all of a sudden, instead of light comes on hit the lever and you get a food reward, now suddenly without warning the deal is light comes on and it's if you don't hit the lever you get a food reward. You have to completely reverse what it is you've learned. That's a hard thing to do except if you are vastly sleep deprived because it becomes much easier to do a reversal task.

How come? That's because in the first place you didn't learn this association very well. You didn't consolidate this rule that when the light comes on hit the lever, so the next morning you're not sitting there saying, "Light comes on, hit the—remember hit that, OK it's different now, don't hit it. OK this is very" ... because you haven't learned the first thing very effectively at all. You haven't consolidated it, and thus, individuals, animals, humans who are sleep deprived are better at reversal tasks the next day. Nonetheless, this is within a larger framework of sleep is a good thing for memory consolidation. Dreaming has all sorts of advantages there. Yes, you want to get enough sleep, and the right distribution of subtypes of sleep. Again, as a warning, we will get to depression where one of the things that goes dramatically wrong is not only trouble sleeping but sleeping with a very particular pattern and a complete disorganization of the structure of sleep.

With the various pieces now in place, what is sleep about metabolically in your brain? What purpose might sleeping serve? What purpose might dreaming do? What we now need to do is, of course, superimpose stress on top of this. What's going on with sleep deprivation? Very simply, it's a stressor. If you don't get enough sleep your levels of glucocorticoids go up in your bloodstream. In fact, there's a very interesting explanation for this, back to the lecture of the basic organization of endocrine systems, the hypothalamus releases a hormone which stimulates the pituitary to release its hormone, remember luteinizing hormone releasing factor and luteinizing hormone, on it goes. What I failed to mention just as one of those miserable elaborations, some of those brain hormones are releasing hormones. They stimulate the pituitary to release its particular hormone. Some of those brain hormones are inhibitory hormones, ones that decrease pituitary activation.

What everybody discovered early on was a releasing hormone coming from the brain which activates the pituitary to release its hormone. Down at the adrenal, you start secreting glucocorticoids. Just to give you the horrible terminology, CRH, corticotropin-releasing hormone, that's the hypothalamic hormone, the brain hormone, that stimulates glucocorticoid secretion. What has always been lurking in the background is the fact that there's a hormone that does the opposite, corticotropin-inhibiting hormone, and what that seems to do is inhibit activation of glucocorticoids. Nobody has quite isolated what the chemical is, but the best evidence is that it's a chemical that is called delta sleep factor. In other words, it's a hormone that does something else in the brain. It helps onset of sleep. The very chemical messenger that transitions you into sleep effectively is the same one that decreases glucocorticoid levels. Obviously what we deal with is a flipside which is if you don't get enough sleep, your glucocorticoid levels are going to go up. Furthermore, particularly so if you don't get enough REM sleep, your glucocorticoid levels are going to go up. That's a bad thing. That's a bad thing, and deprivation increases the levels of that stuff. You can show that that messes up cognition in a very typical way. For example, get somebody truly sleep deprived, and the next day their cognition isn't very good, and what does that look like in a brain scanner? What you would expect is give somebody some task and the relevant part of their cortex doesn't activate a whole lot, and what you see in fact is the exact opposite. In order to pull off the same degree of competence, you have to activate even more of your cortex than usual. What has messed up that ability to focus in, in your cortical activation? The elevated glucocorticoid levels. That's not good.

Now we have the flip side. We've seen this first piece here which is sleep deprivation increases glucocorticoid levels. Just to complete this loop, elevated glucocorticoid levels disrupt sleep onset, and that takes all sorts of forms. Glucocorticoids when they get in and soak your brain make it harder to transition into slow-wave sleep. Particularly they're doing something to a brain chemical called serotonin. Stay tuned, lots of serotonin news coming down the pike in a few lectures. Serotonin, which has something to do with the onset of slow-wave sleep, and by that point, once you have a lot of glucocorticoids, a lot of stress, and you're getting less sleep, you're not doing as much energy restoration in the brain. It's a total mess here. If you think through it, what we've got here is something very disturbing which is a vicious cycle, a dread vicious cycle going on there of the following sort. Sleep deprivation raises glucocorticoid levels. Elevated glucocorticoid levels disrupt sleep. We have a dread vicious cycle. Before you know it, you stay up late one night to watch some late night TV, and you're sunk because thanks to staying up 15 minutes later than usual and your glucocorticoid levels are higher, and thus the next night you're not going to be able to sleep as well, and it's just terrible, this vicious cycle. Just as one is on the edge of panic there, this vicious cycle is not all that vicious. These 2 loops do not connect all that much.

For one thing, when you are sleep deprived, yes indeed, glucocorticoid levels go up; not that much, though. On the other side of this circle, no matter how high your glucocorticoid levels are, if you're exhausted enough, you're eventually going to sleep. In other words all sorts of the other regulatory factors that have some input as to how much sleep you get, eventually they can override the effects of stress. You break that vicious cycle. Nonetheless, you can have periods of quite dramatic problems with sleep built around periods of stress. As we've seen, a big consequence of that is your brain isn't restoring energy as efficiently as usual. For example, when glucocorticoids get into the brain, they make it harder for the energy restoration to occur. We've got this vicious cycle here which turns out not to be quite as vicious as one might initially panic into, but nonetheless, here's a pattern by which lots of stress will decrease your total amount of sleep. Lots of decreases in sleep elevate glucocorticoid levels, and you've got this pattern here. The net result is the impact of stress on the total amount of sleep you get. We now transition to something much more subtle which is what does stress do not to the quantity of sleep, but to the quality of it. Here you see some particularly disturbing news because the deal is you can get lots of sleep, but if it's not of the right type, a predominance of the slow-wave sleep, you don't get the energy restoration that's the type of sleep that's really important for that going on. Get a lot of glucocorticoids, get a lot of stress going on there, and not only do you tend to decrease the amount of total sleep, you also decrease the percentage of your sleep time devoted to that really helpful slow-wave sleep stuff.

You sleep, and thanks to all sorts of problems, you have elevated glucocorticoid levels while you're sleeping. You take all sorts of troubles to bed there or any sort of plumbing problems there that elevate your glucocorticoid levels. When you are actually sleeping, there's going to be less slow-wave sleep. It's going to be less efficient sleep. It's going to be poorer quality; there's going to be less energy restoration. Another feature that stress can do is wreak havoc with more aspects of sleep, and this is where it tells us something very informative about the relationship between stress and sleep quality. This was some brilliant work done a few years ago by Jan Born at the University of Lübeck, and they did the following. Normally, when you're sleeping, you've got this pattern of glucocorticoid release which we heard about a few lectures ago, which is nice low levels throughout the night's sleep. Somewhere near when you're getting ready to wake up, you begin to have elevated glucocorticoid levels in anticipation of the fact that the most stressful thing every single day in a day without major stressors is that mere process of getting up in the morning and beginning to function. That's what happens when you have free-running sleep. You sleep until you're ready to wake up. Somehow your brain senses that it's getting near the end of your sleep period so send that signal, that CRH, to your pituitary, off you go, and glucocorticoid levels begin to rise.

What if your sleep is disrupted, though? In the first version of the experiment what they told these volunteers—and they got volunteers who slept such that on the average, they woke up around 7 o'clock in the morning—what they told them was, well, you're going to sleep now. We're going to wake you up at 5 o'clock in the morning instead. In other words, we're going to disrupt your sleep at a predictable time in a way that's going to compromise the quality of your sleep. What happens now? Around 4 o'clock in the morning glucocorticoid levels begin to go up.

There is anticipation of the fact that there is going to be disruption of sleep, and the quality of sleep goes down the tubes then. I experienced this myself some years ago where I was doing these nutty, impossible experiments where I had to take blood from some subjects every 3 hours or so around the clock for days, and days, and days. In other words, you get the blood sample, you process it for 16 1/2 minutes, and then you go and crash until 30 seconds before the next one. Overall I was getting collectively about 11 hours of sleep each day because I was spending most of the in-between time just sleeping, and I felt lousy. I felt totally exhausted despite having more sleep because the quality of it was disrupted, because my glucocorticoid levels were cycling up every 2 1/2 hours or so.

What we see here is it's not only the amount of sleep you get, but how continuous it is, how many pieces it's broken into. One additional detail they did in this study, which really shows the vulnerability of sleep distress, now what they did was they told these people, OK you're getting your good night's sleep, and sometime during the night we are going to wake you up. Transition from fragmented sleep to unpredictably fragmented sleep. Now what you essentially got were elevated glucocorticoid levels all night long.

What's this about? This is the world of medical residents who deal with some crisis at 2 in the morning and finally crash to sleep, and it's not clear to them if they're now going to get to sleep 5 hours or 5 minutes. What's this hierarchy? Total amount of sleep, the extent to which it is continuous as opposed to fragmented, and if there's fragmentation, it's at least at predictable times.

What we've hopefully gotten here is a distressing amount of information convincing us that sleep really is quite an important thing. With all that distress in hand now, I personally feel like running off to the refrigerator and getting something filled with carbohydrates. Perhaps you want to do the same. Again, punch line here, this is something you want to get enough of, and on the average, we get way too little.

Stress and Aging
Lecture 16

The picture of aging, it's wonderful. When it works right, you become wise, you become peaceful, you become self-actualized, you wind up looking like Jessica Tandy or someone, and it's all great. As far as I can tell, I am not hurdling in that direction at all. I do not anticipate being wiser, calmer, any of that. Instead, I suspect I'm going to be paying the price of way too much agitated stress throughout the years. What this lecture is about is trying to look at the actual science underlying that distressing outcome.

What is aging about? Your body begins to fall apart after a certain time of life; you become increasingly fragile. You have all sorts of advantages earlier in life that increase evolutionary success, that is, increase the number of copies of genes you pass on. There's no free lunch; eventually the bill comes. There's even a technical term for this—negative pleiotropy, the notion of some genetic trait that gives you advantages earlier in life at the cost of disadvantages later on.

Where does stress intersect with aging? From virtually the day the concept of stress was identified in the 1930s, people have theorized that stress and aging must be intertwined in some basic way. This theorizing took 2 forms. The first one is that aging is a time of life when organisms don't deal with stress very well. The second is that lots of stress throughout the lifetime will accelerate the aging process. It seems we've got another vicious cycle on our hands: Lots of stress makes you get older faster, and being older and more fragile can make you less able to deal with stress.

What's the evidence for these 2 ideas? There is endless evidence for the first one at all different levels of body functioning: Aging is a time of life when you don't deal very well with stress. Naturally what we want to do is translate this into one of our greatest markers of stress: What happens to glucocorticoid levels as we get older? They stay reasonably flat until extreme old age, and then they take off. The stress-response, the amount of glucocorticoids you could pump out in response to a stressor, doesn't change a whole lot during aging. What does change is the recovery time, how long it takes to get back to baseline. These elevated glucocorticoid levels in old age decrease the rate of neurogenesis in the hippocampus. So aging is a time of life where you don't deal very well with stress, and you pay a price: decreased DNA repair, decreased ability to regulate temperature, and decreased cognitive ability.

Not only is aging a time of life when you don't deal very well with stress, but lots of stress over the lifetime can also accelerate the aging process.

It turns out there's plenty of support for the second of these twin theories as well: Not only is aging a time of life when you don't deal very well with stress, but lots of stress over the lifetime can also accelerate the aging process. There is substantial literature supporting the notion that a history of lots of stressors accelerates the cognitive decline of aging. Some examples of this can be found in topics covered earlier in this course. In the research in which experimenters picked up baby rats and neonatally handled them, it was seen that as long as the handling was for a very short period, after the baby was returned, the mother was more attentive. It was also found that these rats have a much more successful old age, that in their old age, they haven't lost as many hippocampal neurons. Their cognition is better, and their overall health is better. The Dutch Hunger Winter fetuses are another example. Their prenatal starvation led to a thrifty metabolism, which hurdled them at a significantly higher rate toward diseases that are more common with aging: metabolic syndrome, obesity, hypertension, and diabetes. This does not only apply to prenatal stress: Stress throughout the lifetime increases the likelihood of and accelerates the progress of metabolic diseases of aging. ■

Suggested Reading

Kirkwood, "Healthy Old Age."

Sapolsky, *Why Zebras Don't Get Ulcers*, chap. 12.

1. What is the evidence that aging is a time of life when organisms are less capable of dealing with stress?

2. What is the evidence that stress can accelerate aspects of aging?

Stress and Aging
Lecture 16—Transcript

As you will hopefully recall, the last lecture was about sleep and stress. I began it confessionally saying it's my least favorite topic in the whole field of stress because I can't talk about it and think about it without getting all agitated, because I'm lousy at getting enough sleep. However, truth be told, *this* is my least favorite lecture because I appear to also be lousy at getting older.

What's the picture of aging? The picture of aging, it's wonderful. When it works right, you become wise, you become peaceful, you become self-actualized, you wind up looking like Jessica Tandy or someone, and it's all great. As far as I can tell, I am not hurdling in that direction at all. I do not anticipate being wiser, calmer, any of that. Instead, I suspect I'm going to be paying the price of way too much agitated stress throughout the years. What this lecture is about is trying to look at the actual science underlying that distressing outcome. What does stress have to do with aging? Lots, and to begin to appreciate that, where we have to start off with is what's aging about? What is the biological process? How could you define aging?

We all know how to define aging in a very technical sort of way. Aging is the time of life where your body goes to hell on you. We could probably define that a little bit more precisely. Aging is the time of life where you become more fragile. Aging is the time of life where if you take a 20-year-old and an 80-year-old, and they both slip on the ice, the 80-year-old is more likely to get the broken pelvis. Aging is the time of life where, as just described, you become more fragile. For the same insult, you are more likely to get injury; for the same degree of challenge, you are more likely to get injured—fragility, lack of resiliency.

Given that, and that's a pretty good technical definition of what aging is about, increased fragility over time, I've got to give you at first absolutely stunning fact about this whole field which is, by that definition, an awful lot of species on this planet don't age. Absolutely remarkable, they don't age; they don't show this property of becoming more fragile over time. That's amazing. Mind you, these are not some of the most exciting species on Earth.

These are amoeba, fungi, liver warts, who knows what. This is not to say that they live forever. If you get hit by a meteor, and you're an amoeba, it doesn't matter really what age you are because it's going to do you in, nonetheless, you don't see that pattern of increased fragility during time. A 500-year-old redwood tree is just as likely or just as unlikely to be done in by some beetle infestation as a 50-year-old redwood. A large percentage of the species on this planet do not age by this rule of increased fragility over time.

The second amazing feature of this field, when you think about that as the definition of aging, the species that do age are some of the most recently evolved ones. They're some of the fanciest ones out there. They're vertebrates; they're mammals; they're primates. And you have this boggling realization: Aging is a recent invention. Aging is in the evolutionary avant-garde. The genes that are central to this process of becoming more fragile over time, by the standpoint of the glacial pace of evolution, evolved relatively recently in some of the most complex species on this planet. What is this about? This is totally bizarre. What you begin to see, though, is a hint about what aging, what this increased fragility might be good for. You look at a pattern of what aging is like, what population dynamics are like in those species that, in fact, don't age. You can chart this in a way where you start off with obviously 100% of the population, and somewhere out the other end, you're going to have 0% of the population still alive, but the rate at which they disappear is an absolute straight line. For those of you who care about such mathematical minutia, it's on a logarithmic scale.

Nonetheless, over the course of time the number of individuals in that population declines at the same exact rate. There's no aging. No matter how long an organism has been around, it does not become intrinsically more fragile. When you look at those recently evolved species that show aging, that show this property of increased fragility, you can see that in a way that is, in fact, definitional as you start with 100% of the population, and as time goes by, at some point, it stops being a straight line. At some point the population declines faster than that straight line would predict. What's that? That's the aging process. That's beginning to fall apart after a certain time of life. That's beginning to be more fragile.

Again, this notion, this stuff might have evolved relatively recently. Evolution does not bring about the sort of processes that make you fall apart as you get older. There's got to be something adaptive about it. You look at those population dynamics, and then you see something interesting because the species that show aging—in other words, at some point, instead of population number declining in a smooth line, it suddenly crashes a lot faster—you notice something else, which is earlier in life, the survival rate is better than that straight line would have predicted.

This is really interesting, and what this is is, now, if you want to term it, this is the "there's no free lunch" hypothesis about aging, which is as follows. What aging is about is not the genetics, the evolutionary adaptiveness of falling apart as you get older, it's about all sorts of advantages earlier in life that increase evolutionary success, increase the number of copies of genes you pass on. There's no free lunch, eventually the bill comes which is now falling apart faster than anticipated. When framed this way, this is great. When framed this way, this is not the evolution of falling apart; this is the evolution of all sorts of genetic advantages earlier in life, and eventually you pay the bill. There's even a fancy technical term for this—and do not even dream of memorizing this—this is called negative pleiotropy, the notion of some genetic trait that gives you advantages earlier in life at the cost of disadvantages later on. That's what aging really is.

This is very abstract. Let me give you one example. In primates, you see this pattern, in male primates, in fact, which is you've got prostate glands, and prostate glands do something or other to your sperm, and I don't know what they do. I once knew it for a final exam for about 3 hours, but your prostate makes your sperm happier and faster and jump higher. Primates tend to have prostate glands with very high metabolic rates. In other words, they're really good at making your sperm all perky. That's the early stage in the curve. That's where the fertility rate, that's where the passing on number of copies of your genes is doing better than expected. What's the bill that eventually comes? You can't spend your whole life with your prostate having this blasting high metabolic rate without the danger being that metabolism will spiral out of control into uncontrolled growth, into cancer. Thus, we have an explanation for why male primates, in particular human ones, are so vulnerable toward prostatic cancer as they get older.

There's no free lunch theme. Most organisms do not show this classic pattern of aging. Those that do, they're more in the evolutionary avant-garde, and those that do, it's not really selection for falling apart, it's selection for a trait that's advantageous earlier in life and along comes the bill. We now have some sense of what the aging process is about. Where does stress intersect with it? From virtually day 1 in the 1930s with Selye popularizing the term, with the whole field taking off as a subfield of medicine, from day 1 people were already thinking, OK, stress and aging, stress and aging, they've got to be intertwined in some sort of very basic way. This theorizing took 2 forms, and we're going to spend this talk exploring these two. The first one, aging is a time of life when organisms don't deal with stress very well.

Second notion, lots of stress throughout the lifetime will accelerate the aging process. As you can immediately see, we've got yet another vicious cycle on our hands, stress, lots of stress, makes you get older faster. Older, more fragile, can be translated in our language into less of an ability to deal with stress.

What's the evidence for these 2 ideas? Focusing on the first one, the notion of aging being a time of life where you don't deal very well with stress. There is endless evidence for this at all sorts of different levels of body functioning. At the cellular level we know a little bit about DNA from the earlier lectures, and DNA, in fact, every time cells divide you make a copy of the DNA. That's great, and with a shockingly high rate, there are mistakes. There are little hiccups of mistakes in copying your DNA into the new cell, little mutations that slip in not infrequently, lots of the time, and fortunately, we come with some spanking efficient overactive, ADD-ish sort of enzymes in there that repair your DNA. Typically they keep up just fine, lots of little random mistakes in your DNA which quickly get fixed up. Of course, we've got here a grim finding, and one that fits in with this picture of aging being a time of life where you don't deal with stress very well, in this case, the stress of having DNA damage, your capacity of doing DNA repair goes down as you get older.

Another example, now rather than at the cellular level, at the level of sort of organ, whole organism physiology, take someone and experimentally drop their core body temperature a couple of degrees, and then see how long does it take the body to get it together and overcome this hypothermic stressor. How long does it take for core body temperature to get back to where it was? What you see is the older the individual, the longer it takes. Resting body temperature does not change with age. For the most part, the basal, the baseline function does not change. What changes is the capacity to recover from a temperature stressor. Aging is a time of life where you don't deal with stress very well. Final example, very much on the whole-organism level, what happens to IQ with aging? Notice, I am not saying, what happens to intelligence with aging to the extent to which IQ tests test intelligence, I'm not going within a mile of that one; but in the much more narrow sense, what does the aging process do to IQ performance?

The answer is, it depends. It depends on all sorts of factors, including how much time pressure there is to the test. You give somebody some cognitive sort of test, an IQ test perhaps or other versions thereof of cognitive function, and what you see is the less time pressure there is, the longer somebody can spend on it, the less of an age-related decline there is in performance, often no decline whatsoever. Now throw in a stressor, not the stressor of DNA mistakes or the stressor of hypothermia, now throw in the stressor of time pressure, less and less time to carry out this task. The more time pressure there is, the more there's an age-related decline in performance.

What we see here is lots of evidence, cellular level, organ level, whole-organism level for this notion that aging is a time of life where you don't deal with stress very well anymore. Naturally what we want to do is translate this into one of our greatest markers of stress: What happens to glucocorticoid levels as we get older? What happens to patterns of activation of the sympathetic nervous system? The general pattern that you see in a bunch of species, lots of rodents for example, is as you get older, your resting basal levels of glucocorticoids begin to climb. In other words, as you get older, in the absence of stress, your body is acting as if there's a mild stressor. What about humans? The picture is a little bit more complicated in that you look in an older literature, and you look at what happens to resting glucocorticoid levels as you become geriatric, and the answer that was in the literature was there's no change. Levels stay just fine, and you look at those older studies, and you find something that I thought was kind of humorous way back when—when I was a grad student, and horrifying now—which is back in the old days, they would do studies where geriatric populations were defined as say age 50 or higher. My God, what things were like back when. Now when you have studies and gerontological ones, aging is thought to really count as blasting along, extreme aging, age 80 or so.

When you look at that literature, glucocorticoid levels stay reasonably flat until extreme old age, and then they take off. They tend to rise. Similar pattern as well with the sympathetic nervous system; you've got one marker of your body not dealing very well with stress and old age, elevated basal levels of glucocorticoids. A second problem comes in. This is one that is screamingly familiar by now conceptually from some of these earlier lectures, which is the stress-response, the amount of glucocorticoids you could pump out in response to a stressor, that doesn't change a whole lot during aging. What does change, and this will make perfect sense, is the recovery time, how long it takes to get back to baseline. The sort of changes you see during aging in this whole stress hormone world, predominantly the glucocorticoid one, is a tendency, a very delayed tendency in humans, toward resting levels of glucocorticoids rising, and a longer recovery time after a stressor is over with. We know by now all the bad things that happen.

What's the price of these elevated glucocorticoid levels that you see in old age? There's no problem, no challenge here in coming up with all sorts of versions of it. One very striking one, extremely interesting one, was work done some years ago by Heather Cameron at the National Institutes of Health. Looking at that revolution we heard about earlier on, that business that, no, it's not the case that the adult brain doesn't make any more neurons, there is adult neurogenesis, in the hippocampus as we've heard. Maybe it's essential for certain types of learning, and what Heather Cameron has observed is the rate of neurogenesis in the hippocampus goes down during aging. In a very clever, insightful study what she did was, well, we've got these aged rats with their elevated glucocorticoid levels. What if we turned their glucocorticoid levels into the sort you would see in young rats. Do that, and the rate of neurogenesis pops up again, what's happening is those elevated glucocorticoid levels with age are one of the factors inhibiting senescent neurogenesis, and that's pretty interesting.

We've seen now the first half of this sort of story that has been set up, the notion that aging is a time of life where you don't deal very well with stress, cellular evidence, organ evidence, organismal, endocrine evidence. What the glucocorticoid profile looks like, and what we've seen is, you pay a price, less DNA repair, less ability to regulate temperature, less cognitive ability that's rapidly available to you, and all the prices that are paid by having an excess of glucocorticoids. Now let's switch to the second half of these twin theories, the notion that not only is aging a time of life where you don't deal very well with stress, but lots of stress over the lifetime can accelerate the aging process. It turns out there's plenty of support for this idea as well.

Let's start off with an extremely dramatic version of it, which is mostly just flashy but ultimately quite informative. Any of us who endlessly watch all those National Geographic specials, there are all these realms of animals doing amazing, phenomenal, heroic tasks. This is the world of male penguins standing on top of the egg all winter long while mom is out shopping. This is the world of desiccated camels going weeks and months without water, all of which fall under this sort of umbrella of, wow, animals do some amazing things. Out in that world of heroic National Geographic–worthy animal exploits, one of the most amazing ones is salmon. Salmon when they come back to spawn and that whole world of swimming upstream and leaping over dams and all of that is extremely impressive.

Here's another thing that is extremely interesting about salmon, which is they go and spawn, they get back to where they were born, the pond, whatever, they get back there, they spawn, they lay their eggs, and a week or 2 later, all the salmon are dead. What is that about? This is termed a programmed die-off, the process of spawning, mating, sets this rapidly emerging clock into action which kills you a couple of weeks later. What is this about? It turns out there might be some evolutionary logic to this. There are all sorts of theories. For example, there's the notion that after dying, the purpose of this is, the salmon's body disintegrates and leaves all sorts of great nutrients from the body on the floor of the water there and the new guppies and new puppies and whatever you call baby salmon, they now have stuff to feed on.

This is a model that reminds me actually of a talk I once heard by a very accomplished neuroscientist who was giving a talk to a bunch of young scientists and telling them not about the technicalities of the science, but instead telling them about how you do a career in science. It was that sort of advice. At one point, one of these starting-off-in-the-field, young scientists said to the guy, "Well, what could somebody in a senior position like you do in order to help out this younger generation?" His answer was, die. "Die and get out of the way." One of the leading theories as to what this programmed die-off is about is salmon get out of the way for the next generation, and in fact their body parts feed the next generation, and all sorts of evolutionary theories.

You now ask, why does this programmed die-off occur not at the level of evolutionary explanations, but instead at the nuts and bolts level of what's going on in the body. What is it that happens right after salmon spawn that send them hurdling into this inevitable programmed death soon afterward? A number of decades ago, people got the answer to it, and this is so interesting and instantly makes a lot of sense, glucocorticoids. The second those salmon spawn, they've got an explosion of glucocorticoid secretion like nothing you see elsewhere in the animal kingdom, and it just goes blasting through the roof, and you'd better bet at this point you can make a long list of what goes wrong in these guys. They get immunosuppressed, they have hypertension, they get parasites, they get ulcers, they probably get depressed, and get cognitively impaired and all that sort of stuff. It is driven by this burst of glucocorticoid secretion in the aftermath of spawning. How do you know?

Now you do a really striking study. You take these salmon and right after they've spawned, you go in there and you adrenalectomize them. You take out their adrenal glands; you take out the source of their glucocorticoids, and instead of dying 2 weeks later, they live another year. Here we have this programmed process of accelerated aging. What's weirdest of all is it's not just salmon who have evolved to this. There are all these Australian marsupial mice where after they give birth, they're all dead 2 weeks later.

Then there are some sort of eels that migrate back to the Sargasso Sea, and I actually haven't a clue where the Sargasso Sea is and why eels do this, but they've got the same deal as well which is programmed death. Remarkably, it's the same mechanism again. It's this burst of glucocorticoids right after that period which gets you old really fast. What we see is here, at least 3 times evolutionarily, in totally different branches of the animal world, eels, and fish, and marsupial mice, if for whatever strange evolutionary reason there is that you want to get old really fast, the way to do it is with lots and lots of glucocorticoids, really a remarkable finding. Despite that being remarkable and all the insight and fascination of this, we're not salmon. Most of us are not Sargassoian eels or marsupial mice, and our process of aging is nothing dramatic like that.

What's it doing in terms of response to stress? What is seen by now is a very substantial literature supporting that notion. Naturally, back when, it started off not as data, not as actual findings, but instead lots of theorizing. Selye was the very first to start this with all sorts of wear and tear models which made perfect sense, lots of stress, and that will accelerate the aging process. That was wonderful and heartwarming, wear and tear as the core of aging. The trouble, of course, was nobody knew biologically what wearing and tearing is about. These were very undefined terms. In the aftermath, some other scientists put a lot more structure to these notions of wear and tear, the notion of using up certain amounts of adaptive energy, resiliency, and this was only slightly less than mythology and folktale in terms of being able to translate it into actual science. But very soon you've just got all sorts of versions of the faster you are exposed to all sorts of stressors, the more severely so, the faster you are going to get the little bits of cardiovascular problems, metabolic problems, all the stuff we know oh-so-well by now, lots of theoretical reasons why that should be the case.

What's the actual evidence for the notion that lots of stress will accelerate the aging process? By now, there are tremendous amounts of evidence. Some of it we heard about earlier, the work of Sonia Lupien, again, at the University of Montreal, that business about looking at these populations of aged humans where she's able to do the gold standard of these sorts of studies, a longitudinal prospective study. It's the same folks that she studies year after year, and what she sees is a history of lots of stressors and the cognitive decline of aging is accelerated. That's not good.

Another version of this, a closely intertwined one, and another scientist that we've discussed earlier, Michael Meaney of McGill University, you'll recall that he did that research where you pick up the baby rats and you neonatally handle them and you put them back with mom, and mom is more attentive as long as it's a very short period. What he discovered was that these animals have a much more successful old age, that what you see is get the right amount of neonatal stimulation, and in their old age, they won't have lost as many hippocampal neurons. Their cognition is better, their health is better, and all sorts of things work better. What's the mechanism for this? This was actually some work I did in collaboration with Meaney. What is one of the most interesting consequences of that neonatal handling, mentioned earlier on? As an adult you've got lower basal glucocorticoid levels. What you see is over the course of a lifetime, lower those levels, lower the cumulative exposure to glucocorticoids, and you get older slower. Another version of support for this notion, stress can accelerate the aging process.

Here's more evidence. We've seen that stress can increase the likelihood of metabolic wear and tear. We've already heard this one, a very specialized type of stress. Remember back earlier, those Dutch Hunger Winter fetuses, this was stress very early in life, prenatal starvation, and what that set these individuals up for is a body which, thanks to its changed, thrifty metabolism, hurdles you at a highly significantly highcr rate toward some of the diseases that are more common with aging.

As we saw, metabolic syndrome, obesity, hypertension, diabetes, yet another realm, and what experiments have shown since then, it's not just the prenatal stress. Stress throughout the lifetime and you're accelerating, you're increasing the likelihood of these metabolic diseases of aging, and that makes perfect sense. Deprivation at any point in life, and you're going to set yourself up with all sorts of stressors, the increased appetite afterward. We heard that before, the role of glucocorticoids in the recovery phase of appetite, and what that's going to do is give you a bigger girth. Make you more of an apple, the abdominal fat, and this will make you more likely to get those metabolic diseases of aging.

Final example, and this is a study that has gotten an enormous amount of attention in the years, the recent years since it came out, and this was work done by Elissa Epel at UCSF. This was the same scientist who did some of the work referred to earlier about stress profiles and people who have lots of abdominal fat. This was an area of research she moved into subsequently, and this is one that has just taken the field by storm. You've got your DNA, and long stretches of DNA form chromosomes. It turns out they're fragile in all sorts of ways, and one of the ways they are is this is like a long string of genetic information. It's like a shoelace. It's wrapped around all sorts of stuff. It has this potential problem of fraying at the ends, and this is always the metaphor everybody uses so I'm obliged as well. What you thus have to have at the ends of your chromosomes are the same things you get on your shoelaces, those little plastic, layered wrappy things which stabilize the end of your shoelace DNA, keep them from fraying.

It turns out that these exist, and these are called telomeres. Telomere is the stabilizing end of DNA, and in fact, the discovery of them resulted in the 2009 Nobel Prize in Physiology [or] Medicine, incredibly interesting stuff. Telomeres, this is not a part of DNA that codes for a gene. This is just a little plastic wrapping at the end of the long shoelace of DNA. What you see is, over the course of time, the telomere shortens. It gets a little bit more frayed. It shortens, and when it eventually gets to the point where it's short enough, frayed enough, that there's no longer really a functional telomere there anymore, the DNA gets all ratty and ragged, and all of that and the cell has hurdled into some degree of genetic senescence.

This is a version of DNA damage, and as we already heard about, there are DNA repair enzymes. There is a specialized one in this case which fixes telomeres as they're getting shorter, an enzyme outrageously called telomerase. What telomerase does is, as the telomeres get shorter, they build them back up again. That's great. What Epel did was show that sustained stress disrupts the activity of those telomeres and thus the telomerase, that enzyme that fixes them, isn't working as well, the telomeres get shorter faster.

What was the most remarkable thing about this finding? It was something that broke one of the standard patterns of laboratory science, which is, you first study something in rats, then non-human primates, and eventually see does it work in humans. Her very first subjects were humans, healthy young women who were the mothers of children with chronic diseases of some sort where they were the primary caregiver, enormously stressful, and what you see was accelerated molecular aging of the DNA.

What we've seen here is plenty of evidence for the 2 halves of the story, aging is a time of life when you don't deal with stress very well, lots of stress, accelerating the aging process, and the dread possibility of a vicious cycle. This is awful news, awful news, stay tuned. It's not all awful news.

Understanding Psychological Stress
Lecture 17

You get a baboon who has just had a scare, a lion has almost gotten him, and what does he do afterward? He runs over and grooms somebody. You get the entire troop where something scary has happened, some lion has leapt out and everybody just barely made it into the trees, and when the lion is gone, everybody comes down and sits and grooms for the next half hour. It is very socially calming.

What is it that determines how stressful psychological stressors will be? There are some very powerful psychological factors that modulate the stress-response. The first one is whether you have an outlet. In work pioneered by Jay Weiss, then at Rockefeller University, he would take a rat and shock it every now and then. With enough of these, the rat would develop an ulcer. Then he took a second rat. Every time the first rat got a shock, so did the second, with the same intensity, duration, everything, except one critical difference: Every time that second rat got a shock, it could go over to a bar of wood and gnaw on it with its teeth. That second rat would not get an ulcer. It had an outlet for the frustration caused by the stressor. It soon emerged that all sorts of outlets worked for rats under those conditions: going into a running wheel and running off the stressor, overeating—all of these would wind up protecting from a stress-related disease.

What about in humans? Are stressors capable of being modulated by outlets? We have hobbies; we work off tension in the gym; we scream in the stairwell after that stressful meeting. Why should physical outlets reduce the stress-response after a stressor? For a number of reasons. First, they release muscle tension, especially if it is a psychosocial stressor. Next, they distract you; that's what some of the most basic human hobbies are about. They can also work because they can remind you of what's really important in life. For example, at the end of your long day of traffic, striving, ambition, and shallow wishing, you can come home and have the outlet of playing with your children.

Lecture 17: Understanding Psychological Stress

248

There's one type of outlet that pops up frequently and is really distressing. If the first rat is allowed, after getting its shocks, to run over to the other side of the cage and bite a second rat, guess what happens? The rat doing the biting does not get an ulcer; it is carrying out displacement aggression onto an innocent bystander, and disturbingly, this works very well. This is why during periods of economic duress, rates of family violence go up. Displacing aggression onto an innocent bystander is one of the most common and efficacious things that social organisms do to feel less stressed.

Studies on rats have shown that having an outlet is a great mitagator of stress.

But there is a more positive factor that affects stress outcomes. Take that first rat, but now after the shocks, let it run over to the other side of the cage where there's a rat that it knows and likes. They groom each other, and the first rat doesn't get ulcers. This is social support. If the second rat is a complete stranger, the logical thing to do is displace aggression on it. But if it's a rat the first one knows, it grooms it, which is protective and is stress reduction.

What does this look like in humans? This is the whole world of social affiliation. It's also pertinent in all sorts of very acute circumstances. Take somebody going through a short medical procedure that's kind of stressful. Have somebody there who they know and like to hold their hand, and their stress-response is decreased. Social support is a highly protective factor.

The next factor is predictability. If the rat sees a little warning light 10 seconds before each shock, it doesn't get an ulcer. Predictive information is enormously powerful. If you know when something bad is coming, how bad it is going to be, and how long it is going to last, you can plan coping strategies. This is the principle behind one of the most central questions any of us might ever ask, which is, how much time do I have left? ■

Sapolsky, *Why Zebras Don't Get Ulcers*, chap. 13.

Questions to Consider

1. What sort of findings made stress a subject of interest to psychologists as well as to physiologists?

2. What are 2 key psychological modifiers of the stress-response?

Understanding Psychological Stress
Lecture 17—Transcript

If you ever spend a lot of time hanging out with physiologists, and I'm not necessarily recommending this, but you'll notice something, which is physiologists love toilet bowls. They're wild about toilet bowls; they dream of them. They spend their childhood taking apart toilet bowls. When they sleepwalk, they wind up there. They paint toilet bowls. Toilet bowls teach you everything you need to know about the body as far as physiologists are concerned.

Here's what happens in a toilet bowl when you take the lid off and you've got your microscope going there. You flush the toilet, and you've got a problem. You have a problem, which is a depletion of water. Your toilet bowl is dehydrated and needs to fill up with water. Fortunately, you have a source of water which is a source of water spraying the water out thing. You've got the pipe there which goes and secretes water, as we introduce a term here that will come back to seem quite relevant. You've got the first step there in a toilet bowl doing its thing. It secretes something that is necessary which is water. Water is pouring out, and eventually, the water level begins to rise, and there's something in the toilet that senses what the level is of water in the system. The flotation device there, which begins to go up as it heads up there.

The next thing you have as a critical feature is a set point in the system which is an optimal level of water, a notion as to how high water levels should go before you turn off the source of the water, before you turn off the secretion of the water. The final thing you have is a mechanism that turns the information about water height, that sensor, the floating thingy, and what that is able to do is transduce the "we've gotten up to the set point level" into a signal to stop the source of water. What we have here is what toilet-oriented engineers might call a negative feedback system, where you send a signal out, and you have to have a set point. When you reach that set point, that turns off the secretion of that.

There are all sorts of physiological systems that work that way. Your brain decides how much growth hormone you want to have in the bloodstream, one of those hormones, whatever. It goes and secretes it by way of this whole axis we've heard about. What it needs to do then is measure how much of the stuff there is in the circulation. It needs a floatation device. What that is is parts of the brain that are sensitive to levels of that particular hormone.

There's got to be a set point, some rules somewhere in the part of the brain that initiated the secretion of growth hormone, and there's got to be a way of transducing the sensor signal into shutting off the secretion. There has got to be projections, cables coming out of the part of the brain that's measuring the hormone, heading down onto their negative feedback regulation. There are all sorts of fancy versions of it. You can have your set point change. That happens during the ovulatory cycle for example, the optimal level of estrogen is very different on day 0 versus day 14. You can have feedback systems that are responsive not just to the level of some hormone, but to the ratio of 2 hormones. Basically though, it's great. What it is is taking engineering principles and sticking it into physiology showing that these systems make sense, showing that these physiological systems are tightly regulated.

Selye loved this subject, and this actually makes a great deal of sense. You're Selye, starting the field in the 1930s, and as we talked about many lectures back when he first proposed this stress concept whether you're injured, starving, too hot, too cold, you turn on a very similar stress-response. People, physiologists, thought he was out of his mind in the early years, and because of that principle we talked about earlier when you have a specific problem in your body, you come up with a specific solution. Here's this nonspecific stress-response thing. Everybody thought Selye was a crackpot. What they mostly thought was he was a type of crackpot who was not systematizing in his physiology, who was not organized, who was not hard-nosed, who was not following all sorts of rules about how physiological systems work. Not surprisingly, Selye had all this engineering/bioengineering envy. He wished that he could have the credibility in stress physiologically of things being as clever and clear-cut as those negative feedback loops and the things that would make engineers happy.

Fortunately, in the years subsequent to Selye and stress first bursting on the scene, fortunately what began to emerge was lots of evidence suggesting that is just how the stress system worked. This was enormously exciting to Selye and his disciples because this system was making sense. It was a regulated system. For example, you take an individual, and experimentally, you infuse them with a drug that drops blood pressure a tiny bit. What you could then see is increased secretion of a hormone that counters this by increasing blood pressure. Now instead of dropping blood pressure one smidgen and seeing one smidgen of this hormone coming out, you drop it 2 smidgens, and 2 smidgens of the hormone come out, and 3 and 4, and 3 and 4. It was logical. There was this tight regulation, the amount of stressful challenge to the system in a very tightly predictable, organized, regulatory way predicted the magnitude of the stress-response. This worked in all sorts of realms. You would stimulate say one pain receptor by pressing here and the stress-response of heart rate increasing would be one smidgen, one smidgen, now you stimulate 2 pain receptors, and it goes up a little more.

Suddenly it was just like the greatest dream come true for the stress physiologists, they had to talk to mathematicians. They had to talk to statisticians. The field was becoming really hard-nosed, and this was wonderful, and Selye, this was just a golden age for stress physiologically. Then, something happened that ruined all the fun. This came in the 1950s. You would do an experiment that in the stress-regulatory bioengineering world, you knew exactly what was going to happen. For example, you have a test organism, and you do something like what was just described, you have this much pressure placed on a pressure pain receptor, and glucocorticoid levels going up this much and the next individual, you press this much and it goes this much, the usual, the usual tight mathematical relationship.

Now you do something a little different. What you show is you have your test organism and you put in a certain stimulus of a certain intensity and you've got your calculator and your abacus out there and counting your toes, and as a result, you know exactly how much of an increase in stress hormone levels there should be, except something different happens. When you stress this organism, the organism has the opportunity to now get up and run over to mommy and hold on to her, and it doesn't secrete the glucocorticoids. This was flabbergasting. Nothing in Selye's wonderful clean world of stress-responses being a tightly, logically regulated engineering system as wonderful as a toilet bowl, nothing could have predicted this. This was horrifying, the notion that this tightly regulated system, this organism goes and screws up everything running over to mommy, and mommy would blunt the stress-response. This was very unexpected obviously, and this was the worst news that came down the pike for Selye in a long time because what do you do with this? This doesn't make any sense. Nothing could possibly explain the fact that this tightly regulated world was modulated instead by perception, by appraisal, by evaluation. This was really quite shocking. We've seen one version of how this works, which is these appraisal factors, this world of running over to mommy could modulate how the body would respond to a stressor. You put in a stressor, and suddenly some weird un–toilet bowlish variable like hugging mommy, and you would change the output. You could modulate the magnitude of the stress-response by these appraisal evaluative factors.

There was a remarkable study showing this a few years ago, showing just how much of a stress-response you could get. This was a remarkable study. This was published in the *Journal of Science* some years ago, and it showed some evidence for rat empathy. Here's what was done. You give a rat what's called a hotplate test, which is you put them on a perfectly cold surface, and you slowly begin to increase the temperature of this plate. At the very point where it has gotten warm enough that the rat picks up a paw for the first time, take him off, and you've just finished the study. You've determined what their pain threshold is for this. It's kind of distressing, but it's not massively so. What you see in this study is you're doing this to one rat. You put another rat right next to it, and you give it the same painful stimulus. What you see is if the first rat is getting exposed to the stressor, it lowers the pain threshold of the second rat right next to it, some of the time. Here was the remarkable thing. Put 2 strange rats next to each other, and it doesn't work. Put 2 cage mates next to each other, and you get this empathic lowering of the threshold for the stress-response.

What do we got there? In rats, it's something akin to empathy. I know this rat and this rat is giving off signals of being stressed. I am going to lower my threshold for my stress-response modulating in the most unexpected realms. Go hug mommy and you don't secrete as many stress hormones. Go sit next to a rat that you know and like that's getting exposed to its own stressor, you become more sensitive to stress, so modulatory factors. Then the most outrageous thing came along, people showing that you could turn on the stress-response in the absence of any stressor, in the absence of any physical toilet bowlish sort of insult, of this much of a drop in blood pressure, or this much of a stimulus. You could turn the stress-response on without anything happening physiologically. To appreciate that, all you need to do is look at a classic demonstration of that. Sit there and watch a loved one go through a painful medical procedure, and your heart rate will increase, and your breathing rate will increase. You are turning on a sympathetic nervous system stress-response.

What is this? This is the very core of this entire course, the notion that we smart humans, and even some other species as well, have the sophistication to turn on the stress-response to circumstances that make no physiological sense. We could turn it on in response to psychosocial stressors. This was the establishment that this could go on. Selye hated this, and during the '50s there was this sort of wildly florid animosity that evolved between Selye and a man named John Mason at Yale who was the one who did this pioneering work. This was the battle between stress physiology as a tightly regulated engineering system, and stress physiology as this mucky, weird, world of mommies hugging test organisms.

In one very, very widely read debate that that 2 of them had in the press, they slashed at each other and argued about what sort of system the stress physiology system really is. The general consensus is that Mason mopped the floor with Selye, because you couldn't look at results like mommy hugging and argue that the stress system is nothing but a tightly regulated engineering wonder. Selye managed to get a couple of hits in there at the end pointing out there are a few cases where there's not this appraisal yucky stuff happening. For example, anesthetize somebody for surgery and slice into their belly and you turn on the stress-response. No degree of mommy hugging them, no degree of framing of the experience, nothing is going to change that. Some of the time, the stress physiology system was responsive to the pure mechanical magnitude of the stressor, but the general view though was in all sorts of realms, the most common realms of the stress-response, aspects of appraisal and evaluation and perception would greatly modulate stress-response.

What have we just done here? What happened in the late 1950s, suddenly through the back door in the field, in snuck the psychologists. Suddenly stress and disease and health were as much the purview of psychologists as it was of these hard-nosed endoneuromechanoengineering types. Thus, the field was changed forever after. Once again, as the very core of this course is the fact that when we think about our stressors, we are dumped into the world of psychology, stress and health, rather than the world of tightly regulated endocrine systems. Selye was vanquished as a result and apparently nursed a great grudge for the rest of his life about it. For everybody else in the field, slowly, those low-class, swarthy, unkempt psychologists slowly got some manners, some gray hair and eventually were allowed to eat at the dinner table, and slowly, psychology has come to be viewed as at least as interesting in making sense of stress and disease as the purely mechanical aspects.

That moves us now to this critical issue of: What is it about psychological context that is stressful? What we're talking about here is what makes stress stress when it's psychological stress. We're talking about certain types of stressors. What we just saw was a stressor, a certain degree of stimulation could be highly modulated by hugging mommy. Nonetheless, there are circumstances where it can't be modulated by psychological factors. Go outside for a walk to the supermarket, unexpectedly get gored by a rhino, and you're going to have a stress-response. There's no degree of psychological reappraisal you can do. You can't decide this is a chance to grow from adversity, or I've always hated this shirt so now I could finally throw it out. You're going to have a stress-response. When you get to the world of much more intermediate, moderate stressors, the capacity of psychological context to modulate is enormous.

Thus we begin with this critical question: What is it about psychological context that makes some stressors more stressful and other ones less so? What we'll see over this lecture and the next one, there are some very powerful psychological factors that modulate the stress-response. First one, in the aftermath of a stressor, do you have an outlet? This was work pioneered by Jay Weiss—then at Rockefeller University, now at Emory University—and here's the paradigm that he did. Just as a sort of note up front here, the experiments that dominate the next few days, or the next few lectures, are some rather painful ones to hear about. Hear these in the context of this is where the next antidepressant drug is going to be invented from, information like this, psychological stressors.

Here is what Jay Weiss would do. He would take a rat who would be exposed to a physical Selyian stressor. Every now and then, it would get a shock. With enough of these, the rat would develop an ulcer. Now there's a second rat. Psychology jargon, the second rat is yoked to the first rat. Every time the first rat gets a shock, so does the second, same intensity, same duration, same everything. According to Selye in the 1930s, the 2 bodies are being knocked out of homeostatic balance to the exact same extent, except there's a critical difference which is, every time that second rat would get a shock, it could go over to a bar of wood and gnaw on it with its teeth, and it wouldn't get an ulcer. It had an outlet for the frustration caused by the stressor. What soon emerged was the recognition that all sorts of outlets would work for a rat under those conditions, the rat going into a running wheel after shocks like that and running off the stressor an outlet in that form. All of these, overeating at that point, all of these would wind up protecting from a stress-related disease, outlets.

Then you look at the same thing in humans and you ask: Are stressors capable of being modulated, being blunted by outlets? That's hobbies. That's going for a run. That's working off the tension in the gym. That's screaming in the stairwells after that awful stressful meeting. Humans do the exact same thing. Why should this work? Why should physical outlets work, reduce the stress-response after a stressor? It would for a number of reasons. First off because it releases the muscle tension, especially if it is a psychosocial stressor. Again, back to the very beginning, what's the stress-response about? Getting your body ready to run, to sprint all of that, and here you are having that all turned on for purely psychological reasons. Go exercise and you decrease that muscle tension. This is found in a particularly interesting realm.

Now throughout the early part of the course, a very similar metaphor kept coming up, the zebra running for its life away from the lion. It needs its energy in its thigh muscles. Not all animals deal with predators that way. Consider for example, gazelle. Gazelle are mostly hunted by cheetah, and what gazelles do if there's a cheetah around is they don't run away because cheetahs run faster; what they do is they crouch down and stay as still as possible in the hopes the cheetah won't spot them. In other words, the stress-response in this case is not about running for your life, it's about being as still as possible, and if need be, a quarter second from now, beginning to run for your life. It's a very different physiology, and it is demanding even more so than the running for your life scenario this absolute stillness amid this absolute preparative muscle tension. What do you see after the cheetah disappears and the gazelle has gotten away with it? It gets up and it runs around like mad to dissipate some of that muscle tension.

Why else do outlets work? They do because they distract you, and that's what some of the most basic human hobbies are about. Why else do outlets work? They work, because if it's the right kind, they remind you about what's really important in life. They remind you for example, that at the end of the day, of rushing in traffic, striving, ambition, and shallow wishing, coveting what everybody else has, after a day of that, at the end of the day in those stressors, if it's the right setting, you come home and have the outlet of playing with your children. Suddenly you remember what things really matter in life.

We've got this world of outlets. There's one type of outlet that pops up very frequently and this is a really distressing one. You take the rat that is yoked to the first one. It gets the same shock, same intensity, all of that, and now what it's allowed to do after getting its shocks is run over to the other side of the cage where there's another rat it could sit down next to and bite the bejesus out of it. You know what? This rat who's doing the biting isn't going to get an ulcer. He's got a particular type of outlet. He's doing displacement aggression onto an innocent bystander, and disturbingly, this works great.

Among baboons, about half of aggression is displacement aggression. Male looses a fight who chases a subadult who bites a female who lunges at a juvenile who slaps an infant.

What does that mean? At each one of those steps, an individual is taking the stressor, the frustration of what just occurred, and having an outlet, dumping it on somebody else. This makes very disturbing sense. This is why during periods of economic duress, rates of child abuse, of spousal abuse, go up. This is the word of displacing, really, really depressing finding, and this came out of some of my work with baboons, wild baboons. You look at being a very stressed type of baboon, a relatively low-ranking one, elevated glucocorticoid levels, you know the whole business by now. What you see is the greater the tendency that baboon has to dump on somebody else to displace aggression when something stressful has happened to them, the lower the glucocorticoid levels. In other words, this particular type of outlet, displacing aggression onto an innocent bystander is one of the most common and one of the most efficacious things that social organisms do to feel less stressed, really bad news. It's the core behind one of the great truisms of stress management, don't avoid getting this ulcer by giving it to somebody else.

Next variable, in addition to outlets, here is now the variable. You take the lab rat that's getting the same shocks, all that sort of deal, and now this time, it could run over to the other side of the cage where there's a rat that it knows and it likes. They groom each other, and it doesn't get ulcers, social support. Harking back to that empathy study, it's not just doing it with any rat. If it's a complete stranger of a rat, the logical thing to do is displace aggression on them. If it's a rat you know, the social support, the grooming there, is protective.

Same thing in baboons, what you see there is social grooming, and this is one of the archetypical things nonhuman primates do which is sitting around and taking the parasites off of each other and eating them, and what's grooming good for? All the initial theories were, number 1, if you're being groomed, it reduces your ectoparasite load. Number 2, if you're grooming somebody else, you get all this great nutrition from eating the little ticks and stuff. That has got nothing to do with it. When you look at how grooming works, what it is is social calming, it's stress reduction. You get a baboon who has just had a scare, a lion has almost gotten him, and what does he do afterward? He runs over and grooms somebody. You get the entire troop where something scary has happened, some lion has leapt out and everybody just barely made it into the trees, and when the lion is gone, everybody comes down and sits and grooms for the next half hour. It is very socially calming. A remarkable study was done a few years ago by Dorothy Cheney and Robert Seyfarth at the University of Pennsylvania looking at baboons in one of the worst stressors that could happen to any female primate, your child has died. What they show is for quite a long period afterward, elevated glucocorticoid levels in these females, and the more grooming they did, the less it rose.

What does it look like in humans? Obviously, this is the whole world of social affiliation, and we are going to come back and look at it like crazy. It's also pertinent in all sorts of very acute circumstances. Take somebody going through a short medical procedure that's kind of stressful. Take somebody going through an experimental stressor, rapid mathematics pressure, and have somebody there they know and like and hold their hand, and they don't have as much of a stress-response. Social support, social support, that's a highly protective factor. The next one is predictability.

Predictability, back to those 2 rats, both getting shocks, and now the second rat 10 seconds before each shock, a little warning light comes on, and the rat doesn't get the ulcer. Predictive information, enormously powerful in that regard, and we know that principle. It tells you when something bad is coming, how bad is it going to be? How long is it going to last? How severe, what it's like afterward, and what that does is it allows you to plan coping strategies. We all know that principle, and we use it all the time. Every time you're sitting there in the dentist chair, and you say are we almost done? Give me some predictive information. We all know the difference between the dentist that says 2 more bits of drilling and the one that says, I don't know, you could be here for weeks. What does predictive information do there? It does lots of things. One of the things it affords you is the ability to plan your coping strategy during the stressor, and that's one that's very effective, knowing that this stressor is going to last for 4 and a half days versus 3 seconds, that's very useful to know. That allows you to plan your effective coping strategy.

You even see this in the realm, somebody is going through a surgical procedure, and what they tell you is the first day or so it's going to hurt like crazy, and by the second day, you're just going to be uncomfortable and tired. What that tells you is your coping strategies, you should plan on watching the exciting, tawdry adventure action movies the first day, and work on your composing those delicate haikus the second day instead of the other way around. It allows you to plan your coping strategy. What it also allows you to do is know when the stressor is over with, when you're finally safe. For that rat getting the shocks without any warning light coming on, any second you could be a half second away from the next stressor. This is an extremely powerful principle in terms of being told when is it going to happen, how bad is it going to be, how long is it going to last, and that works as effectively in a human and a nonhuman primate, a rat. In all of them it is a very powerful variable for controlling things. That whole notion of what predictability allows you to do is know what your coping strategy is going to be, know how long the stressor is going to last. That's the principle behind one of the most painful, one of the most central, one of the most defining, one of the most poignant questions any of us might ever ask somewhere down the line, which is, how much time do I have left.

What we've seen here now is the first of the powerful psychological variables. Powerful is the defeat of Hans Selye and the psychologists suddenly taking over the whole field and the starts of these variables. What is it that makes psychological stress stressful for the same degree of objective challenge to the system? You are more likely to subjectively feel stressed; you're more likely to activate the stress-response; you're more likely to get a stress-related disease if you lack outlets for the frustration caused by the stressor, if you lack social support, and if you lack predictive information. At this point, it seems like there is a very clear take-home message from this lecture, which is when stress hits, get as many outlets as possible, get as much predictive information as possible, try to socialize with everybody on Earth. What you're going to see is if that's what you take as the lesson here, it's not going to do you any good. What works, what buffers the stress-response, is far more subtle psychological variables. That's what we'll consider in the next lecture.

Psychological Modulators of Stress
Lecture 18

> They looked at patterns of stress, subjective senses of stress, health, all of that in 2 groups of musicians, those playing professionally in symphony orchestras and those playing professionally in small ensembles, string quartets, and things of that sort. What they saw was the chamber music folks were far less stressed. What's this about? ... [There] is a miserable lack of control on the part of the instrumentalists in [orchestras] because the conductor controls everything. It was, in fact, until not that many years ago the unions of orchestral musicians got the right to demand bathroom breaks with some regularity.

What is it about psychological stress that is stressful? We covered 3 key variables in the last lecture—outlets for frustration, social support, and predictability. Another major factor is a sense of control. As a general rule, the more of a sense of control you have, the less stressful the stressor is.

A major area of focus in this field is the amount of control people have in the workplace. Who do you see getting stress-related disease in the corporate world? It's not upper management, as previously believed; it's middle management. A key feature of life in the middle is you have high demand and low control—high demand in that you're in a position of great responsibility, low control because you're not the one making policy. Second on the list of bad work scenarios are ones with the combination of low demand and low control, because these people have a lack of control plus boredom. For the folks in upper management, as long as they are doing a job that they like, the high degree of control and high degree of demand make a great combination.

The next variable is more subtle: the perception of whether things are getting worse or better. Here's a possibility in a corporation: A worker in the mailroom is making $7 an hour while the CEO is getting a gazillion dollars a year. People suddenly discover that the mailroom person is the most skillful mailroom person on the entire planet, and management decides to reward this. Starting tomorrow, he will have $100,000 a year salary. Meanwhile, the CEO has done some disastrously imprudent things and practically bankrupted the company. She is told she too will have $100,000 a year salary. You can bet that $100,000 a year means very different things depending on which direction you're coming from.

> **For the folks in upper management, as long as they are doing a job that they like, the high degree of control and high degree of demand make a great combination.**

So how can we live our lives successfully with what we've learned in these 2 lectures? If you think the rule is to get as much control in your life as possible, get as much predictive information as possible, and have as many outlets as possible, that's actually not going to reduce your levels of stress. That's going to increase it in lots of ways because it turns out these principles don't apply all the time; they apply only with certain parameters. Predictive information only works during a certain window—it is of no use when you don't have enough time to activate a coping strategy, and having it too far in advance for a major stressor can actually makes things worse. The nature of the predictive stressor is also a factor: Predictive information helps only for stressors with a moderate likelihood of occurring. It doesn't help in cases of a stressor so rare that you don't even worry about it or a stressor so common that you take it for granted.

So predictability helps only some of the time. How about a sense of control? The easy conclusion to draw is that you should have as much of a sense of control as often as possible. In reality, a sense of control can be a disaster at times. One of the most compassionate things we ever do is to try to decrease somebody's sense of control: "Nobody could have stopped the car in time, the way that little girl darted out." We let people know there's nothing they could have done about it; it's not their fault. One of the worst things that we ever do is magnify somebody's sense of control: "What do you expect if they refuse to assimilate into society? Of course people are going to turn against them."

What have we learned about stress and control? In the face of stressors that are mild to moderate in severity, you want to increase a person's feeling of control, whether it's realistic or not. It feels great; it builds up a sense of efficacy. In the face of disastrous stressors, you do not want to inflate a person's sense of control, because you're setting him up to think that he failed. ■

Suggested Reading

Sapolsky, *Why Zebras Don't Get Ulcers*, chap. 13.

Questions to Consider

1. When is (and isn't) a sense of control stress-reducing?

2. When is (and isn't) information about an impending stressor stress-reducing?

Psychological Modulators of Stress
Lecture 18—Transcript

It's dawn here at The Teaching Company. The cows have been milked; things are going terrifically. Over last night, the sound technicians switched me from New York accent to the lovely lilting Scottish brogue you're hearing now, and thus we are ready to plow into the next subject, the next subject being the second half of the last lecture.

What the last lecture did was introduce us to the piece of history, the loves of Han Selye, the hatreds of Hans Selye, the great triumph Trojan Greek battle between Selye and the psychologists, and the emergence of the recognition of how important psychological factors are in modulating the stress-response. That transitions us to the absolutely critical question: What is it about psychological stress that is stressful? We covered the first 3 of some of the key variables, the role of outlets for frustration, the role of social support, the role of predictability, and what we do now is continue into some more of those key factors. The next one is a biggie, which is a sense of control. Here's a general rule, and we will see soon how impossibly simplistic that general rule is, but the general rule is: The more of a sense of control, the less stressful the stressor is.

You can show this cleanly with a lab rat, the same sort of experiments as in the last lecture. In this case, though, a rat that will be getting shocks now and then has been trained, has been trained to press a lever. By pressing the lever, it decreases the likelihood of getting a shock. Here's what's happening. Scenario number 1: You've trained that rat to be able to do that, and the rat is put back into the room where it gets the shocks, except you've taken away the lever. The lever isn't there, and the rat has a massive stress-response, far more so than it would have gotten had it not gotten that lever training. It's obvious what it's doing. It's sitting there saying, "Give me the damn lever. I know exactly what to do to get this under control," and it has lost the opportunity to do that.

Or you could see the flip side of it. You've got the rat who has been trained to press the lever, and back there in the room and getting the shocks and the levers there, but today, you've disconnected the lever. It's doing nothing; it's a placebo. Pressing it doesn't at all decrease the likelihood of a shock, but the rat is in there pounding away on the lever saying this is great; just imagine how many shocks I'd be getting otherwise. It thinks it has a sense of control. What we see here is the power of control to modulate the stress-response, a very, very potentially powerful one.

What else can you say about control? What else can you do in terms of making sense of it? You begin to transition to what does this look like in humans, and remarkably, it looks exactly the same. There was a study done by Owen Wolkowitz at UCSF, and what he did was essentially translate the rat study into humans. Volunteers were sitting in a room, and every now and then, unpredictably, there would be a blast of high-decibel noise, very unpleasant, up goes blood pressure. Now instead, the volunteers are sitting there and they've been told by pressing this little button here, you decrease the likelihood of the blast of noise happening. You don't get as much of a rise in blood pressure amid the exact same number of those shocks, same deal as in the rats, same exact model. You can see this playing out as well in all sorts of human occupations, a realm of occupational psychology, stress management, and an awful lot of what it's about is the amount of control you have in your workplace.

To begin to make sense of this, we have to start with one of the great myths of stress physiology, and this is the myth of the executive stress syndrome. This emerged in the 1950s, a study that ostensibly showed that having a high degree of control and of responsibility ulcerated you like crazy. This was a study where there would be 2 monkeys that would get shocks now and then, and one of them had the power, by pressing a lever over and over and over, to decrease the likelihood of both of them getting shocks. What they showed was this executive monkey with his hands at the wheel of the ship and captain of his own fate and this other one's fate would have more stress-related diseases. Executive stress, and this permeated through everybody's consciousness, especially sort of the bloated robber barons, who were saying

"Oh, my God, now it turns out that yacht is not such a great thing because I am under so much stress. What a victim I am."

It turned out there was an extremely flawed piece of that study in that the researchers, for typical reasons, wanted to get a good result and wanted to get it quickly, so what they said was, "Hey why don't we pick out the monkeys who seem to be the most hyperemotional and reactive. We'll make them the executive monkeys." No wonder they got the stress related disease. They had blown the design; they didn't randomize the subjects. That trashes the notion of the executive stress syndrome. Who do you actually see getting stress-related disease in the large corporate world? It's not upper management; it's middle management. It's middle management because of a key feature about life in the middle there which is you have high demand and low control. High demand in that you've got to do all sorts of difficult things, you're in a position of great responsibility, low control because you're not the one making up the policy, you're getting the orders from on up high. It's middle management that has the most problems with stress-related disease, and when you look at individuals, it's the ones who most interpret their job as involving low control, high responsibility, high demand who get into trouble.

Second on the list of bad work scenarios would be ones where you have the combination now of low demand and low control because now you've got the double whammy of lack of control in your life, plus boredom. What's the best possible way of framing all of this? These are the folks with high demand and high control, and this is typically upper management. This is the folks running things, and as long as this is them doing some sort of job that they like, and it's usually some sort of job that they're obsessively attached to, the high degree of control and the high degree of demand is a great combination.

This came through subtly in a fascinating study that was done some years ago, and it had at a very atypical pair of authors. One of the giants of behavioral endocrinology was a man named Seymour Levine at Stanford University. Everyone knew him as Gig, and Gig Levine published a paper with his son, his son who was not a scientist. His son, who was a professional musician who played in, I believe, the Minneapolis Symphony, and they did the following study: They looked at patterns of stress, subjective senses of stress, health, all of that in 2 groups of musicians, those playing professionally in symphony orchestras and those playing professionally in small ensembles, string quartets, and things of that sort. They did all the same controls on their lab-rat musicians that they should have done. They matched the 2 groups for the total amount of time they traveled, for income, all of that. The sole difference was these guys were playing in a symphony, and these guys were playing chamber music.

What they saw was the chamber music folks were far less stressed. What's this about? One of the things that's constantly emphasized when people think about successful aging is the remarkable longevity of symphony conductors. They're all conducting into their 90s, and they've got the perfect job which we will get to in a few lectures. They've got the aerobic exercises we've heard, but they also have control; they're the head of the orchestra. What that often translates into is a miserable lack of control on the part of the instrumentalists in there because the conductor controls everything. It was, in fact, until not that many years ago the unions of orchestral musicians got the right to demand bathroom breaks with some regularity. Look at this, you're an adult playing there, and the conductor is the one who decides when the oboe people can go to the potty, marked lack of control versus chamber musicians, far more control as to what's going on in their lives.

This is also thought to be a factor, this combination of high-demand, high-control of people who thrive in one of the all-time stressful occupations, people who are air traffic controllers. A researcher named Robert Rose spent much of his career looking at the physiology of the stress-response in air traffic controllers and trying to figure out how that maps on to job performance. Apparently, there's essentially a bimodal shift, 2 separate profiles of air traffic controllers. There are the ones who come in, and after a remarkably short number of months are sopping stressed messes and can't continue the job. Then there are ones who just go on for decades and are great at it. What's the difference? What he saw was a very different style of how they did the work, a very different way of doing it. You have the folks who lasted almost no time at all, and what you would see is the morning they were going to work to do whatever shift it was, they already had an elevated stress-response blasting through the roof. They get into their job, and the stress-response is still way up there. They finish the job and hours later, they're still recovering from the stress-response.

We should know by now that's not a harbinger of a good outcome. Then you look at the folks who did wonderfully, who lasted forever, and what you would see is up to 3 seconds before they would sit down in the chair and start working, no stress-response. Everything's fine, start the stressful work, blast it through the roof, and the second it's over with, they're off thinking about dinner. What they're doing is having a stress-response only when it was needed. What these people are about was having an enormously highly demanding job, but what they tended to also see psychologically was they viewed themselves as having a lot of control, and that took away the psychological stress of the anticipation they're recovering from.

That's this key variable of control. On to the next variable, and this is a rather subtle one, a perception as to whether things are getting worse or getting better. Let me give you an example of this in the experimental realm. Two rats, first day one of them gets 50 shocks, the next day it gets 25, in other words a total of 75 shocks. Meanwhile over here is the rat who's getting 10 shocks the first day and 25 the next, total of 35 shocks, 75 versus 35. Who's more stressed? It's absolutely obvious, the guy who's gotten a total of 75, far more shocks than this guy. No, that's not what you see. Who has a worse stress-response, the guy going from 10 to 25. The one going from 50 to 25 is sitting there saying, 25, piece of cake; this is fabulous. Things are getting better. What you see is this very important variable. It's not just how much of a stressor there is, but it's which direction are you coming to in order to get to that stressor.

You can show this also in a very subtle study that I did with my baboons some years ago. You've got dominance hierarchies, you've got number 1 and number 10 and number 20, and the quality of life is very different depending on your dominance rank, and high ranking guys very aggressively enforce their high rank. Except, every now and then, the ranks change. In other words, every now and then, the relationship between 2 baboons with their known ranking difference becomes unstable and maybe even changes. What does stability look like? You see the interactions between this pair of baboons, number 5 and number 6, and number 5 is winning 95% of the interactions with number 6. That's stable. In contrast, number 5 and number 6, number 5 is winning 51% of the interactions with number 6. What's that about? That's an unstable diet. They might very well be just about to flip.

Thus, what we begin to see is an issue of control, predictability, and stability. Nice stable relationships are much more predictable. Suddenly you would come up with this prediction that instability in and of itself is a stressor. You look at these interactions amongst these male baboons, and you keep track of how stable, how unstable the dyadic relationships are between these baboons with a very simple prediction. The more instability, the closer you are to that 51% versus 49, the more instability, the more stressful, the higher the glucocorticoid levels. That's not what you see. For example, you look at number 5, and if he's having a lot of unstable interactions with number 6, number 5 has a huge stress-response. You look at number 5, and you look at how many unstable interactions he's having with number 4, and he's got no stress-response. How could this be unpredictability, the same number of fights. A critical difference, if you're number 5 and you're having a lot of stressful interactions with number 6, that means number 6 is breathing down your neck, is about to toss you out, and you're about to get a demotion. If you're having a lot of unstable interactions with number 4, it means you're about to supplant him. You're about to get a promotion. Number 5, instability in this direction bad news, in that direction great news. It's not just in this case the amount of instability; it's what it means. When it means good news, you don't get as much of a stress-response.

You see similar things in humans, and you can even see it under remarkable circumstances where you get interactions between the absolute reality of a stressor, and how you actually interpret it. OK, here's a possibility in a corporation. You've got this huge corporation, and there's some guy working in the mailroom getting $7 an hour or some such thing. Then you've got the CEO of the company who's getting a gazillion dollars a year. People suddenly discover that this guy in the mailroom is the greatest mailroom person on the entire planet, the most skillful one, and management comes in and says we need to reward this. Starting tomorrow, you have $100,000 a year salary. Meanwhile you notice that the CEO has just done some disastrously imprudent things and practically bankrupted the company. In a shocking, shocking exception to the usual rule, the guy is actually held responsible for this. They say, "OK, because you have screwed up royally, starting tomorrow, you have $100,000 a year salary." You can bet the mailroom guy is not going to be going to a headhunter to find another job, and you could bet the next day the CEO is; $100,000 a year means very different things depending on which direction you're coming from.

Where this can wind up being relevant is when you see these interactions between control, predictability, outcome, interpretation, where you can even see interactions between some of these pieces. Where it could be fascinating, not just in the realm of how much of a stress-response you have to bad stressful things, but remarkably what the response is in your body to great news, to wonderful things. This is the world of somebody from out of nowhere wins the lottery, it's great, and it has transformed their life, and it winds up being unsettling for a number of reasons. One is it totally messes up their relationships with everybody else, and the other is the sense of the randomness is very often reported by these folks as being quite unsettling.

Or you can have somebody who wins the lottery in a much deeper, more important way. This is someone who is desperately in need of an organ transplant and is on the waiting list, and who knows and who knows. The clock is ticking for how much longer they can survive, and suddenly from out of nowhere, it happens. The transplant, the organ becomes available. This is wondrous. Suddenly it's there, and their life is saved. In the aftermath, amid the gratitude, the pleasure, the joy, what is also very often seen amongst these transplant individuals is a tremendous agitated sense of stress built around the lack of control. "My God, if that person on the motorcycle had taken that curve 5 miles an hour slower, he wouldn't have died, and I'd be sitting here dying for lack of that organ." "My God, if one of the other people on the donor list had a slightly better genetic match with that organ, it wouldn't have been me, the sense of I'm going to live but I have so little control over what happened," that winds up being quite unsettling. A world of stress and a world of psychological modulators of stress where it even plays into things that are not stressful, things that could be good news, fun news, wondrously lifesaving news.

What have we gotten to at this point? We've now gone through some important modulators of the stress-response from the last lecture and this one, outlets for frustration, social support, predictive information, a sense of control, and interpreting things as getting better. All of those are great, thus you need a punch line for how to live your life successfully with these factors in mind from what you've learned here. If you think what you've learned is as follows, it would be a disaster. If you think the rule is: Get as much control in your life as possible, get as much predictive information as possible, have as many outlets as possible, if you turn this into this mantra of more and more and more control and more predictability, that's not going to reduce your levels of stress.

That's going to increase it in lots of ways because it turns out these principles don't apply all the time. They apply only with certain parameters. Only some of the time does a sense of control, this predictive information, actually help. The first one is predictive information. We've already gone through that scenario which is the lab rat is getting the shocks now and then and 10 seconds before each shock it gets the little warning light. Great, and it's quite protective. That's wonderful. When does it not work? You've got the same rat, and instead of getting the warning light 10 seconds before each shock, it gets the warning light half a second before. That does no good whatsoever. How come? Because the rat doesn't have enough time to activate its coping strategy.

On the other hand suppose that you've got the warning light coming instead of 10 seconds in advance, it's coming 3 1/2 weeks in advance, it does no good at all either for obvious reasons. What you wind up seeing is predictive information helps only within a certain time span, when it's not too far in advance and when there's enough time to plan your coping strategy. Have it far enough of advance when it's a really major stressor and not only doesn't it protect, it makes things worse. Just imagine if you have this omnipotent voice that suddenly comes in and gives you some predictive information saying 3 years, 27 days, and 4 hours from now you're going to have a horrible accident and your leg is going to be amputated. Oh, I feel great having gotten all this predictive information. If it's far enough in advance, not only doesn't it protect, it could make things worse.

Next realm where it may not work very well, next realm, and again this has to do with predictive information, and the point is: What is it predicting? What is the nature of the predictive stressor that is now being considered by you? Here are 2 scenarios. Here's the first one. This very odd one, where this voice, again this omnipotent voice, comes in and suddenly says, "Oh my God, I just heard that yesterday there was this disaster. This meteor hit Earth, and in the process, hit your back yard and took out all your flamingos. But you know what, I've got some predictive information for you. It's never going to happen again." "Oh, that's wonderful, at least I know in the aftermath of that disaster, I don't have to worry." Predictive information there doesn't do you any good whatsoever because it's predictive information about a stressor that is such a low probability that the predictive information doesn't help. You're not worrying about it happening anyway.

Or you can have the converse. You can now have the omnipotent voice in some other sort of scenario, and now what it is, is the voice comes in and says, "Remember driving into work today how awful the traffic was? I've got predictive information. It's going to be awful tomorrow also." "Whoa, all that predictive information, I feel wonderful now." That doesn't help in the slightest because that is such a common stressor that you already take it for granted. Predictive information helps only for stressors with a moderate likelihood of occurring. If it is such a rare stressor that you don't even worry about it, it doesn't help. If it's such a common stressor that you take it for granted, it doesn't help. You can even have predictive information where it does no good whatsoever when it's even giving you predictive news about something good. Omnipotent voice again saying you know how you drove to work today and there was horrible traffic, well 3 months and 4 days from now when you drive to work, there's going to be no traffic whatsoever and the police are going to pull you over and insist you share their donuts with them. Oh, that's wondrous. This does not count as useful predictive information even in the face of it carrying good news.

Predictability helps only some of the time, and very importantly, what we saw was if it's far enough in advance of the stressor, it could actually make things worse. How about control? How about a sense of control? The easy solution from the control section is have as much of a sense of control as often as possible and just magnify it and control, control, control. I'm the master of my fate, and you need to think that way all the time. Absolutely not, a sense of control can be a disaster at times. Some of the most compassionate things we ever do is to try to decrease somebody's sense of control. Nobody could have stopped the car in time the way that little girl darted out. It doesn't matter if you had gotten dad to the doctor sooner. It was an incurable disease. There's nothing you could have done about it. It's not your fault. It's not your fault. You didn't have any control. Some of the worst things that we ever do societally is magnify somebody's sense of control. "Oh, what does she expect if she's going to dress like that walking around a bad part of town." "Oh, what do you expect if they refuse to assimilate into society. Of course, people are going to turn against them."

One of the worst versions of that in medical history concerns schizophrenia. Schizophrenia, a horrible disease, has had an awful major impact for decades and decades on mental health, and of course, people have wondered what causes schizophrenia? Up to the 1950s or so, there was an absolutely clear answer given in the field which is schizophrenia is caused by the mother. It's a certain mothering style named schizophrenogenic mothering style, and it's the mother's fault. In other words, the mother had the control to determine whether or not the child became schizophrenic. As the years went by, it was viewed as this was a little harsh, and then a more compassionate version of this theory came in which was they allowed the possibility that it was the father who screwed up the parents' parenting style as the cause of schizophrenia.

Then in the 1950s there was a revolution. People discovered some of the first drugs, the antipsychotics, that could control schizophrenia. This shockwave went through the psychiatric community. Oh, my God, it's got nothing to do with parenting style; it's a biochemical disorder. Schizophrenogenic mothering went down the tube overnight, and you could see amazing editorials in some of those journals, the pain some of these health-care professionals felt when realizing what they had done by inflating a sense of control. They would write editorials like, "I have spent my entire life battling this nightmare of a disease. I have tried to do good. I have tried to help. I have done the best I could do with the information available as to what causes this disease, this mothering style idea. My God, the damage I have done over the years." We see this pattern here. You can, in some cases, be wildly compassionate, wildly stress-reducing by decreasing somebody's sense of control. Some of the most awful, stressful things you can ever do to someone could be increasing their sense.

How do you get some rules coming out of this? Basically what you see is as follows: In the face of stressors that are mild to moderate in severity, you want to increase somebody's feeling of control, whether it's realistic or not. You want them to feel like they were in control because what you're biasing the person to do then to feel is to think just how bad it would have been if I hadn't had a sense of control. It feels great, it builds up a sense of efficacy. When do you not want to inflate the sense of control in the face of horrible, disastrous stressors because all you're doing is setting somebody up with a sense of control to think, oh my God, I could have made it so much better and I didn't. Sense of control works for only mild to moderate stressors. You can see how powerful these variables are in terms of that. Also lurking in there is a remarkable of realization. One of the great golden rules of psychiatry of mental health professionals is that truth and beauty and mental health go hand in hand. What you're seeing here is in some circumstances, the most compassionate thing you can do is disabuse somebody of a notion that is actually for real to decrease the sense of control.

What have we gotten to here? We now see the enormous power of these psychological variables, a sense of control, a sense of predictability, outlets for frustration, social support, and a view of things getting better. What we've also seen is amid these being enormously powerful, they don't work all the time. They work only within certain parameters. Get outside those parameters and you make things worse. What this has set us up for now is moving past our world of all those preceding lectures of inflammation in your blood vessels, decreased numbers of receptors on your pituitary, and what this transitions us to is the trenches of the interaction between stress and mental health. What does stress have to do with clinical depression?

Stress and the Biology of Depression
Lecture 19

> As I said before, I think major depression is among the worst diseases that can possibly happen to you, and it's because of this main symptom. Think about a remarkable feature of humans. You get somebody with a nightmare of a disease, with cancer, terminal cancer. To a surprising extent people will wind up saying things like, "Obviously I didn't want this disease and don't want to die, but it wasn't until I got the cancer that I realized how important family is to me, or what good friends I have, or I found my God, or, I almost feel grateful for it." We humans have this bizarre ability to find pleasure in the most unlikely places, and the defining symptom of depression is ... you lose the capacity to feel pleasure.

This and the following lecture are devoted to major clinical depression. We devote so much time to depression because it's a complicated subject and because it affects so many people. Current estimates by the World Health Organization are that depression is the fourth leading cause of disability in the world. By 2020, it is expected to be in second place, after metabolic syndrome.

What are the symptoms of depression? The core symptom is **anhedonia**, the inability to feel pleasure. Many people with depression experience grief and guilt so severe that they begin to distort the way they interpret the world around them. There is also the tendency of people who are highly depressed to injure themselves, to attempt suicide, or to succeed at committing suicide. Many experience social withdrawal, loss of libido, and changes in sleep patterns. The tendency is to fall asleep fairly normally but wake up very early in the morning. The architecture of sleep patterns is disorganized in people with depression; their brains work differently. There are also changes in appetite and in many aspects of metabolism. In a substantial percentage of sufferers, there are increased levels of glucocorticoids, which means stress, and which also indicates that depression is a biological disorder. Another feature of the disease also screams biology: the fact that there are patterns to when people have their depressions. The most striking example of that is people who get depressed only at a certain time of year, typically the winter months.

What is wrong biologically in depression? First let's look at how brain chemistry works. The figure below shows the basic flow of information between 2 neurons (or brain cells). One neuron sends a projection to another through a small space in between called a **synapse**. The first neuron releases a chemical messenger, which floats across the synapse. The messenger comes out of the extreme end of the neuron, called the axon terminal, and floats across a tiny distance to the dendrites of the next neuron, allowing it to interact with its neurotransmitter receptor. The neurons talk to each other by way of these neurotransmitters, leading to a change in the second neuron, such as it becoming more excitable.

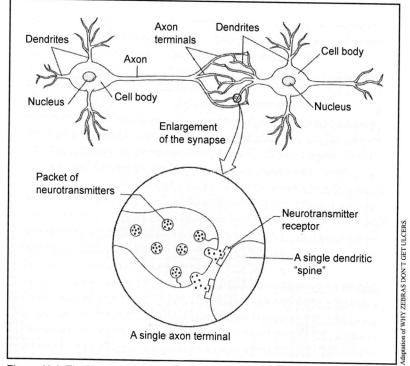

Figure 19.1. The functioning of brain chemistry.

There are many different chemicals that appear to be neurotransmitters. What is happening with the neurochemistry of depression? Here is an extremely simplified summary of what we know now: **Norepinephrine** has to do with energy; so the absence of norepinephrine begins to explain the psychomotor retardation of depression—how it feels exhausting to do everything. **Serotonin** has to do with the rumination on grief, despair, and guilt. And the shortage of dopamine has to do with the anhedonia. What about the neuroanatomy of depression? A depression is when your frontal cortex, in particular a subarea called the anterior cingulate, comes up with abstract sad thoughts and manages to get the rest of your brain to go along with it as if it were a real stressor. So we have demonstrated that this is a biological disorder, as biological as diabetes, but we see in the next lecture that if we only look at the biology, and do not focus on the psychological aspects as well, we are not going to be in a position to help someone who is clinically depressed. ■

Important Terms

anhedonia: The inability to feel pleasure; a defining symptom of depression.

norepinephrine (a.k.a. **noradrenaline**): A type of neurotransmitter closely related to epinephrine. There is good evidence that its release in one region of the brain is blunted in depression; in a different part of the nervous system, it plays a central role in the sympathetic nervous system (along with epinephrine).

selective serotonin reuptake inhibitor (**SSRI**): Any of a class of antidepressants (e.g., Prozac) that increase serotonin signaling in the synapse by blocking their reuptake (i.e., removal) from the synapse.

serotonin: A type of neurotransmitter. Of greatest relevance, evidence suggests that a shortage of serotonin in some brain regions contributes to depression.

synapse: The microscopic gap between the branches of two neurons; excitation in one neuron leads to the release of specific neurotransmitters, which float across the synapse, bind to specialized receptors, and alter the function of the other neuron.

Suggested Reading

Cohen, Janicki-Deverts, and Miller, "Psychological Stress and Disease."

Sapolsky, *Why Zebras Don't Get Ulcers*, chap. 14.

Questions to Consider

1. What sort of evidence shows that depression is as biological a disease as diabetes is?

2. What does stress do to the brain chemistry that is most relevant to depression?

Stress and the Biology of Depression
Lecture 19—Transcript

At some point you have to admit there are some very cool bizarre diseases out there. There are all sorts of exotic ones too that are, on a certain level, just irresistible. There's elephant man syndrome; there are multiple personality disorders. There are the sorts of diseases that get turned into the movie of the week. There's this really bizarre one, a disease called kuru, which is only found amongst cannibals in the New Guinea highlands, and it produces a disease a little bit like mad cow disease. It is transmitted by eating the brains of somebody, and these are cool, bizarre ways in which biology can go wrong. If you want uncool, unbizarre meat-and-potatoes disease versions of just profound human sadness, there's nothing out there like a major clinical depression.

Depression, as we transition here, slowly over the recent lectures, moving from the world of your heart, your liver, your kidney, and now moving into the realm instead of your psyche, your psychiatric status. We've been making this transition. Beginning in the last few lectures to see what does psychological stress comprise, and how powerful can it be? This is a clear transition to what we will focus on in this lecture, the starts of psychiatric disorders, ones that are absolutely deeply intertwined with depression.

Depression, it's going to be 2 lectures worth of material to cover, and this is for a number of reasons. First off, it's a complicated subject and there's actually an awful lot known about the biology of depression. Second reason, there are oceans of people out there with major depression. Current estimates by the World Health Organization are that depression is the number 4 leading cause of disability on this planet. The estimates are, by the year 2020, that it is going to be up number 2 following things like metabolic syndrome, those disorders we know about by now.

Complicated, so it takes a lot of time, incredibly prevalent, so it's really worth going into, and another reason why it's really worth going into, it's a disaster of a disease. I will make the argument in here that a major depression is among the worst diseases anybody could possibly suffer, and we'll see why I think that. What we'll be doing in this lecture is starting off in one domain of understanding depression, understanding the biology of depression. After the initial part of focusing on what the symptoms of depression are, some of which are absolutely intuitively obvious, and some of which are quite surprising, after that introductory stretch, we will begin to focus on what is the biology of depression.

What is the brain chemistry? What's the brain chemistry that goes wrong? What are the structural features of major depressive brains which wind up being abnormal? Transitioning into the next lecture, what hormones are out of whack? What do hormones have to do with depression, perhaps even nutrition? At that point, what you will have is everything needed to be a cutting-edge biological psychiatry maven. You'll know about hormones, neurochemistry, and neuroanatomy, and what we will see at that point is, if that's all you know about the subject, you don't have a prayer of being able to do a whole lot to contain depression. What we'll transition to at that point is the other half of the equation, what are psychological factors, and how are they part of the whole process of clinical depression. What you're going to see there is what seems to be at the end, 2 completely different worlds, different languages, the world of depression as funny neurochemicals and hormone ratios, the world of depression as problems with a sense of control, a sense of despair. What we're going to see is the way these 2 very different views are pulled together is by recognizing the absolutely essential role of stress.

What will run through all of this and is implicit in the very subject of this lecture is the biology of depression, which winds up being one of the things that is challenging when dealing with depression. There's a weird sort of moralistic thread that runs through how people think of depression where it's almost a sense of well, hey, we all get depressed. Bad things happen, we get depressed, we feel lousy, and we come out the other end. Depression is this disease of people who don't quite pull it together, who kind of indulge themselves. There's a weird tinge of sort of moralistic judgment about a depression. What will be a main theme ultimately in this and the next lecture is depression is a disease. It is a disease. It is as real of a disease as is diabetes, and you don't sit down a juvenile diabetic and say, oh, what's the deal with this insulin stuff. Stop babying yourself. This is a real disease. We start off by looking at what depression looks like, and we start off immediately with a semantic problem, which is we use the word "depression," again, in an everyday sense. Oh, something disappointing occurs, something that sort of gets you down and you get depressed. Oh, I've been feeling depressed. This is a depressing day. That sort of thing. When talking about a major clinical depression, this is not oh, feeling kind of down, this is a disorder where you are so crushed by the sense of depressiveness that you can't get out of bed, that you don't do laundry for months on end. That your entire life is ruined. You can't get out of your house. You can't function, you can't work, you don't see anyone. It is a disease that absolutely cripples you.

What are the symptoms of major depression? As I said before, I think major depression is among the worst diseases that can possibly happen to you, and it's because of this main symptom. Think about a remarkable feature of humans. You get somebody with a nightmare of a disease, with cancer, terminal cancer. To a surprising extent people will wind up saying things like, "Obviously I didn't want this disease and don't want to die, but it wasn't until I got the cancer that I realized how important family is to me, or what good friends I have, or I found my God, or, I almost feel grateful for it." We humans have this bizarre ability to find pleasure in the most unlikely places, and the defining symptom of depression is it's a biochemical genetic environmental disorder where you can't appreciate sunsets, where you lose the capacity to feel pleasure.

This is the core symptom, anhedonia. Hedonism is the pursuit of pleasure. Anhedonia is the inability to feel it. Moving on and getting a sense here of the sheer severity of depression, along with that lack of pleasure, the anhedonia, there is deep grief, deep guilt, and this again is not like everyday depression. Ooh, you feel kind of down about something, you sort of grieve about something going wrong, some transient failure. When we're depressed in the everyday sense, we tend to obsess over things in the past that we feel guilty about. Again this is not what major depression is about. It is so severe in the elements of grief and guilt that at an extreme, it could even take on a delusional quality. This is not delusional in the way of a schizophrenic might be, but it's delusional in the sense of how you interpret the world around you.

Let me give you an example. Older guy, perfectly healthy and one day from out of nowhere he has a heart attack. He's in the hospital, he's recovering from it. The reality is that he is going to recover, and his life can pretty much get back to normal, but he falls into a major depression as a result. He's in there every day getting a little bit stronger, and every day talking about how he's falling apart, he's declining, he's going to die, and there's no hope for him. It happens the hospital is circular and the nurses get him up and as he begins to get some strength back, he's able to walk 1 loop around the hospital. That's great. The next day, getting stronger, he walks 2 loops around. That evening his family is there, and he's going on yet again about oh, I'm dying. I'm dying; I wish you could at least tell me the truth. I'll say, you're just depressed, you're getting better. You're getting better. Look, we heard from the nurses, today you did 2 loops around the hospital and yesterday you did 1. He'll say, no, no, no. You don't understand. They've been doing construction. They've been doing construction here at the hospital, and they had to close down the main corridor, and they had to make a new shorter one, a little one last night, so 2 loops around that is, in fact, a lot shorter than the big one and I'm falling apart and I'm dying.

This is delusional thought. This was actually an engineer, the father of a friend of mine, an engineer going on about angles, diameters, and radii and expecting them to believe that last night, folks came into the hospital like little beavers and dug this out. This is delusional thinking, and it's sufficiently so that there is this view, the typical view, that depression is a disease of emotion. Ultimately, it's also a disease of distorted cognition. You view the world around you and you so intensely see the glass as half full, even the ones brimming over the top, that there's ultimately a cognitively distorted, even delusional quality to it.

What are some of the other symptoms of depression? Of course the one that is among the most horrifying is the tendency of people when highly depressed to injure themselves, to mutilate themselves, to attempt suicide, to succeed at committing suicide, and it happens with a very high rate. The current numbers are about 15% of people will come down with a major clinical depression at some point in their lives, and a substantial subset of those people will be depressed enough at various points to feel suicidal. Not good, this is horrifying on a certain level. What's the self-injury about? It begins to tap into a subject we'll hear about later when we begin to look at the psychology of depression and the notion that depression has something to do with unresolved angers. We're going to see about that. There are some pluses and minuses to this one, but there's a sound bite that came out of that literature. Depression is anger turned inward, and the self-injury component of that certainly makes sense

What else goes wrong with a major depressive? You have social withdrawal, that's an obvious extension of the anhedonia. Loss of libido, an obvious extension as well, but then you get a whole bunch of symptoms that are fascinating, a whole bunch of changes in the body of a depressive, these symptoms that are collectively called vegetative symptoms. For example, sleep changes during a depression. What's your guess? Well, when most of us are kind of feeling depressed for some period, we tend to sleep more, we're just without energy, and no, people who are clinically depressed, majorly so, the tendency is to sleep less. They're depressed, they have trouble falling asleep. No, the tendency instead is to fall asleep fairly normally, but wake up really early in the morning. Wake up at 4 in the morning, you are awake, you are not remotely rested, and that's it. Come into an emergency room some day with a deep incapacitating depression and one of the things they better ask you is, so do you wake up early in the morning? Early morning wakening, that is a real clear marker of the disease.

Next, when you actually do fall asleep, we've learned already from the previous lecture, there's a whole structure, a whole architecture to sleep. The different sleep stages, slow-wave sleep, REM sleep, and it tends to be about 90-minute cycles. When you look at the brains of depressives when they're sleeping, and the structure, the very architecture of their sleep patterns is disorganized. Indulging yourself, absolutely no way. This is someone who when they're asleep their brain is working differently. More abnormalities, a change in appetite, in most people decreased, and in a subset of people increased. A change in all sorts of aspects of metabolism, and for our purposes probably the most interesting thing, in a substantial percentage of depressives, increased levels of glucocorticoids. What that screams to you is stress, and as we'll see that makes perfect sense, and what that screams to you, I hope, is this is a biological disorder. There are hormones that are out of whack, sleep cycles. This is not "stop indulging yourself."

Another feature of depression also screams biology, and this is the fact that there are patterns to when people have their depressions. There will be a person with a cycle of being symptom-free for a certain amount of time. Fall into a deep depression, come out the other end at a certain schedule. There could be rhythmicity to the disease. The most striking example of that is people who get depressed, more likely, at only a certain time of year, and it tends to be the winter months. This is someone who, in July, things are going perfectly fine. Then something disastrous occurs and they feel depressed. They come out the other end, and they cope, they heal, and along comes January where there's nothing wrong whatsoever, and just like the previous 6 Januaries, they fall into a winter depression, and they have to be hospitalized and there's this rhythmicity. This particular one is referred to as a seasonal affective disorder; affect, emotion. Seasonal affective disorder, SAD, and this is another thing that screams biology. The biology of rhythms, daily rhythms, seasonal rhythms, and there's something wrong with those rhythms. This is not, ooh stop babying yourself. This is a disease that's all about biology.

This transitions us now to asking: What is wrong biologically in depression? Where we start off is brain chemistry. What's going on normally, and what's going on that's not quite normal in the brains of people with depression?

This is best covered in a diagram, which you could find in the Guidebook, and this is one that shows the basic flow of information between 2 neurons, 2 brain cells. You'll remember from the earlier lectures, one neuron will send a projection, a cable to another neuron, and that's what was going on, the spinal cord, the fast acute pain, the chronic pain, all of that. In actuality, that projection from one neuron to the next doesn't actually touch the next neuron. There's a little space in between called a synapse. Synapse, that's what a synapse is. It's a tiny space between 2 neurons, and what that means then is if a neuron is going to talk to the next neuron, it releases a chemical messenger which goes floating across the synapse. It comes out of this end of the neuron. It comes out of the extreme end of the neuron, that's called the axon terminal, and it floats across this tiny distance to what is called the dendrites of the next neuron, goes across, and yes indeed, as we know by now, that neurotransmitter will interact with its neurotransmitter receptor. Suddenly something or other changes in that second neuron. The 2 neurons have talked to each other. Something or other, as we saw in the pain lecture, something or other sometimes can make the form of making the second neuron more excitable, sometimes less excitable. The neurons are talking to each other by way of these neurochemicals, neurotransmitters.

Looking at that, there's one additional piece that you have to make sense of which is the first neuron has released these neurotransmitters across the synapse, they bind to the receptor, they do their thing there, and they come floating off the receptor, and then you've got to clean up after yourself. You've got to finish what you've done. You've got to get rid of the neurotransmitter you released, and it's floating around now, and there are 2 options. You could be ecologically minded, you can recycle your neurotransmitter. It is taken up by a fancy pump in that axon, the end of the neuron that released it. It's taken back up. It's repackaged, ready to be used again, or you can really be unecologically minded, you can throw out your neurotransmitter. There might be some enzyme in the synapse that takes the neurotransmitter, rips it into a lot of little pieces, flushes it down the toilet, down the toilet into your cerebral spinal fluid and such. We've got this general role of neurochemical communication which is a neuron, when excited, releases a neurotransmitter, floats across the synapse, stimulates the next neuron by way of binding to its receptor, comes floating off, at which point you finish the whole thing, either degrading neurotransmitter or recycling it.

This is the general rule about neurotransmitters, and amid these general rules there are a gazillion different chemicals that appear to be neurotransmitters that meet at least some of the criteria for them, and what we now know and what was sort of the first bit of information in the depression field is, there's something screwy with neurotransmitter called norepinephrine. Wait a second. I've heard the name norepinephrine before, oh-so-many lectures ago, that sympathetic nervous system releasing epinephrine, norepinephrine, norepinephrine down at your heart. This is norepinephrine in a different part of your nervous system doing something completely different that has something to do with depression. You can use the same letter in all sorts of different words, you can use the same chemical messenger.

There's something wrong with norepinephrine in a part of the brain that has something to do with pleasure, and the absence of norepinephrine gets you into trouble there. Stay tuned, we'll see that area in a bit. What's the evidence that there's something wrong with norepinephrine? You go back to the very first drug that was developed as an antidepressant. It's called an MAO inhibitor—do not worry, this MAO inhibitor and the name will make sense. In the synapse, there's an enzyme, which rips up norepinephrine into little pieces, it degrades it, that whole thing you just heard about called MAO, monoamine oxidase. MAO, and what does an MAO inhibitor do? It inhibits MAO, and as a result, you don't rip up the norepinephrine afterward. It sticks around longer, sticks around longer and it's got nothing else to do. It might as well hit that receptor on the next neuron a 2nd time and a 5th time and a 20th time, and what happens then is you're sending more norepinephrine signaling. Depressives tend to get less depressed at that point.

What's your hypothesis at that point? What does it have to be? Ooh, if throwing in a drug that increases norepinephrine signaling makes depressions less depressive, maybe the initial problem is a paucity of norepinephrine. This gave rise to the norepinephrine hypothesis that there's a shortage of norepinephrine in one relevant area of the brain as the cause of depression. More evidence rolled in. By the 1960s, 1970s, a next class of antidepressant drugs had become popular called tricyclic antidepressants. It turns out they do essentially the same exact thing. They don't work on MAO which rips up the norepinephrine; remember that other step where you can also recycle it? The first neuron takes it back up and repackages it. What do tricyclics do? They block the reuptake. They block the reuptake, and thus the norepinephrine sticks around in the synapse longer, and for lack of anything else to do, hits the receptor a 2nd, 4th, or a 50th time, and the person gets better. Ooh, yet another way of increasing norepinephrine signaling and depressions get less depressive. I bet there was too little norepinephrine.

More evidence, more evidence, there's a drug, it's used very rarely now, but there's a drug that lowers blood pressure called reserpine. What does reserpine do? It destroys some of the packages of norepinephrine at the end of neurons whose axons release a lot of norepinephrine. Back to the sympathetic nervous system, less norepinephrine on the scene, blood pressure is going to decrease, that's great, that's great, but there's the side effect which is if you get the levels too high of this reserpine and you wipe out too much norepinephrine, the person gets clinically depressed.

We've got bidirectional evidence here. Take drugs that push up norepinephrine levels, and you take depressives, and they get better. Take drugs that drive down norepinephrine levels, and you take undepressed people and they get depressed. So, yes, I'm convinced by now. What does a shortage of norepinephrine cause in the brain? Or flip the other way, what does norepinephrine normally do? Amid its roles, all sorts of things, you've got a very interesting role for norepinephrine. It's got something to do with pleasure.

Back in the '50s, researchers, neuroscientists discovered something very interesting. They found this one area of the brain, the limbic system, where if you put an electrode down in there, in a rat's brain, and here's what you did. You set things up so the rat could press a lever a certain number of times, and by doing that, it would get buzzed in that part of the brain. This buzzing, this stimulation of this part of the brain, caused rats to be unbelievably happy. Of course the question is, how can you tell when a rat's unbelievably happy? It will just press the lever over and over and over. Rats would work themselves to death in order to get stimulated in this part of the brain. It was soon called the pleasure pathway. It's got more technical terms, but as soon as people saw this, of course the question is do you find this in humans? Do I have one? Can I get a new one? Can I get a second one? Soon neurosurgical studies with humans in the process of going in to get out a tumor for example, in classical neurosurgery, people would be awake. Studies were done stimulating those areas, and it would generate a pure, absolute sense of well-being, That's great.

Now what do we have? The next finding, which was that that pathway makes heavy use of norepinephrine. Ah-ha, so you got a shortage of norepinephrine in this pathway, this pleasure pathway is not working very well, and suddenly, what have you just generated? Anhedonia, that defining symptom of depression. That's great. That describes everything; that explains it. It's all about norepinephrine. Here's where the problems come in. Three reasons, first one, first one is you throw norepinephrine into one of these neuronal systems, and it starts changing What's happening? You throw in one of those antidepressive drugs, trycyclics, monoamine oxidase inhibitors, you throw in one of those, and within minutes they're changing stuff going on in the synapse. You throw them into a depressed person, and they don't start feeling better for 2 to 3 weeks. Something doesn't fit.

Next problem, people soon learned that, yes, norepinephrine had a role in those pleasure pathways, but they soon discovered another neurotransmitter played a much more critical role, dopamine. Then came along the drug that really messed things up, a drug like Prozac. Prozac, which is an SSRI, a serotonin, a selective serotonin reuptake inhibitor, this one works just like the tricyclics. It makes it impossible to take back up the neurotransmitter, but it was a different neurotransmitter, serotonin. Suddenly the norepinephrine hypothesis wasn't looking all that exciting and very flawed there and people were punching it out. You want a resolution at this point, a very, very simplistic one in terms of what's going on with norepinephrine, serotonin, and dopamine during depression, here's an extremely, extremely simplified one, and don't hold me to this. Norepinephrine has something to do with energy. The absence of norepinephrine begins to explain the psychomotor retardation of depression. It's exhausting to do everything. Serotonin has something to do with this rumination on grief, despair, guilt. The shortage of dopamine has something to do with the anhedonia, super simplistic.

We've now gotten a bit of a sense about the neurochemistry. Very quickly looking at something about the neuroanatomy of depression, we already know one thing, which is the hippocampus tends to get smaller. That's not what we'll focus on here; instead, we hark back to many lectures ago, that triune brain concept. You've got that ancient reptilian brain that does mechanical regulatory stuff; you've got the limbic system superimposed on top. Then you've got the cortex, the cortex is abstract thinking. Think for a second what a depression is about: sad things, sad thoughts, sad memories, and sad emotions. Go out and once again get gored by a rhino, and you're going to turn on the stress-response. You will secrete glucocorticoids. You will not feel like having sex all that much. Growth will probably be delayed. Sleep will be disrupted. Sit there instead and think about children in refugee camps, think about childhood leukemia. Think about any of those things, and suddenly your body does something similar to that with vegetative symptoms. Up go glucocorticoid levels, disruption of sleep, anhedonia all of that. On a certain level then, what is a depression? A depression is when your cortex comes up with some abstract sad thoughts and manages to get the rest of your brain to go along with it as if it was a real stressor. What the cortex is about is the abstractions, the very, very subtle poignant features of what stresses us, of what saddens us, of what depresses us where it is then able to send projections down to those ancient reptilian areas as we heard earlier, and stimulate them into a stress-response.

This is very simplistic, obviously, and now let's take this one step further, with really an idiotically simplistic idea. If the problem with depression is you got your cortex thinking, ooh, too many sad thoughts and whispering it down to the reptilian part of the brain, and kicking things into gear there. What's the cure for depression, then? Take yourself a little pair of scissors, cut underneath the cortex, and disconnect it from the rest of the brain. Oh, that's really a terrific therapy, that's really going to do a whole lot for you. Remarkably, a version of that which is used in very, very rare circumstances of severe intractable depression actually makes people feel a bit better, something called a cingulum bundle cut, and that supports this notion of the cortex coming up with sad ideas. It's not just the cortex, it's a subarea, a subarea found very much intertwined with the frontal cortex, an area called the anterior cingulate. The anterior cingulate comes up with the sad things. Watch your loved one being poked in their finger with a pin, the anterior cingulate activates. Have a sad thought with a sense of dread, it's the anterior cingulate, that's the area that is talking downstream, and what you find in depressives is overactivity of the anterior cingulate. That, in effect, in a supersimplified way, that's the part of the cortex that's coming up with those sad, sad thoughts and getting the rest of the brain to go along with it.

292

Where are we at right now? We've now come over the basic symptoms of depression, and we've now looked quite a bit at the brain chemistry, the neurochemistry of it. We've just looked at a little bit of the neuroanatomy of it. What we need to do next in the next lecture is look at some of the endocrinology of depression. What this should be screaming throughout all of this is, this is a biological disorder. This is not "stop indulging yourself," this is as biological as diabetes. There's something wrong with the brain chemistry, the brain structure, the sleep cycles, all of that. It's biology, but what we'll see in the next lecture is if all you do is think about the biology and not focus on the psychological aspects as well, you're not going to be in much of a position to help someone who is clinically depressed.

Stress and the Psychology of Depression
Lecture 20

> Men and women have the same rates of bipolar; women have roughly
> twice as much diagnosis of unipolar depression. What's that about? All
> sorts of possibilities, all sorts of theories. One is the diagnostic criterion
> problem, which goes as follows: Men, when depressed, are more likely
> than women to self-medicate themselves with alcohol, with various
> drugs, and they're more likely to be labeled as an alcoholic than as a
> depressive. There's not actually difference between men and women,
> it's just that a lot of the men get categorized in another way.

The previous lecture covered a number of aspects of the biology of
depression. What about hormones; what do they have to do with
depression? It turns out a whole lot. On average, women have higher
rates of depression than men do, and the risk of depression in women
tends to peak at certain times in life: during the 2 weeks after giving birth,
around menopause, and around one's period. These are all circumstances
where there are very dramatic changes in levels of certain hormones. Two
of the most pertinent ones, estrogen and progesterone, have a great effect
on the brain. The next one that comes in is **thyroid hormone**, which plays
a large role in maintaining your metabolic rate. When people become
hypothyroid, they have a greatly increased risk of falling into a depression.
In fact, the numbers suggest that something like 15%–20% of depressions
are not due to a primary depressive disorder but instead are secondary to an
undiagnosed hypothyroidism.

What's the evidence to think there's a link between stress and depression?
The first is epidemiological: People who have just had major stressful events
are statistically more likely to fall into a depression. Furthermore, people
who are given high levels of synthetic glucocorticoids for autoimmune
disorders or inflammatory issues have greatly increased risk of going into
a depression.

At this point, we know a bit about the neurochemistry, the brain structure,
and the endocrinology—but we are not going to be very good at curing

depression. To begin to put the pieces together, we now have to transition from depression as a biological disorder to looking at the psychological aspects of depression.

Sigmund Freud had some remarkably insightful things to say about depression. Freud wrestled with figuring out the difference between mourning and melancholia, that is, a reactive, transient depression and a major clinical depression. The core of Freudian thinking is that whom or what you love, you also hate; there is this ambivalence. In this view, depression comes out of a circumstance where you lose something or someone whom you loved, and there is hatred and ambivalence mixed in. Freud posited that in the aftermath of this loss, if you were able to put the anger and resentment aside and focus purely on the sadness, the love, the loss, you get simple mourning. If instead you can't put the hate aside, you have melancholia, major depression.

It's at the intersection of the organic basis and the psychological (or psychosocial) basis of a disease that we get the most insight, and very frequently, that intersection is about stress.

We learned earlier the key building blocks of psychological stressors: lack of outlets, lack of control, lack of predictability, lack of social support, and the perception that things are worsening. A depression, in a sense, is a pathological extreme of those perceptions. This fits with the fact that a child who loses a parent to death at an early age is permanently at greater risk for depression. A lot of childhood is about learning what things you can control and what things you can't. When you learn not only that there are things that you can't control but also that some of them are incredibly awful, you begin to learn in an overgeneralized way that you don't have much control over anything. This sets you up for the cognitive distortion that this is what life is like. This is **learned helplessness**.

This is a powerful model and one that I think gives us the most insight into the psychology of depression—depression as caused by extremes of psychological stress. We've got 2 very different views—the neurobiology and the experiential cognitive distortion—and we begin to fit them together in an elegant way that's built around stress. We have seen the intertwining of the two—the role of stress as impacting the biology of depression and the role of stress as an outcome of certain adverse aspects of your life. This brings us back again to an absolutely critical point: It's at the intersection of the organic basis and the psychological (or psychosocial) basis of a disease that we get the most insight, and very frequently, that intersection is about stress. ■

Important Terms

learned helplessness: A term often used in the context of depression, describing a state where an individual, due to repeated psychological stress, has lost the capacity to recognize circumstances where it is possible to effectively cope with a stressor.

psychomotor retardation: A key symptom of major depression, in which thought and action seem exhausting.

thyroid hormone: Secreted by the thyroid gland, its main function is to increase metabolism. Abnormally low thyroid hormone levels (i.e., hypothyroidism) can give rise to depression.

Suggested Reading

Cohen, Janicki-Deverts, and Miller, "Psychological Stress and Disease."

Sapolsky, *Why Zebras Don't Get Ulcers*, chap. 14.

Questions to Consider

1. What does the phenomenon of learned helplessness have to do with depression?

2. Where do neurobiology, psychology, and genetics intersect in making sense of depression?

Stress and the Psychology of Depression
Lecture 20—Transcript

We return for the second lecture covering this disease of malignant sadness, depression, major clinical depression, and the previous lecture covered a number of things worth reviewing here and the first is emphasizing what an awful disease it is. Fifteen percent of us or so will have a major depression at some point in our lives, one of the leading causes of disability on the planet, and a paralyzing disease at an extreme. We saw something about the symptoms, most defining, it is a disease of lack of pleasure, anhedonia, elements of grief, of guilt, elements of what is termed psychomotor retardation, everything is exhausting to do, to think, the possibilities of self injury, those vegetative symptoms including elevated glucocorticoid levels. That really key point that comes out of vegetative symptomology in this disease is, it's a disease. There are biological problems. This is not, "Oh, stop babying yourself."

What we then shifted to is looking at some of the actual biology of the disease. We started off with the neurochemistry, the famed norepinephrine hypothesis of depression, and how in the years since it has given way to recognizing, yes, too little norepinephrine plays a role, likewise dopamine, likewise serotonin, interactions amongst them. I would bet the farm that there is going to be a gazillion more neurotransmitters that are implicated. Then transitioning to structural features of the brain, and that key role played by the cortex, this area, the frontal cortex, the anterior cingulate, this part of the brain where you think abstract, sad thoughts, and in effect, get the rest of the brain to go along with it as if it were an actual stressor.

Now we transition over to another piece of the biology story: What do hormones have to do with depression? It turns out a whole lot, not surprisingly. The first realm of this is one that almost immediately comes to mind when you think about hormones and depression which is the simple question: Why do women have much higher rates of depression than men do? There are 2 different types of depression. There's what's called unipolar depression, which is your alternate between being depressed and not depressed, depressed and not depressed, depressed and not depressed. Then there's the much rarer and in some ways more disastrous, bipolar depression, manic depression, where you're oscillating around the extremes. Men and women have the same rates of bipolar; women have roughly twice as much diagnosis of unipolar depression. What's that about? All sorts of possibilities, all sorts of theories, one is the diagnostic criterion problem which goes as follows: Men, when depressed, are more likely than women to self-medicate themselves with alcohol, with various drugs, and they're more likely to be labeled as an alcoholic than as a depressive. There's not actually difference between men and women, it's just that a lot of the men get categorized in another way. There's some evidence for this, not huge amounts.

Next explanation for why, legitimately, women have higher rates of unipolar depression is a very sociological, almost anthropological one. As we know by now, lack of control plays a huge role in stress, and in this view, there's a focusing on the fact that in so many cultures across this planet, women traditionally have less control over their lives. In this theory, it is setting up one more readily for depression. Another realm, and this one has to do which emotional, psychological aspects, what people do with upsetting emotions, and the tendency, on the average, that women are more likely than men to ruminate on disturbing problems.

What do I mean by "ruminate"? This is a realm where you do studies which they're so embarrassing how clichéd the results are, but how consistently it comes out. You take someone who has just had an upsetting interaction with a friend, something like that, and you give them a choice of some things to do afterwards, a certain questionnaire to fill out. A huge percentage of women choose to fill out a questionnaire about the nature of their friendship with the person they just had the argument with, when they met, does the person have a good marriage, and all that stuff. A huge percentage of the men choose to fill out some questionnaire like trivia questions about the American presidency. No wonder these guys are such a mess. They can't communicate; they hid their emotions, on the average, once again with obvious exceptions. On the average, women ruminate more on emotions, adverse emotions, than men do. That's pretty clear. What's much less clear is how rumination gets you into a higher rate of clinical depression. All these sorts of possibilities, misdiagnosis, sociological explanations, and motive communicative ones, for my money the most interesting realm is what do hormones have to do with depression? What do hormones have to do with the predominance of depression in women?

Part of what makes this very interesting and makes the endocrine explanation very compelling to me is it's not only the case that on the average, women have higher rates of depression than men do, but the risk of depression in women tends to peak at certain times in life, certain times in one's life history. Shortly after giving birth, the 2 weeks after birth, the postparturition period is the most vulnerable time of life for a human to fall into a depression, around the time of menopause, around the time of one's period, all of these are circumstances where there are very dramatic changes in levels of certain hormones. You know by now what some of the most pertinent ones are, estrogen and progesterone. This is a realm where each has a lot of effects on the brain, remarkably where the ratio of the 2 have a lot of effects.

What we saw previously was all of these reproductive events from ovulation, menses, menopause, birth, involve enormous fluctuations in the levels of estrogen and progesterone, and thus, potentially enormous fluctuations in the ratio of the 2. There are lots of reasons in my mind to think that abnormalities in levels of estrogen, levels of progesterone, levels of their ratio, levels of receptors for these in the brain may have something to do with this predominance of depression in women. At this point, what's known is whatever your favorite theory is about the neurochemistry of depression, if you're a serotonin fan, if you're a dopamine one, if you're a norepinephrine, whichever one you are buying into, there's precedent for how estrogen and progesterone affect some aspect of that system. That's a first hormone that's relevant.

Next one that comes in, thyroid hormone—thyroid hormone, extremely interesting because what you see is thyroid hormone, coming out of your thyroid gland, brain, pituitary, what it plays a large role in is maintaining your metabolic rate. What you see is when people become hypothyroid, a real drop in their levels of thyroid hormone in their metabolism, there's a greatly increased risk of falling into a depression. In fact what the numbers suggest is something like 15, 20% of depressions out there are in fact not due to a primary depressive disorder, but are instead secondary to an undiagnosed hypothyroidism. What we see here is this very important point which should be obvious by now: You can't separate the brain from metabolism, from nutrition, intertwining of all of them. For our purposes here in this course in general, obviously the endocrine world that's most interesting with respect to depression is stress hormones, glucocorticoids. As we've heard already, amid a tendency, somewhat of a tendency for elevated sympathetic nervous system tone in people with depression, there is a very reliable increase in glucocorticoid levels in about half of depressives, and ones with the most serious cases. Suddenly we get pulled in explicitly for the first time, something about the interactions between stress and depression.

What's the evidence to think there's even a link for this? The first is epidemiological. People who have just had major stressful events are now statistically more likely to fall into a depression. That's simply the pattern that you see. You see it with an interesting subtlety which is, suppose you have somebody who has some awful, stressful event happen to them. They fall into a depression, and they come out the other end. This person is no more at risk now for a subsequent depression than anybody else is. A second trauma comes along. They fall into a depression the second time, they recover, the come out the other end, they are still no more at risk for a subsequent depression.

Somewhere around the fourth or fifth round of this something happens, and some endogenous process begins to take place, and the person's depressions begin to cycle rhythmically independent of whether something stressful occurs in the outside world, enormously important to understand this transition. Epidemiologically, stressors are associated with increased risk of early stage depression. More evidence, people who are given very high levels of synthetic glucocorticoids for their autoimmune disorder, their inflammatory issues, not only is there the possibility of the memory problems we've heard about, but you greatly increase the risk of somebody going into a depression. Early stage of treatment with steroids, corticosteroids, people tend to have a euphoria, be in this energized state, very long-term treatment, increased risk of depression. Back to Cushing's syndrome, Cushing's disease, any of a number of tumors where the result is you are secreting enormous amounts of glucocorticoids, and Cushing's disease carries an increased risk of depression.

Possible confound here, well duh, of course you get depressed. You've got this awful endocrine disorder. What are the appropriate controls in studies like these? People who have equally severe disorders, but ones that happen not to involve elevated glucocorticoids, and the Cushingoid folks have the higher levels of rates of depression.

All of this evidence linking elevated glucocorticoids to depression has given rise to a fascinating potential new realm of depression therapeutics. As mentioned earlier, there are drugs that target the norepinephrine system, the dopamine system, serotonin, selective serotonin, reuptake inhibitors. There are drugs that are being tried that target some of the neurochemistry of pain, remarkably, and they can decrease depression, psychic pain using some of the same pathways as physical pain, all these different therapeutics. A new one that's emerging is the notion of knock down glucocorticoid levels, decrease glucocorticoid signaling, and maybe that will work as an antidepressant.

Alan Schatzberg, psychiatrist at Stanford University, has been pioneering some of the work of using these antiglucocorticoids, some decrease the release of glucocorticoids, others block glucocorticoid receptors. The net result is less glucocorticoid signaling, and when you look at depressives with some of the most extreme versions of psychotic depression, with some of the most dramatic elevations of glucocorticoid levels, antiglucocorticoid therapy appears to be helpful and therapeutic. We see here, glucocorticoids intertwined pharmacologically, therapeutically, epidemiologically, so of course the question becomes: How does an excess of glucocorticoid set you up for a depression?

We've seen umpteen different things the glucocorticoids do. Amid the possible candidates, one is extremely interesting, which is truly sustained stress and truly sustained exposure to elevated glucocorticoid levels deplete dopamine from that dopamine reward pathway. This is a direct possible link between major stress and the emergence of the anhedonia, the absence of pleasure typical of major depression. This is a really important link. Commensurate with all of this, you wind up seeing elevated levels of glucocorticoids in a substantial subset of depressives. It can take the form of disappearing the daily rhythm, the circadian rhythm of glucocorticoid levels. The levels don't go down at the time of day they normally do. Other versions are the glucocorticoid system has trouble turning off at the end of stressors. It doesn't sense a negative feedback signal, that sort of minutia we talked about before, elevated levels of glucocorticoids. This supports this picture amid the psychomotor retardation. You can't get out of bed, you're so wiped out, you can't get out of bed because an enormous battle is going on internally, this notion of a depression as a chronic stress state, the notion, as we will see again, the notion of depression as anger turned inward.

At this point, you've got something or other about the neurochemistry; you've got something about the brain structure; you've got something about the endocrinology. At this point, you are practically a card-carrying biological psychiatrist at the cutting edge, the best there is out there. At this point, if all you know about is the brain chemistry, and the structure, and the hormones, you're not going to be very good at curing depression. There are still going to be oceans of depressives out there who are not being helped. To begin to put the pieces together, what we now have to do is transition from depression as a neurochemical, neuroanatomical, neuroendocrine disorder to looking at the psychological aspects of depression.

To begin to do so, God help me, very, very deep apologies here at this point, but I actually have to mention the name of Sigmund Freud because Freud had some remarkably insightful things to say about depression. Freud started off with the same puzzle we had in the last lecture. Hey, all of us get depressed, bad things happen to us, we feel depressed, and we heal. We come out the other end of it, and then there are the folks who bad things happen to, or even no bad things, and they crash into a deep clinical depression. Turn of the century Viennese term, mourning, something bad happens, you mourn and you come out the other end. Melancholia, something happens and you crash into a depression.

In this classic essay, Freud wrestled with the issue of what's the difference between mourning and melancholia, a reactive transient depression and a hugely impacting clinical one? Here's the scenario that he came up with, classically Freudian with all of its possible things to criticize, but there is a kernel that just feels right in there. The core of Freudian thinking is: individuals, objects, whatever, who you love you also hate, ambivalence, confused feelings, in this Freudian view, depression comes out of a circumstance where you lose a loved object, person, idea, principle, who knows what, but you lose something or someone who you loved, and of course, with the Freudian baggage coming along who you also hated and all that ambivalency stuff. What he posited was in the aftermath of this loss, if you were able to put the angers, the hatreds, the resentments aside and focus purely on the sadness, the love, the loss, that's when you get mourning. That's where there's the sadness, the depression and you recover, you heal, and you come out the other side.

In the Freudian view, instead what's going on in melancholia, you have these mixed feelings, the love, the hate, and you can't put the hate aside. You are absolutely awash in the contradictions of the love, the hate and the sheer force, the sheer crushing weight of this is what pushes somebody into melancholia. This isn't terribly scientific in modern terms, but something just feels right about this. You look at this, no wonder there's so much grief. You lose a loved object, a loved individual, and you are able to put aside the ambivalences, and you suffer one type of loss, you've lost this individual who you love. You have the mixed ambivalent state of Freudian confusion, and you lose a loved object, and you mourn 2 things. The first is the loss of that individual you love, and in addition, you have now lost the chance to ever make things better with them, to say the things you always wanted to, to hear them say or do whatever. It's a double loss. No wonder the grief is so much more severe.

Next, the guilt—the guilt makes sense as well which is you're sitting there in this Freudian froth there of ambivalency and you loved this person, you're sad, and you miss them. At the same time there's a part of you saying, thank God I can finally live my life now. How could you think a thing like that at a time like this—guilt, paralyzing guilt, coming in. More of the Freudian symptoms that begin to make sense, that psychomotor retardation—you were in the middle of this enormous emotional battle. You have this individual who you loved, you hated, you had mixed feelings. You wanted to say this and you never got to. You wish they could have told you this, and you wondered if they really felt this way. You just want to—and now they're gone and all you can do is take all that confusion and turn it inward. No wonder you're too tired to get out of bed for weeks on end. This is where that Freudian sound bite of anger turned inward begins to make a lot of sense. You see all these pieces, including at the extreme, the possibility of anger turned inward taking the form of self-injury. This was the classic Freudian view. It doesn't make any sense in terms of modern biology. There's no way you can turn ratios, love hate ratios to translate into estrogen, progesterone ratios, or what ambivalences look like in terms of norepinephrine. You can't do modern science on it. The best you can do is just have this intuitive sense; it just feels right. Nonetheless, that's about all you can do with it.

What sort of psychology winds up being much more pertinent, and this is where we switch over to the world of psychological stressors, we already know by now what the key building blocks are: lack of outlets, lack of control, lack of predictability, perception that things are worsening, and lack of social support. What a depression is about in a sense is a pathological extreme of those perceptions. Here's what you would see, a very disturbing research model with animals, but one again, as you hear this, keep in mind this is where Prozac came from. This is where tricyclics came from, this is where the next generation of antidepressants to treat the oceans of treatment-resistant depressives are going to come from.

Here's the sort of model that's used. You take a rat and you give it a shock every now and then. But it's set up in this contingent way where there is one side of the cage where the shocks come, the other side, the shocks don't come. A little light comes on whenever there's going to be a shock here, and very quickly, the rat learns to shift over to this side. The shock comes on this side, and the rat shifts over to that side, it masters this task fairly easily. Now instead, take a rat where you just shock it. You just shock it without a warning, without any of this possibility of control. It just gets a lot of shocks. The next day you put it into this setting where the light goes on here, you step over here, and you find the light goes on here, you learn to step over here, and the rat cannot learn to do it. It cannot learn this simple operancy, this simple bit of efficacy, this simple bit of control, because what have you done? The day before were those repeated uncontrollable shocks, you've taught that rat to be helpless, thus, the sound bite in this realm of learned helplessness. When you do this to animals like this experimentally, suddenly they get elevated glucocorticoid levels. Suddenly, they've got problems with levels of norepinephrine, dopamine, all of that. Suddenly, you have an animal who could be made less learned helpless with some antidepressant drugs. What this has given rise to is this notion in cognitive psychology that what depression is, is learned helplessness.

This fits as well, this even begins to explain one of the pieces of the picture of depression which is you have a child who loses a parent to death at a fairly early age, and for the rest of their life they are more at risk for depression. This makes perfect sense. Think about this rat. The rat has learned when I'm in this cage and I'm getting these repeated shocks, there's nothing I can do about it. That's what the rat should have learned. Instead what it learns is when I'm in any setting, even a setting where I could do something to seize control, even in a setting like that, I don't do it. I can't learn it; I don't perceive it because I have overgeneralized my helplessness into a cognitive distortion. What's going on with the kid? An awful lot of childhood is about learning what things you can control and what things you can't in the world out there. What happens when you learn not only that there are things that you can't control, but some of them are so, so awful, you begin to learn in an overgeneralized way that you don't have a whole lot of control over anything.

What you're setting somebody up for is that same overgeneralization process, that cognitive distortion where instead of learning this is a setting where I have no control, no predictability, and no outlets, instead, this is what life is like. I am hopeless, and I am helpless.

This is a very powerful model, and this is one that I think gives us the most insight into the psychology of depression. It's the lecture on the psychology of stress writ large. Depression as caused by extremes of psychological stress. Now we've got 2 very different views. We've got the neurobiology end of it, hormones, brain chemicals, and we've got the experiential cognitive distortion, learned helplessness. How do you fit the pieces together? Here you begin to fit them together in an absolutely elegant way that's all built around stress. What this involves is recognizing that depression is a genetic disorder. Depression has a certain degree of heritability to it. Depression runs in families. Oh, environment runs in families also, much more careful studies showing things like identical twins have a higher rate of sharing a depressive trait than nonidentical twins. Adoption studies, someone who is depressive, is more likely to share that trait with their biological parents than with their adoptive parents. There's a genetic component to it. This is not there is genetic determinism. Identical twins, one of them is depressed, there's about a 50% chance that the other one will get depressed also. It's a genetic fact. One of them has depression; there's a 50% chance that the other one won't get depressed. There's a genetic influence; there's not genetic determinacy.

What are the genes of depression all about? A few years back, wonderful finding, fascinating one by Avshalom Caspi and colleagues at Duke University isolating what appears to be one of the most meaningful genes related to depression, where you look and you look at large families that have patterns of depression and ones who don't. You look for what genes are common to everybody with the depression and what genes are different from everybody. Out popped this one gene that was very interesting because it came with 2 different flavors, 2 different variants, and one of those variants seemed to be associated with the chemistry of depression.

Part of what made people so excited was this gene made perfect sense. It would have been a drag if this turned out to be a gene that has something to do with like how many nostril hairs you have. What was this gene? It coded for the protein that removed serotonin from the synapse and recycles it, the serotonin transporter. This gave rise to this landmark study looking at humans and looking which type, which flavor, of the serotonin transporter they had and did this increase your risk of depression. This was a mammoth study focusing on tens of thousands of kids who they then followed for years afterward so that in early adulthood, you knew which ones already signs of clinical depression, which ones don't, and you've genetically characterized them.

Then the critical question of this entire literature, which is: If you have the "bad version" of the serotonin transporter gene, are you more likely to be clinically depressed? If you had the version that was more likely to produce the serotonin chaos that we now recognize to be central to depression, are you more likely to be clinically depressed? Back came the answer, which was no. Having that version of the gene did not increase your risk in the slightest. What's going on there? Something much more subtle, something much more important, having this version of the gene doesn't increase your risk of depression unless you also have had a lot of childhood stressors. In other words, an interaction here between early environment, experience stress, and genetic propensity, and what you see, remarkably, is for each increase in the childhood traumas, the folks with the good version of the gene have a little bit of an increased risk of depression. The folks with the bad version, it just increases more and more. This is a gene-environment interaction. This is the demonstration of how experiential trauma and stress interacts with the brain chemistry. What is remarkable as it turns out, glucocorticoids are able to do something to regulate this gene, the serotonin transporter gene. The pieces are perfect there.

What do we have at this point? We've seen the biological view of depression, and we've seen brain chemistry, hormones, anatomy, and even genes. We've seen the more psychological one, Freudian, the theorizing, and for us, far more importantly, the notion of depression as a pathological extension of psychological aspects of stress. What we've seen, I think, most of all is the utter intertwining of the two, and the intertwining, the interface being the role of stress—the role of stress as impacting the biology of depression and the role of stress as an outcome of certain adverse aspects of your lives. What this brings in is this absolutely critical point. We've had it starting with ulcers and it pops up again and again, if all you try to do is understand the organic basis of a disease or the psychological, the psychosocial basis, you're not going to really know what's going on. It's at the intersection of the two that you get your most insight, and very, very frequently, that intersection is about stress.

Anxiety, Hostility, Repression, and Reward
Lecture 21

There're ... different genetic versions of dopamine receptors, some of which are less responsive; you need more of an umph in the system to keep it from habituating. To appreciate this, think about this, who is that guy? Evel Knievel, that was that madman who would motorcycle over all sorts of like cruisers and things of that sort and had broken every bone in his body over and over. You think about it, once a long, long time ago the young Evel Knievel, who had his driver's permit in his back pocket, raced a red light, just got across in time and got a little bit of a thrill from that. The next day, that wasn't enough.

This lecture examines more areas in which major stress has psychiatric implications. The first one, anxiety, is a psychiatric disorder that affects perhaps even more people than depression. To understand the biology of anxiety, we look at a part of the limbic system called the **amygdala**. The amygdala plays a role in learning to be fearful of new things and in innate fears and phobias. What does stress have to do with this? On a purely behavioral level, stress increases anxiety. The amygdala is extremely sensitive to glucocorticoids. With sustained stress and lots of glucocorticoids, the amygdala gets better at doing what it does, which is learning to be afraid. Its synapses become more excitable, and it can even grow new processes. The neurons get larger and more interconnected, setting you up for an anxiety disorder.

A second realm related to stress is hostility, which used to be called **type A personality**. **Toxic hostility** is a personality style where you think anything that happens around you is proof that everyone is out to get you; you have to watch your back 24-7. You're in the supermarket, and you've picked the slower line. You want to kill the idiot kid behind the cash register for intentionally slowing you down. You're thinking, "Come on, come on, come on!" Instead of checking out the People magazines, you drive your blood pressure up and put yourself more at risk for cardiovascular disease.

A third realm of intersection between personality and stress is that of repressive personalities, which are held by about 5% of the population. By definition, if you are repressive, you don't have depression or an anxiety disorder—in fact, you tend to be really happy. These are the folks who are highly organized and have everything under control. They walk the same way to work every day and can tell you what they're having for dinner 2 weeks from Thursday.

By definition, if you are repressive, you don't have depression or an anxiety disorder—in fact, you tend to be really happy.

They have a lot of discipline and get tons accomplished. Everything is terrific—until something stressful comes along, because they don't deal well with ambiguity or surprises. There are some downsides to it, but these are people who are normally highly functional, very productive, and happy. What is happening in their bodies? The level of metabolism in their prefrontal cortex is above normal, and their bloodstream has elevated levels of glucocorticoids. This makes an important point, which is sometimes it can be enormously stressful to create a world in which nothing stressful ever occurs: There's chronic activation of the stress-response in repressive individuals.

The goal of research in this area is not to get rid of stress. We don't want lives without stress whatsoever; in fact, stress is great when it's the right kind. The right kind of stress is called stimulation. Ask somebody who works in child development or gerontology, and they'll tell you people need stimulation. What counts as stimulatory stress? A moderate stressor that doesn't go on for too long and that you experience in a safe context.

We have entered this terrain of stress, under the right parameters, being pleasurable. What goes on in the brain to explain it? A neurotransmitter called **dopamine**. Dopamine is about reward, or more accurately, the anticipation of reward. It's also about the motivation that comes out of that anticipation. What happens with moderate amounts of stress that are moderately transient, with moderate increases in glucocorticoid levels?

You increase the release of dopamine. Short-term stress improves those aspects of mood; chronic stress depletes you of dopamine, and thus, you have less of a capacity for pleasure or the anticipation of pleasure. ■

The Delayed Discovery of Type A Personality

Here is the fascinating story of how type A personality was first discovered, which I got from the horse's mouth some years ago. Meyer Friedman, the cardiologist who first described it, died a few years ago at age 91. In the 1950s, he and his partner had a new cardiology practice; everything was going fine. But they had this one problem, which was that for some weird reason the armchairs in the waiting room were getting worn out at a very high rate.

Every month the upholsterer would come and fix a couple of the chairs. One month, the upholsterer was on vacation; the replacement upholsterer comes in, takes one look at the chairs, and discovers type A personality. He says, "What's with your patients? Nobody wears out chairs this way." That was indeed the case: The front 2 inches of the seat cushions and the front 2 inches of the armrests were totally shredded. This is the type A profile—people who are literally sitting on the edge of their seat, squirming and clawing nervously. This is what type A individuals look like when they have heart disease and are sitting in the office of their cardiologist. This is what it was.

What happened next? This is where things get really unfortunate. At that point Dr. Friedman should have grabbed the guy and said, "Good God, man, what you've discovered!" But that didn't happen. What happened instead? Dr. Friedman told his nurse, "Get this man out of my face. I'm an important cardiologist; he's wasting my time." Dr. Friedman himself was too type A to listen to the guy. It was about 5 years later that the doctor was collaborating with some psychologists and the type A profile popped up, and they said, "Oh my God, the upholsterer—he was right." To this day, nobody has a clue who that man was. This stands as one of the truly dark chapters in the history of science and medicine.

Important Terms

amygdala: A part of the brain's limbic system that plays an important role in fear and anxiety.

dopamine: A type of neurotransmitter whose numerous functions include a role in anticipation of pleasure; abnormalities in it have been found in individuals with depression.

toxic hostility: A personality style where an individual consistently interprets benign events as being threatening and calling for a hostile coping response. This modern incarnation of the type A personality concept carries an increased risk of cardiovascular disease.

type A personality: A personality style first described in the 1950s that carries an increased risk of cardiovascular disease. In its original formulation, type A individuals tend to be highly competitive, overachieving, time-pressured, impatient, and hostile.

Suggested Reading

Nestler and Malenka, "The Addicted Brain."

Sapolsky, *Why Zebras Don't Get Ulcers*, chaps. 15–16.

Questions to Consider

1. What does stress do to the brain that helps explain the increased risk of anxiety?

2. When do we love stress?

Anxiety, Hostility, Repression, and Reward
Lecture 21—Transcript

By now, we have moved so far away from some of the themes that dominated the first part of this course. Way back when, what were we thinking about: spastic colons, bladders, blood flow to penises, and fat cells as inflammatory. In the recent lectures, what we've done instead is move into the world of emotions and psychology and psychological stress, and as we saw in the last 2 lectures, the way in which psychological stress can bring about one of the worst of psychiatric disorders.

What we'll be doing in this lecture is now shifting over to an additional realm, another realm of major stress having psychiatric implications. What we'll shift to first is another one of the disastrous psychiatric disorders for which there are vast numbers of people suffering from it, arguably, perhaps even more than the number of depressives, anxiety disorders. As one prominent psychiatrist once described it, anxiety is the common cold of psychiatric disease.

A theme that came through very heavily in the depression lecture was you could think of depression as being a disease where people don't deal very well with stress, framed a particular way, which is when there's circumstances where you could control, where you have control, you have predictability, someone who's depressed, is unable to find that. Someone who is depressed is unable to recognize there's the possible control and predictability, and this is the notion of learned helplessness. As we transition now to thinking about anxiety, you have another version of people not dealing well with stress. In this case, it takes the form of, these are people who perceive stressors, and what they do is they try to mobilize 14 different coping responses at once, and they're mutually contradictory, they're endlessly vigilant, and most importantly, they can never recognize when it's over with. They can't recognize safety signals, it just goes on and on.

In beginning to understand the biology of anxiety, we enter a new part of the brain—one that hasn't really been mentioned before after dwelling so much on the hippocampus, the hypothalamus, the frontal cortex—another part of the limbic system, an area called the amygdala. The amygdala is absolutely central to understanding a lot of what goes wrong in anxiety. The amygdala plays a role in learning to be fearful of new things. It plays a role in innate fears and phobias. Very interestingly, the amygdala also plays a central role in aggression. In other words, you can't understand the neurobiology of aggression outside the context of the neurobiology of fear, and one might even conclude that in a world in which no amygdaloid neuron be afraid, you may perhaps have a more peaceful world centered around the amygdala. The amygdala is fascinating, and what you see is all sorts of evidence. If you stimulate the amygdala, you increase levels of anxiety, and this could be measured in a rat. If you destroy the amygdala experimentally, you decrease levels of anxiety. What does anxiety look like in a rat, anyway? Rats are nocturnal creatures; they don't like bright lights. You put them in this arena where it's dark around the periphery and brightly lit in the middle, and you put something wonderful in the middle, some piece of food or whatever. The rat wants it, but it's made anxious by the bright lights. You see this coming-and-going vacillation, and higher levels of anxiety; the rat is less capable of leaving that safe wall.

Manipulate the amygdala in a rat, and you manipulate levels of anxiety. Remarkably, you give a rat an antianxiety drug called a benzodiazepine—and that's a term that came up many lectures ago—a drug like Valium or Librium, and the rat gets less anxious and is more willing to explore the middle of that arena and has an amygdala that isn't as active. What about the human amygdala? You can't do that experimental stuff. But there are some accidents of nature, some very rare cases, where people have had their 2 amygdalae—there's one on each side—damaged, and these are individuals who don't show fear. These are individuals who are bizarrely trusting in circumstances where one should be a little bit skeptical and cautious.

The amygdala has a similar tone in humans. How do you see just how an amygdala is working? The sort of studies you do, once again brain imaging, put someone in one of those imagers. In this case, you can see what circumstances make a part of the brain suddenly become metabolically active. With the amygdala, it's fearful stimuli. It's stimuli that you've learned to perceive as fearful, and in fact, that could be subliminal, that whole business where you flash up a scary picture for a tenth of a second, and you're not even aware that you saw it. Your cortex isn't even aware that it saw it. Your amygdala did. One of the things you wind up seeing is people with post-traumatic stress disorder, their amygdala can get bigger or more metabolically active.

What does stress have to do with this? On a purely behavioral level, stress increases anxiety. You can show this with laboratory rats. Glucocorticoids do the same, and it's got lots to do with the amygdala. What were our hot spots so far of glucocorticoid receptors, hippocampus, frontal cortex, next in line is the amygdala, extremely sensitive to glucocorticoids. What happens there with sustained stress? It's really interesting. Let go back to the hippocampus, lots of stress, lots of glucocorticoids, and the hippocampus doesn't do its job as well. The synapses are less excitable, less of that LTP stuff. The dendrites, the processes of neurons retract, all of that. Meanwhile, over in the amygdala, right next door, it's exactly the opposite, lots of stress, lots of glucocorticoids, and the amygdala gets better at doing what it does which is learning to be afraid. The amygdala has its synapses, its connections become more excitable. The amygdala will even grow new processes. The neurons will get larger and more interconnected, and what we see here is stress remarkably doing, on a nuts-and-bolts level, exactly the opposite of what it does in the hippocampus, but on the most fundamental level, it sets you up again for another psychiatric disorder.

This brings us into another realm where things can go wrong, where you pay a psychiatric price, and where stress has something to do with it, hostility. Hostility, hostility, way back when, used to go under the name of type A personality. Type A was first described by a pair of cardiologists in San Francisco in the 1950s—Friedman and Rosenman—and here was the original type A formulation: time pressured, impatient, low self-esteem, joyless striving, anger, and this was what the picture was. What these guys reported at the time was, if this was your personality profile, you were more at risk for heart disease— type A personality increasing the risk of cardiovascular disease. Cardiologists hated these guys. You're some 1950s cardiologist, and all you think about is like heart valves and lipid levels in the bloodstream. Here are these guys saying, no, you got to sit down your patients, talk to them, and find out how they feel about their life. They hated the concept, total resistance to it. It wasn't until the 1980s enough studies had been done to make clear that the type A personality profile was for real in

315

terms of increasing the risk of heart disease. It was in fact a bigger risk factor than if you smoked, than if you were overweight, than if you had elevated cholesterol levels, hugely endangering factor.

By the 1980s, what became clear, though, was the critical component of that type A profile, which was the hostility. The hostility of a certain style, which is now known as toxic hostility, and this attributional style where anything that happens around you is proof that they're out to get you. They're out to get you preferentially; all you can do is watch your back 24-7, and this is the style. This is the style where you're in the supermarket, and you've picked the slower line. You want to kill the son of a bitch kid behind the cash register intentionally slowing you down, and no, don't ask the old lady how she is today. Come on, come on, come on, I'm going to die someday, and I don't want to spend my whole life in supermarket lines. This is your interpretive style. Instead of checking out the *People* magazines there, and you're blood pressure is going to go up, and you will put yourself more at risk for cardiovascular disease. In a lot of ways, the central research question of what toxic hostility is about is insofar as you are toxically hostile, what's worse for your cardiovascular system? Expressing the hostility or keeping it repressed inside. What's clear is expressing it is worse for everybody else's blood pressure, but this is a big issue. What is the physiological cost of repressing strong emotions, so really fascinating.

What's also fascinating is the story of how type A personality was first discovered, and I got this from the horse's mouth some years ago. Meyer Friedman, the cardiologist who first described it, died a few years ago at age 91. He saw his last patient a week before he died working a full-time cardiology clinic. As he used to say, I still have type A personality, but I'm a type A tortoise now. Here's the story he would tell: 1950s, he and his partner had this new cardiology practice; everything was going fine. They had this one problem which was for some weird reason the armchairs in the waiting room were getting worn out at a very high rate. What's this about? Who knows what this is about? This is part of the overhead. Every month this upholsterer would come and would have to fix a couple of the chairs, and that's how it works. One month, the upholsterer is on vacation. In comes a replacement upholsterer, takes one look at the chairs, and discovers type A personality. He says: "What's with your patients? Nobody wears out chairs this way." That was indeed the case, the front 2 inches of the seat cushions and the front 2 inches of the armrests were totally shredded like beavers were in there every night pulling away at the chairs. This is the type A profile. The person who is not just figuratively, but literally, sitting on the edge of their seat and squirming and clawing nervously. This is what a type A individual looks like when they have heart disease sitting in the office of their cardiologists. This is what it was.

What happens next? This is where things get really unfortunate. How should things have occurred? At that point Friedman should grab the guy and like, good God, man, what you've discovered. Or like upholsterers having midnight meetings with cardiologists, or teams of young idealistic upholsterers sweeping across America and coming back with the news, that no, you don't find chairs like these in podiatrists' offices. That didn't happen. What happens instead? Here's where Dr. Friedman starts looking all sheepish. He said, "I told my nurse, get this man out of my face. I'm this important cardiologist. He's wasting my time. Give him this damn check." He was too type A to listen to the guy. It was about 5 years later that Friedman was collaborating with some psychologists and out popped the type A profile, and they said, "Oh my God, the upholsterer, he was right." To this day, nobody has a clue who that man was. This stands as one of the truly dark chapters in the history of science and medicine.

Moving on, another realm of intersection between personality and stress, and this is a fascinating personality profile. This isn't even a disease. It's a personality style. These are people who have what is termed repressive personalities; maybe 5% of the population fits this profile. By definition, if you are repressive, you don't have a depression, you don't have an anxiety disorder—those have to get cleared out—and in fact, you tend to be really happy. You claim that you're happy, and they can even prove that you're happy with little psychological tests. Who are these people like, these repressive personality individuals, these are the folks who are so organized. These are the people who have everything under control; these are the folks who cross all their Ts and dot their Is. They've got everything organized. These are the folks who walk the same way to work every single day, they can tell you what they're having for dinner 2 weeks from Thursday. These are folks who are like that. These are the people like the college roommate you had where you looked at them and you said, oh, God, I wish I had like even remotely as much discipline as this person does. They get tons accomplished. Everything is terrific. Until something stressful comes along, until something of a particular type of stressor, which is some ambiguity, and they don't like surprises. They're not good with surprises. They don't express emotions very readily, they repress them. They don't read subtle emotions in other people very readily, and they're able to recognize the big ones. Oh, this person is in a rage, and that person is euphoric. They can't pick up this person is in rage but has an undercurrent of melancholy. The secondary emotions they don't express, and they don't pick up very well. There are some down sides to it, but nonetheless, these are people who are normally highly functional, doing well, very productive, and happy.

What are we doing talking about them in a stress course? What are we doing? You go find something interesting. Look at how their bodies work. First interesting hint, you look at the prefrontal cortex, put them in one of those scanners and you can see the level of activity in the prefrontal cortex, and you ask what are the levels of activity there? Prefrontal cortex is the part of the brain that makes you do the harder thing when it's the right thing to do, long-term planning, gratification postponement, it's got repressive, disciplined personality written all over it. People with repressive personalities, the level of metabolism in their prefrontal cortices are elevated above normal. What is that? It's like their fontal cortex is spending all the time squeezing their psychic sphincters closed as tight as possible. This is the regulation. What about hormones? You look in the bloodstream of these folks, and what you see is elevated levels of glucocorticoids. This makes no sense at all. This makes no sense because these people aren't depressed, they aren't anxious, they're happy, they're productive. What are they doing with elevated glucocorticoid levels? I think what repressives tell us is something very interesting, which is sometimes it can be enormously stressful to create a world in which nothing stressful ever occurs. Here we've seen yet another realm in which stress is bad news; you want to get rid of it. We've got all our organ systems, we've got these psychiatric disorders, we even have the ones that aren't psychiatric disorders that look like a good deal, but nonetheless, there's chronic activation of the stress-response in repressive individuals. This just underlines our theme of stress, bad news, get rid of the stuff, and get rid of every type of stressor.

What's worth talking about right now is that's not how it works. The goal of research in this area, the goal of any of this is not to get rid of stress. We don't want lives without stress whatsoever; in fact, we love stress. We love stress when it's the right kind. We leap up to experience it. We pay good money to get terrified by some scary movie. It's not that you don't want stress; we want the right kind, and that's clearly apparent in all sorts of realms of life. What do we call the right kind of stress? We call it stimulation. You look at somebody who works with child development, and the goal is not to have a stress-free life. You need stimulation. You look at gerontologists and the exact same punch line there. Our goal is not to have stress-free lives; we love stress when it's the right kind, when it's stimulatory.

What counts as stimulatory stress? One is stress in the perfect range, and it has a couple of parameters to it. First off, it's a moderate stressor. Here's the example. You get on a roller coaster, and this counts as wonderful, active stimulatory stress that you want to experience. You get on a roller coaster, and part of going on there is you're expecting unpleasant things to happen to your body as part of it. Maybe by the end of it you're going to feel a little queasy and nauseous, and that's part of the stressful menace of getting on a roller coaster, you may feel queasy afterward. You don't get on a roller coaster where there's a fairly high probability that you're going to be decapitated instead. You want a moderate challenge there. You want a moderate menace. What else? What else are aspects of when stress is working just right? It's transient. It doesn't go on for too long. What you've got there is the same logic. It's not by chance that roller coaster rides are 3 minutes long and not 3 weeks long, you want transient stuff. Most importantly, you want to feel those experiences, that transient challenge, that moderate challenge in a context that's safe, where overall you are in a benevolent setting.

We've just defined something very interesting. A benevolent setting where you are willing to stress yourself as long as it's not too severe and doesn't go on for too long. Where you are willing to stress yourself by giving up a certain degree of control, of predictability of outlets, all of that. What have we just defined? This is what play is. Play is giving up control in a circumstance where you feel safe. Look at 2 dogs when they're playing. What happens? The higher-ranking one squats down low, takes the subordinate position, saying, hey, the hierarchy is suspended for the moment, and I'm willing to take this position because we're going to play; we're going to play, play. What you do then is you give up all the control and predictability, that the subordinate animal has to make sure the dominant one knows they're groveling. They're rolling around and they're communicating vulnerability, and before you know it, you're allowing the other dog to put his teeth on your neck, your private parts, and all that. This is what play is. Play is the world in which, in an overall benevolent setting, we're willing to give up some control. We're willing to be stressed. We love play. An absence of play is a very serious problem during development and probably during adulthood as well.

We're in this terrain now of stress not being stressful, but under the right parameters, stress being pleasurable. Where does this come in? What does go on in the brain that begins to explain it, and we are back to that neurotransmitter that has already been floating around a lot in these lectures, dopamine. Dopamine, you remember dopamine, the pleasure pathway. Dopamine is about reward. It turns out when you look more closely, dopamine isn't actually about reward. It's about the anticipation of reward. It's not about happiness; it's about the pursuit of happiness. It's even about the motivation, the willingness to work, that comes out of that anticipation in order to get the reward. Very insightful work showing dopamine is more about anticipation than it is about the actual reward. I knew somebody in my dorm in college, an extremely mordent, depressive sort of guy who summed this up very well once by saying, a relationship is the price you pay for the anticipation of it. This guy had an endless stream of disastrous relationships, but you get the point here. Dopamine is much more about anticipation, the pursuit of, than it is about the actual reward. We've now gotten some more insight as to what dopamine has to do with this.

Where has dopamine come in before? Wait, we heard about dopamine before in the depression lecture. Chronic stress depletes you of dopamine, and thus, you have less of a capacity for pleasure, for the anticipation of pleasure. You become anhedonic. That's not what short-term stress does. What happens with moderate amounts of stress that are moderately transient with moderate increases in glucocorticoid levels? You increase the release of dopamine from out of those pathways. Short-term stress improves all those aspects of mood. Short-term stress activates those reward pathways, and where are we? We're back to our starting premise of all of this stuff. Short-term stress-response does something extremely different from long-term. We've already seen short-term enhances cognition, more oxygen delivery to the brain, and all that sort of stuff. Short-term stress releases dopamine. That's great, that's wonderful. It's sufficiently so that you will see there are optimal levels of glucocorticoids in the bloodstream which stay up to just the right amount for just the right duration in order to maximize dopamine release. An absolutely remarkable finding, which is you take lab rats, and you put them in a position where by pressing a lever they can get infused with a certain amount of glucocorticoid. Oh my God, that's terrible, glucocorticoids. Don't do that. Don't do that. It's going to cause a gazillion diseases. What you see is lab rats will press the levers to the point to get the exact level of glucocorticoids in the bloodstream that maximize the release of dopamine.

What we've seen here is this transition from stress being uniformly bad news— glucocorticoids being the steroid of Beelzebub and that sort of thing— to this whole world, we love the right kind of stress. We call it stimulation, and just the right amount of glucocorticoids going hand in hand with that, and we secrete more dopamine rather than less. This brings us now to the realm of individuals where that whole process of pleasure, excitement, stimulation, and anticipation works kind of differently from everybody else. These are the folks who need enormous amounts of challenge, stress, menace, and all of that to get things going. What are we defining here? Adrenaline junkies, and as we've learned something about the biology of them, what has become obvious is it's the wrong term. They shouldn't be called adrenaline junkies; they should be called dopamine junkies. What's happening with them, animal models of this—OK, not adrenaline junkie rats, but thrill-seeking, risk taking, that sort of thing that you could define—what's going on biologically? First hints of 2 different things, one is, as we saw just now, with the onset of a transient stressor or transient stimulus, you go up with dopamine and then you go back down. These rats who are models of adrenaline junkies, they go up, and they go back down a little lower than where they started. Thus, they have to do it again with a stronger stimulus. They go back even lower, and over and over because you're habituating to what's going on. Other evidence suggests there're different versions, different genetic versions of dopamine receptors, some of which are less responsive; you need more of an umph in the system to keep it from habituating. To appreciate this, think about this, who is that guy? Evel Knievel, that was that madman who would motorcycle over all sorts of like cruisers and things of that sort and had broken every bone in his body over and over. You think about it, once a long, long time ago the young Evel Knievel, who had his driver's permit in his back pocket, raced a red light, just got across in time and got a little bit of a thrill from that. The next day, that wasn't enough.

What this begins to bring up here, of course, is the issue of stress and addiction, and they're highly intertwined in all sorts of ways. When you are highly addicted to a drug, cocaine, for example, which releases dopamine, what you find is you down regulate, you decrease the number of dopamine receptors. You've got to release more and more of the stuff to get the same buzz in the system, and dopamine is released in massive amounts in response to some of the dopamine-related drugs like cocaine, amphetamines, and things of that sort.

You've got this happening here, and the question becomes, at what point do you have this transition from wanting to have a drug to needing to have the drug. At what point does the addictiveness kick in? What you see is it's around the point where you're getting a lower and lower baseline after each one of these; you're habituating to the drug where the receptors that might be kind of sluggish in their response are getting even more sluggish, you're decreasing the numbers of them. Suddenly, you've moved from drug abuse as a recreational wanting to addiction, needing. It's right around that point that taking these drugs are associated with very high levels of glucocorticoids, and even more so, craving those drugs and not getting them are associated with astronomically high levels. What does stress do to the system? It does absolutely logical things. You take rats, and what you'll do is they have this task. They can press a lever a certain number of times to get an infusion of a tiny amount of cocaine, for example. It's called self-administration. Stress a rat, and it self-administers more cocaine. Stress a rat, and it's willing to work harder to get that dopamine buzz because it's beginning to get a little bit depleted of dopamine. Another subtle thing as well, which is, often you see individuals who have a history of some addiction, and they're basically cured of it. They're on the wagon, and they're doing just fine. What a standard view in the field is, there's no such thing, as for example, an ex-alcoholic. There are only alcoholics who are not drinking at this point because part of what you see is this phenomenon called relapse. You take someone who hasn't taken drugs in whatever number of years, who hasn't drunk to excess, whatever. They've been fine and going along with their life, and you put them back in the place where they used to take the drugs or they used to drink too much, back on that street corner, or back in that big comfortable armchair in their men's club, whatever it is, and suddenly the craving comes roaring back, you relapse. What also occurs is lots of stress and you relapse more readily, in lab rats and in humans as well. Of course, there are individual differences in it, and there's increasing insight that it's going to have differences in the types of dopamine receptors, and all that sort of thing. There's some evidence that people who have more addictive personalities tend to secrete glucocorticoids longer after a stressor. We're beginning to get a lot of insight there. Somewhere in there, there's a really fascinating issue because all of this revolves around dopamine, dopamine and that reward pathway with the generating of anticipation, it's talking an awful lot to the frontal cortex and getting the frontal cortex all aerobically stoked up to do the harder thing.

Dopamine has a really large challenge because there's a wide range of things that are pleasurable to us. Once, 500 years ago, some medieval peasant hearing an organ cathedral, that was like the loudest man-made sound in their entire life, it must have been just overwhelming, the emotions it pulled out. Now we've got so many big ruckus thundering things that a cathedral organ seems like this quaint little thing. Once, there were hunter-gatherers who would strike gold somewhere in the forest there, or they would find a beehive that they could get a hold of, and they got the greatest of pleasures, they got some honey. These days, you go into a market, and there are hundreds of products that have been carefully engineered by smart scientists to flood our taste buds with far more sugary momentness than some honey in a forest could ever bring about. Or you have some task, which amid a very difficult, demanding life of all sorts of privations, you accomplish something and that's pleasurable. You release some dopamine, and now instead, you take an artificial drug and you release a thousand-fold as much. The only way this dopamine system could handle this where pleasure could take the form of the whiff of flowers in spring all the way up to a massive amount of cocaine, the only way the system could work is, it habituates quickly. That's the only way in which you can have a massive source of pleasure one day, and you can have a dopamine response 2 days later to something as subtle as the right person brushing your arm. What we have is one very sad outcome to this unique range that we humans have of feeling pleasure, one very sad outcome, this ability of the dopamine system to habituate so quickly which is for those feelings of pleasure to habituate so quickly. If we were simply machines of homeostatic balance, the more we consumed, the less we would need. Instead, the more we consume the more we want, and whatever was exciting yesterday is what you expect today and isn't going to be enough tomorrow.

Stress, Health, and Low Social Status
Lecture 22

> To give a remarkable example of this lack of control [among those with lower socioeconomic status], this was a study in the early '90s, looking at a bunch of men who had problems with hypertension and thus were taking antihypertensive drugs. One particular type is a diuretic. In this study, we show that one of the major reasons why working-class men with high blood pressure would stop taking their antihypertensives was because they had to go to the bathroom more often than they were allowed to on their job.

We have learned that you cannot understand the biology of disease outside the context of the person in which the biology is occurring, and now we see that we must also look at the context of the society in which that individual dwells. What does your place in society have to do with your health, and how does stress factor in?

The one clear-cut human hierarchy in Westernized societies is **socioeconomic status** (SES), and it is clear that being at the bottom of the SES hierarchy is bad news. For one thing, you're subject to more physical stressors: You have to haul the groceries upstairs because you live in an old building where the elevator is broken; you have to walk further with the heavy groceries because your car isn't working; you have to do manual labor for a living. The realm of psychological-psychosocial stress is disproportionately focused on the poor as well. You have a relative lack of control—you spend your life working on an assembly

Individuals with lower socioeconomic status tend to be exposed to more stressors.

line instead of being in a position of determining your own occupational fate. You have a lack of outlets—you can't join that expensive health club when you're feeling stressed out. Perhaps most important is the fact that you don't have as much social support as wealthier people. You can't do a whole lot of social support if you're working 2 or 3 jobs or spending all your time trying to fix everything around you that is broken.

In the greater Washington DC area, inner-city residents have a 16-year shorter life expectancy than those in the wealthier suburbs.

What does SES have to do with your health? There is something called the SES gradient of health: Across Westernized societies, the poorer you are, the worse your health is. You have higher rates of a whole variety of diseases: cardiovascular disease, respiratory diseases, psychiatric disorders, metabolic diseases, and vulnerability to diabetes. With some diseases in some societies, there's a 20-fold difference in the incidence of these diseases between those on top and those at the bottom. As one example, in the greater Washington DC area, inner-city residents have a 16-year shorter life expectancy than those in the wealthier suburbs.

What's the cause of this socioeconomic gradient? Numerous studies have shown that about one-third of the variability is accounted for by lifestyle risk factors. Poor people drink more than wealthier people, they smoke more, they eat to excess, and they get less exercise. But what's the remaining two-thirds about? For a while, we didn't have evidence, but stress physiologists suggested it's about stress. Why? In part, it was by default, because other explanations had been eliminated. We also noted that the types of diseases that are most sensitive to stress are the ones that show the steepest SES gradients. Moreover, 100 years ago, there was a completely different set of diseases from today, yet the same SES gradient was there.

In recent years, studies have come through and shown in a major way that stress is the predominant factor in the socioeconomic gradient. A person's objective SES is a predictor of health, and their subjective SES is at least as good. In other words, feeling poor has at least as much impact as being poor.

Another critical variable is how much income inequity a society has. For poor people with the same income, those in countries with greater income inequality have worse health. We can really see here the power of SES to subordinate the health of humans, and to do it in a way that's heavily mediated by stress. ■

Important Term

socioeconomic status (SES): An aggregate measure that incorporates level of education, wealth, and place of residence. Low SES is a predictor of increased risk for a wide variety of disease, as well as for significantly shortened life expectancy.

Suggested Reading

Marmot, *The Status Syndrome.*

Sapolsky, *Why Zebras Don't Get Ulcers*, chap. 17.

Questions to Consider

1. What's the evidence that lack of health-care access has little to do with the socioeconomic status health gradient?

2. What do the distinctions between being poor, feeling poor, and being made to feel poor teach about the socioeconomic status health gradient?

Stress, Health, and Low Social Status
Lecture 22—Transcript

We are now continuing this large arch that this course has basically set up. For the first dozen or so lectures, maybe a few more than that, the primary concern was the biology of the stress-response, the biology of stress-related disease, when it's good news when it's bad news, and all of that. In a recent set of lectures, somewhere around the point transitioning to what makes psychological stress stressful, we went into a second phase bringing up a critical truism that ran through all those lectures which is you can't begin to understand the biology of disease outside of the context of the person in whom that biology is happening.

With this lecture now, we transition to a third layer, a third layer in this case ever-more expansive saying not only can you not understand the biology of disease outside the context of the person in which the biology is occurring, but also in addition to outside the context of the society in which that individual dwells. What this lecture is about is looking at what your place in society has to do with your health, and as we'll see as a strongly intervening variable what your place in society has to do with the sort of stressors you're exposed to.

Following a time-honored rule starting with a subject this complex, I'm going to start off talking about animals and what hierarchy has to do with health. I'm going to start off talking about baboons. I've studied baboons in East Africa on and off for about 30 years, and I've been interested in stress-related disease, who gets the diseases, who doesn't, what does it have to do with social behavior. If you're interested in stress and disease, psychogenic stress, baboons are perfect to study because they're totally untrustworthy, backstabbing, miserable creatures. Here's the deal with baboons. If you're a baboon and you live in the Serengeti ecosystem, which is the animals I study, it is a fabulous place to live. The baboons' infant survival rate is better than among neighboring humans. You live in these big troops so the predators don't mess with you much, and most importantly, you only have to work about 3 hours a day for your calories. Critical implication, if you only have to work 3 hours a day for your calories, that means you've got like 9 hours of free time every day to devote to being just God awful to some other baboon. All they do is harass each other. All they do is generate stress in each other. Overwhelmingly, if you're a baboon in the Serengeti and you're miserable, it's because another baboon has worked really hard to bring that state about. They're perfect models for us Westernized humans. They are no more getting stressed running away from lions than we are, and instead they have the capacity to generate psychosocial stress.

An awful lot of what this stress is built around is dominance hierarchy. Baboons come with dominance ranks, there's a number 1, a number 10, and a number 20, and this greatly influences the quality of your life. What I've been interested in over the years out there is what does your dominance rank have to do with how your body responds to stress? With a great deal of work over the years, I got what I thought was a very clear answer, which is, if you have the choice in the matter, you do not want to be a low-ranking baboon because you get all sorts of grief. You dig some tuber out of the ground to eat, and anyone higher ranking can rip you off. You get somebody to socially groom you finally, and anybody else can disrupt it. You're sitting there minding your own business, and some guy who's in a bad mood comes and slashes your rear end with displacement aggression—lack of control, lack of predictability, lack of outlets.

What I've seen over the years is, if you are a low-ranking baboon, you see exactly the profile of poor health that one would expect. Low-ranking baboons have elevated levels of glucocorticoids, have an inability to turn off the glucocorticoid stress-response very effectively at the end of stress. They have elevated blood pressure, less of the good type of cholesterol, an immune system that doesn't quite work as well, a reproductive system that's more vulnerable to stress, antianxiety chemicals, these endogenous benzodiazepines working differently, over and over you see low-ranking baboons are a wreck. You look at this and you come up with a perfectly obvious punch line, which is you want to be a high-ranking baboon and go win, win, win and compete and aggress and dominate in one big social Darwinism blow-out. It turns out there's something a lot more complicated. This is something that would come up now and then at primatology meetings

I would go to, and I would get up and give a song and dance about what baboons are about with the punch line low-ranking baboons show the greatest indices of stress-related disease. Then there'd be this guy named Dave Abbott from the University of Wisconsin who studies marmosets, these are these little squirrely monkeys that are found in South America, and he would get up and say, well among my animals, it's high- ranking animals who show the greatest indices of stress-related disease. This was very uncomfortable, and mostly what we did with this was like during breaks when everybody's like jostling for the cookies there and stuff, we would avoid each other and sort of stay at different ends.

At some point, we realized we have to tackle this issue. What we started to do was try to make sense of this, and look at what by that time was a dozen different species where people knew something about social rank and stress-related disease and health. What we went through after a great deal of work and recruiting a lot of other colleagues as well was discovering what now makes perfect sense, the relationship between rank and health. It's not so much about your rank; it's what your rank means. It's the social context of the rank, and you see all sorts of critical factors. You will see in some species if you're a high-ranking male for example, you get challenged 3 times a day and have to defend that rank. In other species, like baboons for example, if you're a high-ranking male, you go months without anybody challenging you because all you need to do is like stare at somebody, and it's over with. In species where the high-ranking animals are constantly being challenged, it's the high-ranking individuals who have the worst health. In species where the high-ranking individuals are just coasting on their laurels, it's the subordinate animals with the worst profile.

More issues, you're low ranking, and in your species how often are you subject to displacement aggression. In other words, how often are you sitting there minding your own business and somebody pounds on you. In species where there's a lot of displacement aggression, subordinates have a worse health profile. What else, what kind of outlets do you have? That, in the world of primates, is pretty straightforward. How often are you able to groom somebody else? In species where low-ranking animals have a lot of opportunities for grooming, their health is better than in species where the low-ranking animals don't have an opportunity. Next, what by now should make sense enormously is: You're low ranking in your species according to the structure and gender organization of how your species works socially. Do you have a lot of relatives in your group, or did you pick up at puberty and go wandering over the horizon and join a troop where you've got no relatives? The more relatives subordinate animals have in their species, the healthier they are.

This was really quite a striking finding for us. It's not rank; it's what your rank means. Another factor is how stable is your rank? If you are a high-ranking individual, and you're having lots of unstable interactions with a rival, you're going to have a lousy stress profile. If you have extremely stable, predictable ones, you're really healthy—over and over this theme. Very quickly, what you see is you can take this even one step further. Rather than looking at different primate species where there are enormous differences in social organization and huge, huge variation, you begin to look at individual social groups of primates in the same species, and they have differences. In this troop, the alpha male is a misery and beats on everyone, and in that troop the alpha male spends all his time meditating and grooming. What you see is the particular social atmosphere of your troop is a predictive feature of what does your rank have to do with your health. In some species and in some primate groups, it's better being subordinate than in other cases, you get more or less grief.

All of this winds up being really interesting and leads one immediately to say well, what's up with humans? Of course the first question here is, do humans have ranks in the way that these other primates do? I'm very skeptical about this possibility, mainly because I spent my entire childhood being the last one picked for the Wiffle Ball teams. Thus, I'm not quite sure if we are a ranked-hierarchical species. We're much more complicated than that. We have hierarchies, but one of the things we have going for us is we belong to multiple hierarchies. What happens is, belong to enough of them, and even though you may be at the bottom of a whole bunch of them, there's going to be one where you're doing well, and that's the one that you rationalize into being the most important. You've got somebody who is downtrodden in some miserable job where they're highly subordinated, but come the weekend, they're the captain of the softball team. You'd better bet that's the person who's going to be sitting there saying, 9 to 5 you got to earn a living, but it's stupid, that's just bringing home the bacon and what is important in life is when Saturday comes along. What we have great ability to do is play psychological games with whatever our rank is in particular hierarchies. Often what we can also do is play games with not so much what your rank is, but what it used to be, what direction you're heading, so we're not a ranked species in the way that all sorts of these primates are. We've got a lot more subtle stuff going on.

Nonetheless, there's one domain of human social life in Westernized societies where there's a ranking system that is just a sledgehammer, which is socioeconomic status. Socioeconomic status, an aggregate measure of level of education, level of income, wealth of one's home, average wealth in the community you live in, this aggregate measure, and what's very obvious, given this is there's a hierarchy of socioeconomic status in various societies. On the top are the bloated robber barons, at the bottom are the poor, and everybody in between. That's human hierarchy in Westernized societies.

You look at that, and you begin to ask where are the stressors in socioeconomic status, SES hierarchies? What's clear is being at the bottom of the hierarchy is bad news. For one thing, separate of our world of psychosocial stressors, you're subject to more physical stressors. If you are poor, you have to haul the groceries upstairs because you live in some old building where the elevator is broken again. You have to walk further with the heavy groceries because the car isn't working. The heat is broken down in the apartment yet again. You have to do manual labor for a living. You've got backaches because you can't afford to get a good bed—a whole life full of physical stressors.

We now move into our realm of psychological-psychosocial stress, and it is way disproportionately focused on the poor as well. Lack of control, you spend your life working on an assembly line instead of being in a position of determining your own occupational fate. To give a remarkable example of this lack of control, this was a study in the early '90s, looking at a bunch of men who had problems with hypertension, and thus were taking antihypertensive drugs. One particular type is a diuretic; it makes you pee more. It makes you pee more and decreases your blood volume, and thus your blood pressure goes down and that's great. In this study, we show that one of the major reasons why working-class men with high blood pressure would stop taking their antihypertensives was because they had to go to the bathroom more often than they were allowed to on their job.

Lack of control, lack of predictability, very much intertwined with that sort of stressor. Lack of outlets, you don't do the same deal that wealthier people do. You're feeling a little stressed, so time to take up a new hobby and join that expensive health club. Maybe even let's do something important here, maybe I'll just drop out of the rat race and don't work for 3 or 4 months and spend the whole time making sandals. You don't have that option. You don't have the same outlets. Perhaps, most importantly, you don't have the social support. One of the great myths of poverty is, oh, we were poor, but we were loving. Everyone in our community was poor, so if everyone is poor, no one is poor. Social support, for the most part, this is a myth. The poor have far less social support than wealthier do for some very simple reasons. You can't do a whole lot of social support if you're working 2 jobs or 3 jobs or spending all your time trying to plug the holes in your life there, not a lot of social support.

You look at all of this, and you now have to ask a very obvious question, which is, so if poverty is as battering of one in terms of psychological stress, is there a relationship between socioeconomic status and markers of the stress system? You know what's going to be the easiest one to focus on right now. Is there a relationship between socioeconomic status and resting glucocorticoid levels? The first bit of evidence is coming in for that looking at, for example, kids. How depressing is this? Kids in the first couple of years of school and there's already a relationship between resting glucocorticoid levels and socioeconomic status. This is a very small literature, hasn't been well replicated yet, but first hints that your SES, how you're doing in your society, manifests itself in what your stress-response looks like.

How about asking the next question, though: What does socioeconomic status have to do with your health, have to do with stress-related diseases and such? It turns out, boy is it ever related to socioeconomic status. There is now what is called the SES gradient of health, which is this finding that across all sorts of Westernized societies, the poorer you are, the worse your health is, more diseases of all sorts. A whole variety, cardiovascular disease, the lower your SES, the more likely you are to have problems with that. Respiratory diseases, psychiatric disorders, metabolic diseases, vulnerability to diabetes, inflammatory disorders, all of these become more prevalent the lower you are on the socioeconomic ladder. Maybe these are little statistical predictors, these are huge effects. With some of these in some of these societies, there's a 20-fold difference in the incidence of these diseases looking at those on top and those at the bottom. As but one example, you look in the greater Washington DC area, you look at inner-city populations there, and the wealthier suburbs, and there's approximately a 16-year difference in life expectancy. These are not little statistical phenomena; these are enormously powerful effects.

You look at those, and of course, what comes to mind immediately is trying to make sense of these. There are a first couple of hints. For one thing, it's not a universal rule that there is this SES gradient. It pops up in the weirdest places, one of the grand people in the field doing research—and his name will come up soon—has noted that when you look within gender, there is a very strict socioeconomic gradient between who survived the *Titanic* sinking and who didn't. If you were poor, you didn't get out of there alive. You get SES gradients in all sorts of weird places. You also get a few cases of inverse SES gradients. There are a few diseases that actually become more common among the wealthier. Breast cancer is an example of that, melanoma, multiple sclerosis, endometriosis, and a few other diseases. Nonetheless, there's this big, whopping set of diseases where the poorer you are, the more likely you are to have that disease, and these are meaningful differences.

Where's this coming from? What's the cause of this socioeconomic gradient? A remarkable number of really smart public health scientists have been wrestling with this one for years, and it's fascinating. It's obviously important. Where's it coming from? Right off the bat, you come with a really easy explanation, the causality horse and cart, chicken and egg issue there of saying well obviously, if your health is lousy and you're sick all the time, you are unlikely to be a CEO of a large corporation. Poor health drives down one's socioeconomic status. That makes sense, and you have to go control for that. It turns out in this SES gradient, this SES health gradient, that it's the other way around where poverty, poorer, low socioeconomic status is the predictor of the poor health. The way you see this most readily is to look at somebody's SES at some point in life, and see how predictive that is of what their health is going to be like at a later point. One of the most astonishing examples of this is from a research body of studies that are fascinating having to do with successful aging. This is looking at a population where the goal was where all of these subjects had had roughly the same food consumption all their lives, roughly the same living conditions, roughly the same number of doctors visits. Who can you find this in? In this wonderful body of research, what's researched are elderly nuns. Elderly nuns, they join the convent, the program around age 18, 20 or so, and for the rest of their lives they are living under very similar circumstances, wonderfully controlled experiment. It turns out there's all sorts of features of life experience that predict who's going to have a successful versus unsuccessful old age. One of them is, amazingly, their socioeconomic status at the time you became a nun. The lower your SES, the lower the likelihood that you are going to be hale and hearty in your later years.

We see here a first explanation go down the tubes. Oh, it's just because if you're sick, you wind up being poor because you can't work very effectively. It's the other way around. If you are poor, your socioeconomic status is the driving force on the poor health.

What's another possibility? Once that one is out of the way, it's totally obvious what the explanation is, which is, well, poor people can't afford to go to the doctors. They can't afford to get checkups, preventative stuff. It's an issue purely of health-care access. That makes a ton of sense. If you can't go to the doctor for checkups, you're not going to be as healthy. If every time you're sick, you have to hold on a little longer and see if it will pass because you really can't afford to go into the emergency room, pay those prices, because you don't have a physician of your own because you—this makes perfect sense, health-care access. That explains the socioeconomic gradient.

It turns out, it doesn't in the slightest. How come? For a number of reasons, you see the SES gradient in societies that have universal health care, that have socialized medicine, where everybody has health care that's rather similar. You get the same gradient. It's not quite as steep as in societies like our own that at this point in time do not have universal health care. It's steeper in the United States than in any other country in the world, but the gradient is still there in countries that have universal health care. The gradient is still there for certain diseases where you could go to the doctor for a checkup 18 times a week and get centrifuged on the weekends for good measure, and it's not going to change the likelihood of you getting that disease, juvenile diabetes for example. These are diseases that have nothing to do with how often you get to see a doctor, and they still show the same socioeconomic gradient.

Another version of it is you look at what people were dying of in 1900, and it's mostly completely different diseases than now, but you saw the same socioeconomic gradient. It's not the disease; it's not the health-care access. The Rosetta stone of the whole field showing this fact is a body of research carried out by Sir Michael Marmot who is one of the gods in this field. Michael Marmot of University College, London. What he decided to study was a society of hierarchically organized humans where everybody had sufficient resources and sustenance, that nobody was lacking for calories, but a highly stratified society. He looked at the British Civil Service System where, apparently, there are a gazillion different layers of ranks that you can have. Nobody is starving in there. Everybody has the same universal health-care access, and what he showed was within this system, every step lower in the civil service hierarchy, the worse your health in all those domains, the worse your life expectancy.

It's not reverse causality; it's not health-care access problems. It's obvious what it is, which is poor people drink more than wealthier people, they smoke more, they eat to excess, they get less exercise, all these lifestyle risk factors. Numerous researchers, Marmot leading the way with this, show that you factor all of those in, and it describes one-third of the variability.

What's the remaining two-thirds about? Up until a few years ago, this is where the epidemiology, public health, SES gradient people would really get uncomfortable because all these stress physiology people would suddenly jump up and say, it's stress, it's stress, and ooh, it's stress. Why would you think that this is stress? For one thing, you've run out of all of the easier explanations. Maybe it's about stress, this SES gradient, simply by default. The next thing, and to argue for it is, the types of diseases that are most sensitive to stress, those are the ones that show the steepest SES gradients. Another reason why people would argue in favor of stress is that point I just brought up, 1900 completely different diseases than now, yet the same SES gradient was there. It has got nothing to do with whether or not you were drinking pure water because of public health hygiene or any of that stuff having to do with diseases then versus now. The only thing in common was if you are low-ranking and low-SES, you're enormously stressed.

That's about as far as it would go, which is, they'd have to irritatingly deal with some of these stress people saying, well maybe it's mostly about stress. In recent years, though, beautiful, beautiful studies have shown it's about stress big time. Here's the first one. Some research carried out by Nancy Adler, UCSF, University of California, San Francisco, now there are all sorts of research where scientists have big fancy machines and microscopes the size of this room, and gazillion dollar pieces of equipment, and high-tech science. Nancy Adler has done the most remarkably high-tech science of all time; she does her research with one piece of paper at a time. Here's what she does. She has a piece of paper, and on it is a drawing of a ladder, a ladder with 10 rungs. The person she is studying, she sits them down, and she says something very simple, which is, "When you compare yourself to other people, where would you stand on this ladder, what rung are you on? What is your subjective socioeconomic status?"

Now this has to come with some controls. For one thing, it differs by different cultures, those good old optimistic Americans, the average American views himself as above average on this ladder. In Southeast Asian cultures, the average person there, not wanting to brag in this more communal society, rates themselves lower than average, so you got to factor that stuff in. Another thing you factor in, is when you ask somebody how are you doing, who are they comparing themselves to? Comparing themselves to the next-door neighbor, to Bill Gates, to some fictional TV character? By saying not when you compare yourself to your neighbors, when you compare yourself to people you work with, simply saying, when you think of other people, how are you doing compared to them, you're allowing the person to choose the relevant community that they keep in mind. The extraordinary finding that Adler comes up with is while one's objective socioeconomic status is a predictor of health in a lot of realms, one's subjective status is at least as good. What does that mean? It's not being poor; it's feeling poor.

The next body of work that helps pin this down with stress comes from public health scientist, Richard Wilkinson. What he does is look at a critical variable in various societies, how much income inequity is there? In a community independent of the average income, how much variation is there? What he shows is, the more variation, the more hierarchical income is in a community, the less likely you are to have a peer because everybody is either above or below, social capital breaks down. What he shows is for the same income, the more income inequality, the worse the health of the poor is. He has shown this at the level of states in the United States, cities, actually even particular blocks in Chicago, all of that. What is he showing there? It's not being poor; it's feeling poor. What's the surest way to feel poor? Having your nose rubbed in it all the time surrounded by what you don't have. What this really brings in here is the power of socioeconomic status to subordinate the health of humans and to do it in a way that's heavily mediated by stress.

We get a confusing point here at the end. We go back to the start of this lecture with baboons, marmoset monkeys. What does your socioeconomic baboon rank have to do with how your health is? What we saw was the answer is, it depends. It depends on what it's like to be a dominant individual in the society. It depends on how stable the hierarchy is. It depends on how many relatives you have around you, great complexity. What comes out of the human literature on socioeconomic status, you look at utopian Scandinavian societies, you look at sweaty capitalist societies, and the gradient is there. You look at societies that are diverse in their ethnicities and ones that are homogenous, and the gradient is there. You control for gender, for age, for race, and all of that, the gradient is there. What that's telling you is something that seems rather odd. Wait, are baboons and marmoset monkeys more subtle and more complex than humans? They come with all of these—well it depends. It depends on what the particular non-human primate society is about, and here you see instead, in every single sort of place you look among humans, Westernized humans, there is that SES gradient. It doesn't tell us that nonhuman primates are more complicated and more subtle than we are. It tells us something much deeper and much more fundamental, ultimately much sadder which is: When humans went and invented socioeconomic status and invented haves and have-nots, we came up with a way to subordinate those have-nots like nothing the primate world has ever seen.

Stress Management—Clues to Success?
Lecture 23

> The closest thing our society has to a village elder, being a Supreme Court justice—tremendous longevity, function and quality, and successful old aging in those folks. It makes perfect sense. This is like the world's greatest job. You don't work that much of the year. You only pick the cases that are interesting, all the scut work is done for you by these hyperactive, manic law clerks, and then you decide things that change the course of history. No wonder these guys do wonderfully; it's our equivalent of a village elder.

Thus far, we've had 22 lectures of bad news. At this point, it must seem miraculous that you're still functioning. How is it any of us are still functioning? How have we not all just collapsed into puddles of stress-related disease? We're scraping along; we're coping. It's clear that some individuals deal with stress much better than others, so we begin by looking at what is different about those individuals.

What is one of the big predictors of successful aging? Having a healthy lifestyle. Smoking, being overweight, not getting enough exercise, and drinking too much all shorten your life expectancy. This makes perfect sense. The next thing is to have a long-lasting, good marriage. This too makes sense from everything we have learned about social connectiveness and social support. Other factors are also obvious from earlier lectures: Avoid major clinical depression throughout adulthood, have an extroverted personality, and get treated with respect.

© Stockbyte/Thinkstock.

Nursing home residents thrive when given greater responsibility and autonomy.

I know what you're thinking: This doesn't do me much good. I don't have the option to not be depressed or to have the right temperament in the face of cancer or to go back and make sure my mother touched me the exact right amount when I was an infant. What can I do to make use of these principles? One thing that is clear is change can occur. Some individuals with type A personality who suffer a heart attack, with some very intensive work, change their personality profiles.

Some of the deepest insights into our ability to change have come from experimental studies where people have manipulated psychological variables and brought about change. One study with individuals with chronic pain syndrome discovered that when they are allowed to self-medicate, they actually take fewer painkillers. This change medicated the pain—and also the lack of control. Studies done in nursing homes have demonstrated the ability to counter some of the downsides of the aging process—the loss of control, loss of outlets, and loss of autonomy. Something as simple as giving a resident a plant and telling them that they need to remember to water it every day gives the person some responsibility and autonomy. Their energy levels get higher. Often when the conditions of these studies are reversed, the individuals don't just drop down to the level at which they started; they drop lower.

So what have we learned here? Hope can be an amazingly powerful, sustaining set of feelings, but nothing destroys us more like when there's hope that turns out to be utterly unjustified. This gives us a first warning as we transition into the final lecture on how to apply some of these principles to ourselves. What we see is it's not simple; there are double-edged swords all over the place. You want to get it right, because if you apply some of these notions simplistically, you won't help lessen the effects of stress—and you could perhaps even make things worse. ■

Suggested Reading

Monat and Lazarus, *The Praeger Handbook on Stress and Coping.*

Sapolsky, *Why Zebras Don't Get Ulcers*, chap. 18.

1. What do baboons, nursing home residents, and parents of cancer patients teach about dealing with stress?

2. What sort of experimental manipulations make an individual more resistant to stress?

Stress Management—Clues to Success?
Lecture 23—Transcript

If you've still stuck it out with the course up to here, rather than having tossed it in the fire or into your sock drawer angrily demanding a refund, if everything has worked right, we would have gotten you to a certain point right now. Thanks to research on the part of the big R & D division of The Teaching Company, what we would have accomplished by now is you should be feeling depressed as hell. This is 22 lectures or so into this, and there has been nothing but bad news so far. At this point, it should seem just like miraculous that you're still functioning. Look at all these ways that your body can go wrong. Actually, don't look at it. Let's hold on for one more stress-related disease, and this is as much stress trivia for today as you could get, remember—let's see who was actually listening—remember that disease a number of lectures ago of hair falling out, the version where you don't know why it happened—idiopathic alopecia areata. It turns out there's a stress-related version of alopecia areata where you are so, so traumatized by something or other happening that over the next few days, your hair turns white and falls out. This is for real. This is a real disease. This is like a once-in-a-career of a physician's disease, but this is a real one. Look at this. You're chronically stressed, you get high blood pressure, you get diabetes, you stop growing, you become flatulent, your sex life is ruined, your brain gets damaged, and your hair falls out.

How is it any of us are still functioning? How have we not all just collapsed into puddles of stress-related disease? What's clear is, for the most part, we haven't collapsed into those puddles. We're kind of muddling along. We're scraping along; we're coping. We're coping, and that's the critical point in this last part of the course. What does stress management consist of? What does coping consist of? What is clear from day 1 all the way back to Selye in the 1930s, all the way back to the very first rats that were being experimentally exposed to generalized unpleasantries, what was clear from the very start was variability. Individual differences, translated into sort of our vocabulary for these couple of lectures, that from the very start of thinking about stress and coping, it's clear that some individuals deal with stress much better than others. Some cope better.

Thus, in beginning to think about how to incorporate some wisdom into one's stress management techniques, inevitably where you need to start is asking what's up with those individuals who cope better? What does it have to do with? Why do some bodies, and even more importantly, some psyches, deal better with stress than others? What are the mechanism underlying individual differences, enhanced resistance to stress-related disease? Once that's under your belt and you know exactly how that works, how can you sign up and wind up being more like those folks, those folks who just happen to be good at that. That's where we're going to start, rather than with prescriptions, and rather than even going over the science of experimental manipulations to make individuals better at dealing with stress. Let's start off just seeing some of the wild success stories out there of individuals, individual organisms in some cases, who just happened to be the ones who are spectacular at dealing with stress.

First domain, first domain was promised toward the end of that lecture on aging, which was one of the great ones for nothing but bad news, promising at the very end that in fact there's some good news lurking there, good news being what is now called successful aging. This is one of those scenarios, you go to a gerontology conference and somebody gets up, and they study this organ system. What their talk is about is how it falls apart during aging. The next person gets up and they study this other organ and how it falls apart during aging. It's all really quite cheerful. If you look closely at the data, and you do some math over some of the figures that you're being shown, and what always pops out is there's always a subset of those individual subjects, those individual rats, fruit flies, college graduates, and all of that, there's always a subset where things aren't getting worse with aging. In fact, some of the time, these measures are even getting better. This weird statistical observation is now this whole subfield of successful aging.

What goes into successful aging? Some of the time, as we'll see, it's pretty logical things, some of the time rather unexpected. First version, what is a version of rat unsuccessful aging? We've heard plenty of this by now. We've heard about how during aging, rats' basal resting levels of glucocorticoids begin to rise; about how the hippocampus doesn't work as well, increasing amounts of damage and there are memory problems. In fact, work that came out in the 1980s, some of it my own, showing that in fact there's a connection between the two, we know one of the pieces of that already. Rise in glucocorticoids in the aging rat causing accelerated aging in the hippocampus, for insanely complicated reasons we're not going anywhere near, a more and more damaged hippocampus leads to higher and higher glucocorticoid levels. Yet again, another vicious circle there, and this seemed to be the case until you suddenly realize that's not, in fact, an inevitable feature of aging. There are some rats who don't show this pattern. Which rats are they? We've already heard about them. The rats who way back when had the moms who licked them more and groomed them more, mothering style playing out in old age. Here we see one pathway toward rat successful aging, and we already see one domain in which this is not going to turn in to an obvious prescription for how we go about our mothering styles.

What are other cases where you see successful aging? One of the classic ones, seeing what some of the predictors were, is this famed Harvard aging study. A bunch of Harvard-associated psychiatrists back in the 1940s took the graduating class of 1941, took a random subset of these men—yes, it was all men back then—and did this grand prospect of longitudinal study intensively following these men over the decades since. One of the key issues being, what are the old ages of these men going to be like? What sort of predictors along the way will there be as to who has the healthiest old ages and the longest years? Out of it comes all sorts of interesting findings. Some of them aren't so interesting. What was one of the big predictors? It was having a healthy lifestyle. Smoke, and your life expectancy is going to be shorter even if you're a 1941 Harvard graduate, be overweight, don't get enough exercise, drink too much, all of that, this makes perfect sense.

The next thing that came through in this grand study, have yourself a long-lasting stable, good marriage, and that has just greatly increased the odds of a hale and hardy old age. That sure makes sense from everything we heard about social connectiveness and social support, but there may be little things creeping in the back way. For example having someone who you live with in your later years, you've got somebody who, in addition to all the heartwarming support, reminds you to take your medicine. These are the sort of confounds that go into that literature. What are some other factors? Factors that won't be at all surprising given the previous lectures. Avoid major clinical depression throughout adulthood, and that's a predictor for a longer life span and a healthier, more successful old age. That sure makes sense to us by now, and especially given a finding that has emerged in recent years, major clinical depression, everything else being equal, you've increased the risk of heart disease, a connection there often years and years between the 2 events, another price that you pay.

Try to not be depressed—oh great, really useful advice here. Even more so, try not to be neurotic. That's another marker of unsuccessful aging among these Harvard grads. What else is there? Have a resilient personality, and we will see in more detail what the building blocks of that are. Have an extroverted personality, and that's a good thing, in part because extroversion tends to go hand-in-hand with decreased risk of depression, decreased risk of neurosis. You've got this whole package deal. That's wonderful, that's very informative. This doesn't do me much good. Number 1, I was not 20 in 1941. Number 2, I was not some good old, good solid fellow Harvard graduate from back when. I'm not even male, I don't have the option to not be depressed or to be unneurotic, there's only so much you could do with findings like these.

There are limits also. What else winds up being a predictor of successful old age? This one makes a whole ton of sense the older you get, respect. One of the predictors is if you are in a position in your life, your personal life, your occupational life whatever, where as you get older, you are subject to, if anything, increasing respect, wow, is that a predictor of a healthy old age. What are we describing here? We're describing becoming a village elder, and that's a very rare thing in our society because we've got some awfully bizarre, screwed up feelings about the aging process. You're young, and all you want to do is be older, be old enough to do this, old enough to learn about that, whatever. Then once you hit this magical stage, I'm guessing, I don't know, it's somewhere around 30 or so, there's this horribly neurotic transition and suddenly, you want to be mistaken for somebody younger. Suddenly you want to act younger. Suddenly the greatest compliment in the world is for somebody to say, you're 33? My God, I would have guessed you were 31. Oh, why thank you. Suddenly we have this whole different attitude.

We've got a very weird view of aging. Sit down someone from a traditional African village and say to them at age 50, wow, you look like you're 30, and you've just insulted them. They would much rather look like 70 because that's the time of life where you are most honored, most respected, most powerful. That's something that's often lacking from our society. When you see when it occurs, there are some very interesting consequences. Two of the longest-living associated professions out there have very distinctive features that go along with these professions; one we've heard about already, orchestral conductors. Part of what's good for them is all that aerobic stuff we hear about, but a big chunk of what's good for them is the control, the respect, the authority, the autonomy. My God, you could be a 90-year-old conductor, and you're still determining when all these other adults go to the bathroom as we heard about. That's one occupation that predicts a very successful old age. What's the other one? The closest thing our society has to a village elder, being a Supreme Court justice, tremendous longevity, function and quality, and successful old aging in those folks. It makes perfect sense. This is like the world's greatest job. You don't work that much of the year. You only pick the cases that are interesting, all the scut work is done for you by these hyperactive, manic law clerks, and then you decide things that change the course of history. No wonder these guys do wonderfully; it's our equivalent of a village elder.

These are some of the things that predict successful aging. What are other markers that go along with the folks—the folks, the rats, the primates, the humans—who simply deal with stress better than others? Now we move into an extremely interesting, extremely informative, potentially extremely moving literature having to do with people who have children who have serious, severe illnesses, as most studied, parents of children with cancer. These folks have been studied in lots of settings, but this is one classic study. It took a population of parents of children with cancer, children with serious cancer, and what they looked at were the indices in these parents of stress-related—what were their glucocorticoid levels like, blood pressure, cholesterol levels, all these sorts of things. Looking, there would be as per usual tremendous variability, a whole spread as to some of the parents who were doing horribly in terms of those measures, some who were doing relatively good independent of how serious the child's cancer was, all of these were cases of serious cancer.

In this classic study, they tried to figure out, what are the predictors of the parents who are doing better physiologically in the face of a disaster like this. This fascinating set of studies were, not only are there the medical measurements in these folks, but intensive interviews, psychotherapeutic interviews with these parents trying to see what's different. There were a few markers that came out, a few key differences. The first one was, what do you do with some of the anxiety, some of the fears intrinsic in this whole cancer process. Here would be a typical scenario, like virtually any parent in this position, they are there around the clock. This is just consuming them. They are exhausted.

At some point, friends or family convince them you need to go away for a weekend. You need to do something. You're falling apart here. They're finally convinced. Along comes Friday night. They're about to go away for this weekend, and the psychologist working on the project asks them, well, how do you feel about this? There are 2 different categories. There is the first group that says, "My God, I know this disease. I know this disease. I've seen children on the ward. It could come in from out of nowhere. It could take them in a few days. My God, what if I'm away and my child dies." The other version, they sit there and say, "Well, you know, it's probably a good thing I'm getting away, but I'm kind of worried. I'm worried because I'm worried they're not going to pay enough attention to him. Or, you know, the nurses are busy, maybe one of them will have time to read a book to him, but they're not going to read it like I do, I'm afraid. It's not going to be as good for him." If you take, "Oh my God, what if he dies while I'm away" and turn it into, "Oh my God what if the nurses don't read *Goodnight Moon* as effectively as I do," the ones who could break down these huge worries into these smaller pieces have much better physiological profiles, lower glucocorticoid levels.

Next predictor, this was a period when the kids would go into remission, cancer remission, where there was an issue of are they cured. Is it going to come back? When is it going to come back? Now the psychologists sit down the parents and say, "Well, how do you feel about this period of remission?" There are the ones who would say, "Remission? Remission. Don't even say that word. Remission, it isn't—he's cured. She's going to live forever; it's fine now. I don't even want to hear that word." Then there are the ones who would say, "Well, we're enormously grateful for this period, but you know, the statistics are not great. You know, every day is going to be a blessing, but we have to be realistic about it." Parents who sit there and are realistic about it have much higher glucocorticoid levels than ones who say, "Over with. Done, we don't have to think about it anymore." What does that hark back to? Those control, psychological control issues there of do you always want to have a sense of control, not in the face of horrific stressors; in cases like that, denial might be a very good thing. Here is one of these domains where denial, in fact, was quite protective. Stay tuned, bad news about that, nonetheless, to come.

One additional variable that they found which was did these parents have a religious framework for explaining where the cancer had come from? What do I mean by that? On one hand, you have the parents sitting there saying, "This is the worst thing conceivable. This is the biggest challenge of our lives, but, you know, we're religious people. Sometimes the at worst moments, I think God has chosen us for this task. God knows that we can carry this burden, and this is going to sound crazy, but it almost feels good knowing that God knew that we could carry this." Versus the ones who would sit there and say, "God, don't tell me about God and mysterious ways. I don't even want to hear about God this decade or so." If you could look at your child declining with cancer and think that this is a sign that God knew you could carry a burden, much lower glucocorticoid levels. The starts of some insight here, but again, foreshadowing these particular studies are going to come back to haunt us big time.

What else do we have? Studying baboons, my baboons in fact, and looking at this world of terrible male-male competition where we've already seen if you're a low-ranking male, you have elevated glucocorticoid levels. Wait, not so fast, it was more complicated than that. If you're a low-ranking male, and the hierarchy is stable, and the alpha male is psychologically adept, all those qualifications, but what we also saw was there's another issue lurking in the background there, which is personality. What's your personality like? What's your personality like if you're a baboon? First, do you even have personality? Yes, indeed, and that's one of the hottest topics in primatology these days the fact that nonhuman primates, they are smart, they're social, they're long-lived, they have personalities, they have differing temperaments, and all of that. What sort of personality does it turn out work well for a baboon, a male baboon, remaining healthy in the face of this wildly competitive world? There are a number of predictors that begin to make sense. Number 1, can you, as this male baboon, tell the difference between the threatening and the neutral things in your life? What do I mean by that? Threatening, you're sitting there. Your worst rival on the whole planet shows up, threatens you in your face. This is bad news. What do you do? What do you do? You stop whatever you are doing, and you take this very vigilant defensive stance. Contrast, you're sitting there minding your own business, and your worst rival on the planet shows up and takes a nap 100 yards away. What do you do next? What do you do next? You do exactly what you're doing; this is not a big deal. Pathetically, a large percentage of male baboons can't tell the difference between their worst rival threatening them in their face, and the guy taking a nap across the field. You can see in their minds, that they're just like, "Look at that guy. Look at that guy. Look at the way he's sleeping, and the way he's snoring. I hate him, and he's doing it just to get on my nerves." This is type A personality. This is toxic hostility, seeing challenges others don't. If you sit there and you can't tell the difference between your rival sleeping and threatening you, about twice the levels of glucocorticoids are in the bloodstream.

Next variable, the guy is threatening you in your face. What do you do next? Do you abdicate control and allow him to start the inevitable fight or do you at least seize a little bit of control there. Straight out of our control predictability one, baboons who sit there and make no attempt to control the inevitable fight, have about twice the glucocorticoid levels. Next variable, you've had the fight. You've had the fight. Can you tell the difference between whether the outcome was good or bad? Oh, geez, that's kind of important, and you can tell if a baboon does that by what sort of behaviors they do afterward. A baboon who can't tell the difference between winning and losing has significantly higher glucocorticoid levels. Finally, you've had the fight and you've lost. What do you do next? Do you go and mope by yourself or do you go and do something social? If you mope by yourself, there are higher glucocorticoid levels. Look at this profile. Can you tell the difference between the big things and the little things? If it is a big thing, do you at least get some control over it? Can you tell if the outcome is good or bad? If the outcome is bad, do you have some effective coping mechanisms?

People pay to be taught stuff like this, and some baboons just happen to be more that way than others.

All of this is very exciting, very wonderful, very heartwarming, full of optimism, but what if you happen not to be the right sort of baboon or not happen to have the right temperament in the face of a nightmare of cancer, or you didn't happen to have a mother who licked you the right amount back when? What can you do to, in fact, still make use of principles like this? What can you do to change? What becomes clear is that nonetheless, change can occur. One of the things that we find to be particularly unlikely is stuff can change. Athletic conditioning, people go from being out of shape into in shape. What does being athletically conditioned consist of? You lower your baseline of glucocorticoid levels and heart rate. You increase the ceiling of it. You recover faster. That happens. Certain types of individuals with type A personality who have just shown up with their first heart attack, with some very intensive work, they could change their profiles. We change. We grow, we mature, we harden, we grow together, we grow apart, we get bored, we change. It's possible for us to change. Not only is it possible, but it's hard in terms of there's no free lunch in the next lecture and a half. Nonetheless, change can occur. Where you get some of the most insights into it have been experimental studies where people have manipulated some of those psychological variables and brought about change.

The first version of this has extraordinary studies. You take one of the worst medical things that happens to people which is something goes wrong, disaster, and they have a chronic pain syndrome, constantly in pain. These are people who live for when they can get their next medication, their next painkillers. All they do is sit there in the hospital bed hitting the Call button, is it time yet, is it time yet; it's misery for everyone involved. Some years ago, some researchers tried out something that seemed loony where you have these powerful painkillers, and they said, instead of these patients driving the nurses crazy all day long, what if you gave them the medication, put it on the side of their bed on the nightstand, and whenever they needed some, they would take it. What if you allowed them to self-medicate their painkillers. Oh, my God, the AMA had an apoplexy. You can't do that; they'll become addicts. They're going to overdose, all of that. People tried it, and you know what? Not only don't they overdose, when chronic-pain patients can self-medicate, they take less painkillers. What does that tell you when you are lying in bed there, it hurts, you're not sure if anybody is paying attention on the Call button and when they're going to come, and you need more pain medication, then it tells you 2 things. You're medicating the pain, but you're also medicating the lack of control.

Another domain, nursing homes, the aging process is, in lots of ways, the experience of loss of control, loss of outlets, loss of autonomy, and winding up in a nursing home is one of the front lines of how that can go wrong. Wonderful studies done led by a psychologist named Judith Rodin at Yale at the time, going into a nursing home and manipulating some of the psychological variables there. Things like you give one of these individuals a plant, and in one case, as part of the experiment, you say, "Oh, you need to remember to water it every day." The other, "Well, I'm going to come and water it for you." Give the person some responsibility, some autonomy, something as trivial as that, and people's level of energy, people's level of activation get higher.

Here's a much more subtle version, and this is an extremely important classic study. You go into a nursing home, 3 different conditions, the first one, the control one, there are no differences in how people are living. Second one, you come in and you say, "Oh, we're doing this study here and I'm wondering if this social worker student can come in every Thursday for 2 hours to talk to you about your life." Third version, "Oh, we're doing this study here, and I'm wondering if this social worker student can come talk to you a couple of hours a week about your life. When would be convenient?" When would be convenient, like you have a busy schedule there under these circumstances; but you know what the outcome is going to be. Socialization in interactions with the social worker, and you do better than the ones who are the controls. Have that minimal bit of input in there, though, in terms of when would it be convenient for you, and you do significantly better; remarkable finding, remarkable finding that's just about to backfire on us big-time.

If you read all of this superficially, you come out with the same potentially bad conclusion as at the end of that lecture on psychological factors with stress, which is, what's the solution. You know, slap a smiley face sticker on your forehead and just get as much control as much predictability as possible, and it doesn't work that way. We saw the formal versions of it in a previous lecture. You don't want to get your information too far in advance. What does that look like in the real world? In the first example, in the kids with cancer, what did we see? The parents who could deny the possibility of cancer coming back were doing significantly better, lower glucocorticoid levels. It happens in one of these studies that the children came out of remission. The cancer came back, and the cancer came back fatally. What happens in the aftermath? You take the parents who all along were saying, "This is wonderful, this is a blessing, but, you know, it may very well come back," and their indices of health, stress-related disease got a little bit worse. You take the parents who were sitting there all along saying, "It's over with, it's not coming back, never have to think about it again," back comes the cancer, and they wind up more stressed. The denial worked only until the point that reality overwhelmed it, and then you did much worse.

Here's another example of this, an extremely powerful one as well, going back to those nursing home studies. What did they just do, this wonderful experiment, OK the social worker is coming when it's convenient for you versus coming Thursday for 2 hours all of that. The folks who see the social workers are doing better, the social contact, throw in the element of control as well, does even better. It's great, the study is over with, 14 doctoral theses handed out, it's terrific. You know what happens at this point which is these participants, researchers, these social workers come in and they say "Well, the study is over with so we won't be doing this anymore. Oh, I'm going to come back and visit all the time, all the time," but it's not going to be as regular anymore. You know what happens which is you never see them again. What happens at that point? You have these individuals in the nursing home who, thanks to this social contact, are now doing better, doing better—mood, doing better—level of voluntary activity, doing better— fewer doctors' visits, everything is great. We're at the end of the study and student social workers don't come anymore. Do these individuals drop back down to where they started? No, what they did was they dropped back down to lower than where they started.

Think about this. This makes perfect horrible sense. You're sitting there in a nursing home. You're alone. You're isolated. Your kids come to visit you resentfully once a month or so, and this is pretty bad. Just imagine if you were sitting in this nursing home and you're alone and you're isolated, your kids show up now and then, and up until this past week that young person—that energetic person—would come by every week and seem so interested in you. Oh, you looked forward to it, and now they're not even coming anymore. There are very few of us who have the strength and resilience not to be knocked down a bunch of steps there. What do we see here? Hope can be an amazingly powerful sustaining set of feelings, but nothing destroys us more like when there's hope that turns out to be utterly unjustified. This begins to give us a first warning as we transition into this final lecture, how to apply some of these principles to yourself. What we see here is, it's not simple. What we see is, there's no free lunch. What we see is, there are double-edged swords all over the place. You want to get it right because if you apply some of these notions simplistically, not only don't you help buffer from the effects of stress, you perhaps even make things worse.

Stress Management—Approaches and Cautions
Lecture 24

When you were young, what stress management is about is trying to make the stressor go away. As you get older, what effective stress management is about is learning to adapt to the inevitable. This is a very important difference. This was wonderfully summarized in a quote that I once heard in a Quaker meeting, which is as follows: "In the face of strong winds, let me be a blade of grass. In the face of strong walls, let me be a gale of wind."

Our challenge here at the end of this course is to begin to take some of those pictures of spontaneous success at dealing with stress, and some of those demonstrations of experimental manipulation that make individuals better at stress, and look at how to apply these principles to yourself. This is a grand overview of components of stress management, and of course it comes with many qualifiers.

The first thing you can do is exercise. Exercise helps in all sorts of ways: It decreases your chance of cardiovascular disease, and that seems to protect against certain aspects of brain aging and cognitive decline. If your cerebrovascular system is not getting gummed up, you are going to have a brain that works better and that ages better. Exercise also stimulates neurogenesis and helps your neurons grow new processes and new connections. The one qualifier to keep in mind about exercise is that if you overdo it, it can negatively impact your reproductive system.

There are certain qualifiers that apply to exercise as well as the other techniques in this lecture. First, you cannot save your stress management for the weekend; it has got to be done virtually daily. Next, you need to take the time out for it. It needs to be something that is important enough to you that you are going to say no to all those stressors competing for your attention. In the realm of aerobic exercise, for example, most studies suggest you need to do 20 to 30 minutes to begin to get the cardiovascular advantages. Last, you have got to like doing it: If a personal trainer is forcing you to exercise, you do not get anywhere near as much of the health benefits.

Transcendental meditation also does great things for you. It lowers heart rate and blood pressure as well as cholesterol levels—in particular, bad cholesterol. What is unclear in that literature is how persistent those effects are. There is also a huge confound in that literature—the problem of self-selection. It is not just anybody who decides to meditate on a regular basis; people who do so are probably already somewhat different from other folks.

What else can you do? You can have social support—people you love and trust.

Exercise can decrease the chance of cardiovascular disease and protect against brain aging and cognitive decline.

We have seen how this has a calming effect. There are caveats here, too: In studies on the effects of marriage on the immune system, it was found that for men, getting married improves their immune system. But it is not as simple for women: They don't get a benefit just from marriage; it has got to be a good marriage.

Religious belief tends to increase protection against cardiovascular disease and depression and increase life expectancy. They are not huge effects, but there definitely is some protection. But this is an incredibly controversial field: The effects are hard to measure, there are many different kinds of religious belief, and there is the enormous confound of self-selection bias. Maybe people who are more religious tend to have healthier behaviors. Another confound is that people who are highly religious also have a community of social support. So this is particularly hard to study.

Another principle you can use is cognitive flexibility. This means recognizing when your strategy is not working and it is time to do something different. Some of the time, stress management is about tackling the problem; some of the time, it's about realizing that it is not going to go away and you need to accept it. Inevitably this brings us to that famed Reinhold Niebuhr quote, the Serenity Prayer, this notion of being able to accept the things you cannot change, having the courage to change the things that are changeable, and of course having the wisdom to tell the difference between the two. Very few of us are getting stressed because we are running away from saber-toothed tigers. Instead we have this bizarre, cognitively complex, Westernized lifestyle luxury of wallowing in psychogenic stressors. That is really the final point here: In so far as we are smart enough to make these things up and foolish enough to fall for them, all of us have the potential to instead keep them in perspective. ■

Important Term

John Henryism: A personality style where one perceives oneself to have control over circumstances where, in fact, that is not the case. It has been specifically applied to working-class African Americans and is associated with a greatly increased risk of cardiovascular disease.

Suggested Reading

Monat and Lazarus, *The Praeger Handbook on Stress and Coping*.

Sapolsky, *Why Zebras Don't Get Ulcers*, chap. 18.

Questions to Consider

1. What is the role of social support in stress management?

2. When are traditional stress-management techniques—like meditation, religiousness, and exercise—most effective?

Stress Management—Approaches and Cautions
Lecture 24—Transcript

We are here for the last lecture and this is one built on the previous one, stress management, and now beginning to apply some of these things, so it is probably worth having a recap of the previous lecture. Actually, it was "Oh my God, I feel so depressed. Whoa, there are some people who deal really well with stress. It is not going to be me, because I did not have the wisdom to pick the right womb to develop in. Oh, but there are experimental manipulations that could make people deal with stress better. Oh, but if you do it wrong, it backfires on you majorly." With that recap under our belts here, the challenge now is to begin to take some of those pictures of spontaneous success at dealing with stress, some of those demonstrations of experimental manipulation that make individuals better at stress and keeping the cautionary notes in mind and beginning to see now, how do you begin to apply these principles to yourself. This is going to be a grand overview of some different components of stress management. Of course it'll come with all sorts of qualifiers, which seem to be the habitual thing that I throw in here, but let us see what we can find out.

Starting off, the first thing you can do is exercise. I put that at the top of the list because I manage to exercise every now and then and feel enormously self-righteous about it. I figure by putting it at the top of the list, it makes it seem like that is the most important one and it is going to help me the most. Exercise is a good thing. Exercise really is a good thing. It helps in all sorts of ways. Here is one obvious one, which is it decreases your chance of cardiovascular disease and plaques and occlusions and all of that, and among other things, that seems to protect against certain aspects of brain aging and cognitive decline. That's a great thing. That certainly makes sense. If your cerebrovascular is not getting gummed up, you are going to have a brain that works a lot better, that functions better, that ages better. An interesting additional example of the unexpected advantages of things like exercise is that exercise stimulates the formation of new neurons in the brain, that adult neurogenesis stuff. Exercise causes your brain to make more of types of chemicals called growth factors, nerve growth factor, brain-derived neurotropic factor, things that make your neurons grow new processes, new connections, all sorts of good stuff like that. Exercise is obviously good for you, within a range of benefits that could be obvious, that could be unexpected. One qualifier that comes in already from oh so many lectures ago, about the effects of stress on the reproductive system. You can overdo it. Nonetheless, get it within the optimal range of homeostatic balance and exercise is a great thing, but it comes with certain requirements, certain qualifiers, and these basically apply to everything we are going to hear about in this lecture.

First off, you cannot save your stress management; you cannot save your exercise for the weekend. It has got to be something that is virtually daily. Next, you cannot do it while you are holding the phone for 30 seconds and decide this is a great opportunity to do something like 1-arm push-ups or things like that. You need to stop. You need to take the time out for it. It needs to be something which, by definition, if you were doing it, you were communicating this is important enough that I am going to say no to all those things that cannot be said no to. In the particular realm of aerobic exercise, for example, what most of the studies suggest is you need to do 20 to 30 minutes worth of it to begin to get the cardiovascular advantages. You need to do this sort of stress management thing on a fairly regular basis. It cannot just be in a spare second to grab an opportunity for it. Certain types work better than others: aerobic, and interestingly, unintuitively, until you hear it and then it makes perfect intuitive sense, there is one more requirement with exercise as a means of stress management with virtually any of these, you have got to like doing it. Oh, there is a voluntary element to it, voluntary.

This could be shown with an incredibly elegant study. In this study, you take something that rats love to do, you have a rat in the cage and you give it a running wheel. Rats love running and running wheels. Rats, during their nocturnal awake phase, will run the equivalent of miles on a running wheel. They are scampering around in the world. You have got a rat and it is running on its running wheel, getting its aerobic, working up for its marathon and all of that; in other words, it is running voluntarily.

Going back to a design that we have heard about a lot, you have a yoked design. In the next cage there's a second rat with a running wheel, and the deal is, every time the first rat runs and moves the running wheel, this one moves exactly the same. The difference is, the second rat is stuck inside the running wheel. In other words, it is doing the exact same amount of exercise but it is not doing it voluntarily. What you see is in the first case, you get all the beneficial health effects of exercise and in the second case, when you have got this rat stuck in there and it's health club trainer is forcing it to do this, you do not get anywhere near as much of those benefits. That is real informative for not just things like exercise, and as we will see applying this to lots of these stress management approaches, it has got to be something that you do not dread and you are not made miserable by.

There's one example, meditation. As we will see shortly, meditation does all sorts of great things for you. If it happens to work for you, we will go over the evidence, it happens that this is not the sort of thing that works for me. If I were to do like 20 minutes a day of transcendental meditation, I would have a stroke by this weekend. It is so antithetical to what I am about. Nonetheless, it works for some people. The voluntary element has to come in. That voluntary element, the business about what is it you are using those muscles for, what is it that you are exerting that energy for, that depends on the context, that depends on the meaning, and all of that. It comes in a very interesting way, coming back to that exercise business.

You could be running for your life because the predator is coming after you, you could be running joyously amid the right background music to embrace your beloved in the middle of that field with the blowing blades of grass. In both cases, you are using your thigh muscles. You could be dealing with some sort of horrible, taxing setting where you are working really hard, muscular exertion to save your life, or in the right settings, you could be doing the same very happily using those muscles during sex, and a big question in the field is, wait a second, on a certain pure energetic metabolic level, running for your life or running with the pastel background music to your beloved, you are consuming the exact same energy, you are increasing your heart rate in both cases, you are increasing glucocorticoid levels in both cases. Remember that truism, way back earlier, the opposite of love is not hate physiologically; leap up for joy and leap up in grief and your heart is going to have to do very similar things.

How does your body differentiate between the two; there's a very important finding. Do you remember the amygdala from just a few lectures ago? The

360

amygdala of fear, anxiety, conditioned fear, in general if you were running across the field with the background music and it's great, you are increasing blood pressure, heart rate, you are secreting glucocorticoids, all that sort of stuff, but your amygdala is not activated. Go running for your life and it is the exact same energy demands, the same nuts and bolts, reptilian part of your brain powering it, but in addition, the amygdala is going to activate, and that turns out to be sort of a key way of differentiating. Studies with sex where in terms of running for your life, the amygdala activates, in sex it does not amid using the exact same muscles. You are probably wondering at this point: How did they study that one with those brain imagers and all of that? The answer is fruit flies. Actually, that is probably not the answer, but nonetheless it represents a great methodological challenge, how do you differentiate between the two. Remember this brings us back to that truism, the opposite of love is not hate, your body is working really hard running with joy as with running with terror; so a sense here about the role of exercise.

Let's move on now to meditation. What is clear is when it works, when it is done regularly, when it does not drive you out of your mind, when it is all that sort of thing, it is actually beneficial. It lowers heart rate; it lowers blood pressure. There is evidence that it lowers cholesterol levels, in particular the levels of bad cholesterol. What is unclear in that literature which is quite controversial is, just how persistent are those effects. It is not entirely clear, at least in my read of the literature, but at the very least you can get transient benefits. That seems pretty rock solid. There is one huge confound in that literature though, which is the problem of self-selection, and that is going to run through a whole lot of these techniques. It is not just anybody who proves willing to meditate on a regular basis. People who would voluntarily do so, they are probably already somewhat different from other folks. What is the gold standard of those sorts of studies? You assign people either to the mediation or no mediation group. That is the well done study. You get your lab rats. These lab rats are going to do TM; these rats are not. You come back and see how the blood pressure is. That is the way to do those studies, to get around that self-selection confound there.

What are other possibilities? We know ad nauseam now from a bunch of these lectures, going way back to the building blocks of psychological stress, get yourself more of a sense of control. Increase control in life and it is going to be a great thing. You are going to feel more in control of your life. We saw that low control, low autonomy in the job setting, is a real predictor for bad outcomes. More control there's more control; not always. You may have noticed this pattern by now. Here is a great intervention, not so fast. Control, as we know by now, is not always a good thing. Control in terms of everyday life, in terms of dealing with stress, is not always a good thing.

I heard a wonderful example of this from a friend of mine, a physician, and this was during his medical training, during medical school, and this was the start of his first surgical rotation. On his first day he goes into the operating room and there is some amazingly complex surgery happening, and there are dozens of people around there and working away, and being this lowly med student, he is like 4 layers out up in the bleacher seats, and he is out there and he cannot really see anything. Then suddenly, at one point the people in front of him part, and out comes the chief surgeon who says, "Oh, you are the new med student. First day, that's great. Surgery, you are going to love it. So glad that you are here. Do you want to do something? Yeah, great, OK, good attitude. Come on in here. Here's what I am going to do. Take this hemostat, and you need to clamp it on here." My friend is telling me about this. "You need to clamp it on here and just hold on, because that is pretty important." He is there standing like that and the crowd comes back in again and he is holding it like that, and all he is can see of what is happening is like bloody towels, kidneys come flying over people's shoulders at various points, and he is holding on. Hours of this go by and he is beginning to get lightheaded and he is wobbly and just about to pass out, when suddenly the surgeon is right there in his face and says, "Do not let go because you are going to screw up everything." He finally finishes the surgery and they part, and he discovers that the hemostat has been clamped onto a towel the whole time. This was the big hazing joke for the new kid there. Number 1, teaching you in a case like this, do not let go, you are going to screw up everything. This is not a circumstance where you want to have more of a sense of control than you actually do. Number 2, he did not go into surgery for a profession.

Here now is this whole possibility that, in fact, you can have too much of a sense of control. We have already seen that in a very pernicious way back in the lecture about cancer. That study, women had just gotten the metastatic breast cancer diagnostic, "So what do you think is the cause of your cancer," and as we saw, the most common answer being stress. We saw the really poisonous damaging way in which that lack of information, that lack of validity, can come back to haunt you is if the conclusion you make there then is, "Oh, it's my fault that I had the cancer. I could have prevented it if it is something that is due to stress." That is another realm where inflating, exaggerating a sense of control is not a great thing.

These dangers of an overly inflated sense of control can even manifest itself in the personality style, one where people consistently have more of a belief that they have control than is actually the case. This is a style called John Henryism, first described by Sherman James, Duke University. John Henryism is based on the folk legend of John Henry, which I do not remember in too much detail, but John Henry, who worked the rails with his big old hammer and they brought in some machine that was supposed to do it better than any human, and he went head to head competing with the machine and impossibly he defeated the machine that could not be defeated, hammering away and then keels over dead.

This describes what John Henryism is about. It is enormously energetic optimism and one that is suffused with a belief that there is control in everything. People with a John Henryism–type profile will say things like, "Well, you know, when things don't go right, you just pick yourself up and work even harder." Or things like, "Once I make my mind up to try to accomplish something, nothing can stop me." What's wrong with that? That's wonderful. That's a sense of efficacy. That's an internal locus of control that is a great thing. Why is this a personality disorder which is, in fact, linked to an increased risk of high blood pressure and hypertension? That's because this is a person whose personality style is found among some working-class African Americans. The argument there being from James is if in a setting like this where an awful lot of one's problems in life, you cannot just pick yourself up and dust yourself and you can overcome anything; and gosh, if people just talked to each other, everybody could get along. Face racism, face things of that sort, and there is no degree of "if you just set your mind to it, you are going to be able to accomplish anything" and what do you see as the correlative of that, as I mentioned, an increased risk of hypertension. You do not see that in middle-class African Americans. You do not see that in working-class white Americans. It is a marker of people who feel like they have more control in a setting, where they actually do not.

This whole business about this belief that enough control and you're on top of everything does not necessarily work, as we have seen. It reminds me of this old parable: What is the difference between heaven and hell? As it goes, heaven you spend all of eternity studying the Holy books, whereas in hell you spend all of eternity studying the Holy books. Ahhh. It is how you interpret it. Each of us has the potential to turn our hells into heaven. It is appraisal; it is evaluative. It is not appraisal. It is not evaluative. It is not context-dependent when you are dealing with someone who is a refugee, when you are dealing with someone with terminal cancer, when you are dealing with someone homeless. It is not the place there to sit down and say, "Ooh, did you know how much psychological factors have to do with health and stress-response? You just have to feel like you have more control in life." No, you do not do that, because that barrels you into the realm we have already considered of inflating a sense of control, especially people undergoing adverse circumstances and all you are doing is blaming the victim and setting somebody up to think, "Ooh, it could have been so much better and it is my fault that it did not happen, because I had control." We see here the wonderful advantages, the wonderful possibilities by increasing a sense of control, not in all settings, cautionary note.

We'll now move on to the next intervention. What else can you do? You can have social support. That one is obvious from all those studies we have heard about by now, starting with rats grooming each other, to holding the hand of someone you like and love and trust, and you do not have as much of a cardiovascular response to a scary procedure. Social support, and thus we are going to have a similar theme here, which is that is not a blanket recommendation. There are all sorts of realms in which not only doesn't it do you much good, it can make things worse. Here's one example. A number of years ago, a very humanely-motivated rule came down the pike concerning laboratory primates. In a lot of experimental settings, they are singlely housed. In other words, that's social primates living alone in a cage. The ruling that came down was that even if these are animals that have to be singly housed because of the nature of the experiment, once a week you need to let them be in a large social group in an open space to get some social contact, social support. Anyone who is a primatologist knew this was going to be a disaster, because when you put a whole bunch of monkeys together in a place where they do not know each other, they are going to spend the first year or so punching it out with enormous amounts of social conflict until they figure out the social hierarchy. In social groups of primates it often takes up to a year, and what you do here is if once a week you allow these monkeys to have some social support in this group, all they are going to do is stress each other like mad because every single week, they have to start this process all over again of who is the tough guy. Once this actually stabilizes in to a hierarchy, if it ever happens, the ones who wind up at the bottom of the hierarchy are going to do terrible as well, this being a realm where socialization is not necessarily stress reducing.

Another example in a realm of another type of primate, a psychoneuroimmunological question that has been asked in research is, "What are the effects of marriage on the immune system?" In studies of men the answer comes back absolutely clear: Getting married improves your immune system. That's great. Maybe even back to that Harvard study, stable, long-term marriage, getting married improves immune function in men during the year after they have married. It does not work that way in women. Women are so picky. Women are not just satisfied with marriage, it has got to be a good marriage. These guys, as long as there is somebody who feeds them meatloaf every now and then, they suddenly make a whole lot more white blood cells, here we see the possibilities that marriage is not necessarily a panacea if it does not supply the social support that one may actually be needing.

What we see here is that there are a few things that are as helpful as true intimate social support, and there are as few things that are undoing as when that extensive social intimacy turns out to be misplaced. Within this realm of social support, and social support is stress reducing, one version of social support that, in my opinion, is way underemphasized in this literature is stress reduction, stress management with sociality, making a point of going about helping someone else. There is an interesting cross-cultural pattern with that. In both American and East Asian populations—and this has been well studied—social interactions help to reduce stress. In the United States, what does that typically take the form of? It is good to have somebody else

365

there who you feel close to so you can bitch and moan to them about how awful things are, whereas typically in East Asian populations, what you see is when things are stressed, it is good to have somebody else around so you can reflexively, just obsessively ask them how are things going. The big difference between an individualistic and a communal society, social support works only under some circumstances. Do not mistake social support for being only a realm in which you get to lean on somebody else.

Next potential area of potential good outcomes is religiosity. As you might guess, this is one incredibly controversial field but built around a fairly undeniable fact, which is religiosity, religious belief, is associated with a longer life span and a lot of healthier outcomes; super controversial nonetheless. Part of it is arguments about, well, these effects were there. How big of effects are they? Part of it is that there is this enormous complexity that religiosity does not come in just 1 flavor. There are different kinds of religious belief. A Pentecostalist is a whole lot different from a Unitarian. There is a difference between religiosity and spirituality. It is a very complex sort of field to try to challenge.

Then there is the one enormous confound in there, the same one that came up with the meditation literature, which is the self-selection bias, which is it is not just random who winds up being religious. Maybe people who already have a certain bent that would predispose towards more health are more religious, and it's particularly hard to do a decent scientific study on this. You cannot take your subjects, divide them in half and say, "Okay, you guys go believe there is a benevolent God who loves you, and you guys don't believe anything, and let's meet in a year and see how everybody's blood pressure is." It's very, very hard to do these studies. Here are more reasons why they are very hard. When you look at religious individuals, in general, you are often at a higher than expected rate. Also looking at individuals who do not drink to excess, who have all sorts of lifestyle factors that work better for them, is it due to the religiosity or is due to the lifestyle issues. You have to control for that.

Here we have the next problem. Typically, people who are highly religious, what they get amid their religiosity, they also get a community of social support. So is it the religious belief or is it all the great sociality stuff we've heard of? You have got to control for that as well. You go through all of that, and these are enormously difficult studies to go through, and the people in the field, the best people who really support the notion that there are beneficial health effects of religiosity, the people who really are skeptical about it, one thing they agree on is most of the studies are uninterpretable, exactly because of these confounds. When you cut through it, what do you see in the literature? Religiosity tends to increase protection against cardiovascular disease. It tends to help against depression. It does increase life expectancy. All of those are quite clear. What the literature is also quite clear about is, it has no impact on cancer incidence or progression. That's no surprise; we had an entire lecture about that one.

In general, religiosity is more protective at preventing the emergence of disease than curing it in the aftermath. What is also clear is there are hierarchies of types of belief in terms of tapping into psychological issues of stress. You can have somebody at a certain level, who believes there is a God, and that is all they know, and that comes with a certain amount of protective power, attribution. Then there is a next step where you believe there is a God who listens to you; control, predictability. Then there is the level of the God you believe in who listens to you and listens preferentially to you and people who dress like you, or eat like you, or pray like you, even a higher level of a sense of control. It's a very tough literature to tackle; nonetheless, what the critics and the zealots agree on is they are not huge effects, but there definitely is some protection.

What they also agree on is what this literature should never, ever, ever wind up doing is suggesting that part of clinical medical therapeutics should be the doctor sitting you down and saying "Hey, did you know religion is good for your health? Maybe it is time to start becoming religious." It's a very, very messy controversial field in that regard.

What else can be going on here? What other possibilities can we intervene with? Let's consider cognitive flexibility. This one is extremely important, and this is the whole notion that part of what stress responsiveness, part of what stress success is, is recognizing when your strategy is not working and it is time to do something different. This is very nicely summarized in this view as the stress management over the course of life history, when you were young, what stress management is about is trying to make the stressor go away. As you get older, what effective stress management is about is learning to adapt to the inevitable. This is a very important difference. This was wonderfully summarized in a quote that I once heard in a Quaker meeting, which is as follows: "In the face of strong winds, let me be a blade of grass. In the face of strong walls, let me be a gale of wind." What is this saying? It is saying that some of the time what stress management is about is tackling whatever the problem is, whatever the impediment is, and tearing down walls of constraint and triumphing over your limits, and some of the time what stress management is about, is here is the blasting wind, and the thing to be under this circumstance is a blade of grass and get bent down, and the winds will pass, and they are all over with, and you come bouncing back up. Some of the time, what things are about with stress management and successful stress management is cognitive flexibility. The solution to this problem that is not getting solved is to do the thing that I normally do but do it 17 times as much and faster and more intensely, and that is going to solve things. An awful big challenge is realizing, "You know what, I have go to try something completely different," or "You know what, this is not going to go away and I need to start accepting it."

What this all brings up, amid this complex set of advice here, that yes, control is good, a sense of control is great, unless it is a disastrous stressor, unless it is something that is uncontrollable, predictive information is good, but only within certain parameters. Inevitably what this brings us to here is that famed Reinhold Niebuhr quote, the Serenity Prayer, that we are all familiar with, this notion of being able to accept the things you cannot change, having the courage to change the things that are changeable, and of course having the wisdom to tell the difference between the two. This is a very good place to begin to wind up here.

Stress is not everywhere. Stress is not universal. Stress does not explain all our diseases, but when it does, there are some rules. There's control, but not trying to control the uncontrollable. Where there is control, the journey begins with one step. You need little pieces of taking on these massive challenges. Predictive information is helpful, but only for things where it actually is useful to know about it. Outlets should be benign. You should not give ulcers in order to avoid getting one. You need to have the outlets on a regular basis. Sociality can be wonderful, except there is nothing that does us in more when it turns out that something we thought that counted as intimacy turned out to be grossly misplaced. Yes, all of these rules, all of these rules again in the context that every disease out there is not stress related. Getting things into perspective is not going to help cure your cancer or your homelessness.

The world of what these last 24 lectures were about was predominantly the world of middle-class, harried, neurotic problems, the ones that we are all consumed with, and within that realm, it has much to do with stress. On a certain level, that brings us absolutely back to where we started. Very few of us are getting stressed because we are running away from saber-toothed tigers. Instead we have this bizarre, cognitively complex primate Westernized lifestyle luxury of just wallowing in psychogenic stressors. That is really the final point here. In so far as we are smart enough to make these things up and foolish enough to then fall for them, all of us have the potential to instead keep them in perspective. So, good luck with your stressors.

Glossary

abdominal fat: Fat deposits around the gut. Chronic stress preferentially promotes the deposition of abdominal fat, which is of the type that is worse for cardiovascular health.

adrenaline: *See* **epinephrine**.

amino acids: Approximately 20 different kinds of closely related molecules that are the building blocks of protein.

amygdala: A part of the brain's limbic system that plays an important role in fear and anxiety.

analgesia: The blocking of pain perception. Stress-induced analgesia is the phenomenon where extreme, acute stress blocks pain perception.

anhedonia: The inability to feel pleasure; a defining symptom of depression.

anterior cingulate cortex: A region of the brain's frontal cortex that plays a role in evaluating pain and in empathy. Abnormalities in its function have been noted in people with depression.

atherosclerosis: A disease of the vascular system in which portions of the inner lining of blood vessels are degenerated and inflamed and deposits of cholesterol form plaques that impede blood flow.

autoimmune disease: A disease in which the immune system mistakenly responds to a part of the body as if it is an invasive pathogen and attacks it. Examples include juvenile diabetes, in which insulin-secreting cells in the pancreas are attacked; rheumatoid arthritis, in which joints are attacked; and multiple sclerosis, in which aspects of the spinal cord are attacked.

autonomic nervous system: A part of the nervous system that mediates aspects of the body's function that are often automatic, or involuntary. Consists of the sympathetic nervous system (generally involved in arousal and stress-responses) and the opposing parasympathetic nervous system (generally involved in calm, vegetative bodily function).

benzodiazepines: Anxiety-reducing tranquilizers such as Valium and Librium. The brain contains receptors for them, indicating that the brain makes still-undiscovered natural versions of these drugs.

beta-endorphin: A hormone released during stress, predominately from the pituitary gland. It plays a role in stress-induced analgesia and in some of the disruptive effects on reproduction.

cholesterol: For the purposes of this course, there is "bad," LDL (low-density lipoprotein) cholesterol, which promotes atherosclerosis, and "good," HDL (high-density lipoprotein) cholesterol, which does the opposite.

cortex: The outer surface of the brain, it is the most recently evolved and involved in the most abstract brain functions. Most pertinent to this course is the frontal cortex.

cortisol: *See* **glucocorticoids**.

Cushing's syndrome: A collection of diseases involving pathologically elevated levels of glucocorticoids.

dexamethasone: *See* **glucocorticoids**.

diabetes: Type 1 (juvenile) diabetes is an autoimmune disorder in which the pancreas is unable to secrete insulin. Type 2 (adult-onset; a.k.a. insulin-resistant) diabetes is a disorder, typically brought on by obesity, in which cells throughout the body have become resistant to the effects of insulin.

dopamine: A type of neurotransmitter whose numerous functions include a role in anticipation of pleasure; abnormalities in it have been found in individuals with depression.

epinephrine: A hormone released during times of stress by the adrenal glands under the control of the sympathetic nervous system; it is also known as adrenaline. Epinephrine plays a key role in virtually all aspects of the stress-response.

fetal origins of adult disease (FOAD): This is an emerging concept in medicine, focusing on the fact that events during fetal life can program lifelong aspects of bodily function. As the example covered most in this course, fetal malnutrition often causes increased insulin secretion throughout life.

follicle-stimulating hormone (FSH): A pituitary hormone that stimulates follicle maturation in females and sperm maturation in males.

frontal cortex: The brain region involved in decision making, impulse control, long-term planning, and gratification postponement.

glucagon: A hormone released from the pancreas during stress that helps mobilize energy from storage sites in the body.

glucocorticoid: Any of a class of hormones released from the adrenal gland during stress that play a key role in virtually all facets of the stress-response. The primate/human version is cortisol, also known as hydrocortisone. Synthetic versions often prescribed by physicians include dexamethasone and prednisone.

gluteal fat: Fat deposits around the buttocks.

glycogen: The storage form of glucose/carbohydrates in the body.

Helicobacter pylori: A bacteria that causes a large percentage of cases of peptic ulcer. Chronic stress can impair the ability of the body to repair such ulcers.

hippocampus: A part of the brain's limbic system that is centrally involved in learning and memory and highly sensitive to the effects of stress.

homeostasis: A state of equilibrium, with physiological endpoints functioning in an optimal range.

hormone: A chemical messenger released by glands into the bloodstream, where it travels and has effects elsewhere in the body.

hydrocortisone: *See* **glucocorticoids**.

hyperalgesia: Exaggerated pain sensitivity.

hyperglycemia: Elevated blood-sugar (glucose) levels.

insulin: A hormone released from the pancreas that promotes the storage of glucose throughout the body. It is normally secreted when blood glucose levels rise; secretion is inhibited in the early phases of the stress-response.

John Henryism: A personality style where one perceives oneself to have control over circumstances where, in fact, that is not the case. It has been specifically applied to working-class African Americans and is associated with a greatly increased risk of cardiovascular disease.

learned helplessness: A term often used in the context of depression, describing a state where an individual, due to repeated psychological stress, has lost the capacity to recognize circumstances where it is possible to effectively cope with a stressor.

limbic system: A region of the brain that plays a central role in emotion.

long-term potentiation (LTP): An increase in the ease with which neurons communicate with each other across synapses; this increase in excitability is thought to be a cellular building block of memory formation.

luteinizing hormone (LH): A pituitary hormone that stimulates estrogen synthesis in females and testosterone synthesis in males.

metabolic syndrome: An emerging concept in medicine focusing on the fact that there is often overlap between the causes and symptoms of cardiovascular disease and of metabolic diseases such as diabetes; the syndrome refers to a constellation of symptoms that can include hypertension, obesity, hyperglycemia, and insulin resistance.

neurogenesis: The generation of new neurons. The fact that this can occur in the adult brain has been a revolution in neurobiology.

neurotransmitter: A chemical messenger with which one neuron communicates with another. Examples include serotonin, dopamine, and norepinephrine.

norepinephrine (a.k.a. **noradrenaline**): A type of neurotransmitter closely related to epinephrine. There is good evidence that its release in one region of the brain is blunted in depression; in a different part of the nervous system, it plays a central role in the sympathetic nervous system (along with epinephrine).

parasympathetic nervous system: *See* **autonomic nervous system**.

post-traumatic stress disorder (PTSD): A psychiatric disorder comprising a constellation of symptoms (e.g., sleep disruption, flashbacks, and hypersensitivity to stimuli) caused by severe trauma (e.g., combat trauma, childhood abuse, or rape).

prednisone: *See* **glucocorticoids**.

prolactin: A hormone released from the pituitary gland in response to stress, exercise, and nursing. It inhibits aspects of reproductive physiology.

psychogenic: Generated by psychological factors.

psychomotor retardation: A key symptom of major depression, in which thought and action seem exhausting.

rapid eye movement (REM) sleep: The sleep state during which dreaming occurs. It unexpectedly involves higher levels of activity in some brain regions than during normal waking.

receptor: A hormone or neurotransmitter carrying messages from one cell to another. Each type of hormone or neurotransmitter binds to a specific receptor on a target cell and exerts its actions through that route (e.g., estrogen stimulates uterine growth by binding to estrogen receptors in uterine cells).

selective serotonin reuptake inhibitor (SSRI): Any of a class of antidepressants (e.g., Prozac) that increase serotonin signaling in the synapse by blocking their reuptake (i.e., removal) from the synapse.

serotonin: A type of neurotransmitter. Of greatest relevance, evidence suggests that a shortage of serotonin in some brain regions contributes to depression.

slow-wave sleep: The deepest stage of sleep, in which the most energy restoration occurs. This is the sleep stage most disrupted by stress.

socioeconomic status (SES): An aggregate measure that incorporates level of education, wealth, and place of residence. Low SES is a predictor of increased risk for a wide variety of disease, as well as for significantly shortened life expectancy.

steroids: A class of structurally related hormones. For the purpose of this course, the most important ones are glucocorticoids, estrogen, progesterone, and testosterone.

stress dwarfism (a.k.a. **psychogenic dwarfism, psychosocial dwarfism**): A disorder in which growth in a child is significantly impaired by severe psychological stress.

stressor: An external perturbation that disrupts homeostasis; also, the psychological anticipation of such a perturbation occurring.

stress-response: The array of hormonal and neural adaptations in the body meant to reestablish homeostasis.

sympathetic nervous system: *See* **autonomic nervous system**.

synapse: The microscopic gap between the branches of two neurons; excitation in one neuron leads to the release of specific neurotransmitters, which float across the synapse, bind to specialized receptors, and alter the function of the other neuron.

thyroid hormone: Secreted by the thyroid gland, its main function is to increase metabolism. Abnormally low thyroid hormone levels (i.e., hypothyroidism) can give rise to depression.

toxic hostility: A personality style where an individual consistently interprets benign events as being threatening and calling for a hostile coping response. This modern incarnation of the type A personality concept carries an increased risk of cardiovascular disease.

triglycerides: The storage form of fats.

type A personality: A personality style first described in the 1950s that carries an increased risk of cardiovascular disease. In its original formulation, type A individuals tend to be highly competitive, overachieving, time-pressured, impatient, and hostile. *See also* **toxic hostility**.

ulcer: An area of tissue erosion (e.g., on skin or on the stomach lining).

Bibliography

Adam, T., and E. Epel. "Stress, Eating and the Reward System." *Physiology and Behavior* 91 (2007): 449.

Arnsten, A. "Stress Signaling Pathways That Impair Prefrontal Cortex Structure and Function." *Nature Reviews Neuroscience* 10 (2009): 410.

Bangasser, D., and T. Shors. "Critical Brain Circuits at the Intersection between Stress and Learning." *Neuroscience and Biobehavioral Reviews* (forthcoming).

Blum, D. *Love at Goon Park: Harry Harlow and the Science of Affection.* New York: Berkeley, 2004.

Burke, K., T. Franz, D. Miller, and G. Schoenbaum. "The Role of the Orbitofrontal Cortex in the Pursuit of Happiness and More Specific Rewards." *Nature* 454 (2008): 340.

Caudill, M. *Managing Pain Before It Manages You.* 3rd ed. New York: Guilford Press, 2008.

Cohen, S., D. Janicki-Deverts, and G. Miller. "Psychological Stress and Disease." *Journal of the American Medical Association* 298 (2007): 1685.

Creswell, J., W. Welch, S. Taylor, D. Sherman, T. Gruenewald, and T. Mann. "Affirmation of Personal Values Buffers Neuroendocrine and Psychological Stress Responses." *Psychological Science* 16 (2005): 846.

Dallman, M., S. la Fleur, N. Pecoraro, F. Gomez, H. Houshyar, and S. Akana. "Glucocorticoids—Food Intake, Abdominal Obesity, and Wealthy Nations in 2004." *Endocrinology* 145 (2004): 2633.

Dement, W. *The Promise of Sleep.* New York: Dell, 2000.

Depp, C., I. Vahia, and D. Jeste. "Successful Aging: Focus on Cognitive and Emotional Health." *Annual Review of Clinical Psychology* 6 (2010): 527–550.

Gillespie, C., and C. Nemeroff. "CRF and the Psychobiology of Early-Life Stress." *Current Directions in Psychological Sciences* 16 (2007): 85.

Godfrey, K., and D. Barker. "Fetal Programming and Adult Health." *Public Health and Nutrition* 4 (2001): 611.

Kiecolt-Glaser, J., L. McGuire, T. Robles, and R. Glaser. "Emotions, Morbidity, and Mortality: New Perspectives from Psychoneuroimmunology." *Annual Review of Psychology* 53 (2002): 83.

Kim, J., and D. Diamond. "The Stressed Hippocampus, Synaptic Plasticity and Lost Memories." *Nature Reviews Neuroscience* 3 (2002): 453.

Kirkwood, T. "Healthy Old Age." *Nature* 455 (2008): 739.

Kleinman, A. "Culture and Depression." *New England Journal of Medicine* 351 (2004): 951.

Lue, T. "Erectile Dysfunction." *New England Journal of Medicine* 342 (2000): 1802.

Lupien, S., B. S. McEwen, M. R. Gunnar, and C. Heim. "Effects of Stress throughout the Lifespan on the Brain, Behaviour and Cognition." *Nature Reviews Neuroscience* 10 (2009): 434.

Marmot, M. *The Status Syndrome: How Social Standing Affects Our Health and Longevity*. New York: Henry Holt, 2005.

McEwen, B. "Protective and Damaging Effects of Stress Mediators." *New England Journal of Medicine* 338 (1998): 171.

Meerlo, P., R. E. Mistlberger, B. L. Jacobs, H. C. Heller, and D. McGinty. "New Neurons in the Adult Brain: The Role of Sleep and Consequences of Sleep Loss." *Sleep Medicine Reviews* 13 (2009): 187.

Monat, A., and R. Lazarus. *The Praeger Handbook on Stress and Coping.* Westport, CT: Praeger Press, 2007.

Morgan, D., K. A. Grant, H. D. Gage, R. H. Mach, J. R. Kaplan, O. Prioleau, S. H. Nader, N. Buchheimer, R. L. Ehrenkaufer, and M. A. Nader. "Social Dominance in Monkeys: Dopamine D2 Receptors and Cocaine Self-Administration." *Nature Neuroscience* 5 (2002): 169–174.

Nestler, E., and R. Malenka. "The Addicted Brain." *Scientific American,* March 2004, 78.

Rubin, A. *Diabetes for Dummies.* 3rd ed. New York: Hungry Minds, 2008.

Sapolsky, R. M. *Why Zebras Don't Get Ulcers: A Guide to Stress, Stress-Related Diseases, and Coping.* 3rd ed. New York: Henry Holt, 2004.

Sapolsky, R. M., and J. Wingfield. "Reproduction and Resistance to Stress: When and How." *Journal of Neuroendocrinology* 15 (2003): 711.

Schwartz, B. "The Tyranny of Choice." *Scientific American,* April 2004, 71.

Selye, H. *The Stress of My Life.* New York: Van Nostrand, 1979.

Stansfeld, S., and M. Marmot. *Stress and the Heart: Psychosocial Pathways to Coronary Heart Disease.* London: BMJ Publishing, 2002.

Sternberg, E. *The Balance Within: The Science Connecting Health and Emotions.* New York: W. H. Freeman, 2001.

Taylor, S., L. Klein, B. Lewis, T. Gruenewald, R. Gurung, and J. Updegraff. "Biobehavioral Responses to Stress in Females: Tend-and-Befriend, Not Fight-or-Flight." *Psychological Reviews* 107 (2000): 411.

Tilbrook, A., A. I. Turner, and I. J. Clarke. "Effects of Stress on Reproduction in Non-Rodent Mammals: The Role of Glucocorticoids and Sex Differences." *Reviews of Reproduction* 5 (2000): 105.

Notes

Notes

Notes

Notes

Notes